E. ☙ YO-BCU-007

Lieut., USNR

Excuse My Dust

BOOKS BY

BELLAMY PARTRIDGE

COUNTRY LAWYER
The Story of My Father

*

BIG FAMILY
Small Town Life in the Nineties

*

SIR BILLY HOWE
Life of the Gay Revolutionary General

*

AMUNDSEN
The Splendid Norseman

*

THE ROOSEVELT FAMILY IN AMERICA
An Imperial Saga

"Good-looking wagon," Tom said to Mr. Dorlon. "What's the matter with it?" (*page* 132)

Excuse My Dust

BELLAMY PARTRIDGE

Illustrated by
STEPHEN J. VOORHIES

ST. JOSEPH'S UNIVERSITY

3 9353 00227 2126

PS
3531
.P2
E9

242905

WHITTLESEY HOUSE

New York McGRAW-HILL BOOK COMPANY, Inc. *London*

EXCUSE MY DUST

Copyright, 1943, *by the* McGraw-Hill Book Company, Inc.

All rights reserved. This book, or parts thereof, may not be reproduced in any form without permission of the publishers.

SECOND PRINTING

PUBLISHED BY WHITTLESEY HOUSE
A division of the McGraw-Hill Book Company, Inc.

Printed in the United States of America

FOR

SAMUEL BELLAMY

Who was a little late in joining
the big family

*C*ontents

*F*oreword

Tolerant as he was of dust around his office and on his law books, my father had a strong aversion to it anywhere else. One of the reasons why he liked to drive a speedy road horse was so that he would not have to drag along behind some stodgy team, "eating their dust," as the phrase went. More than once I have heard him sputter and mutter when he came up behind a vehicle on a narrow stretch of road where it was impossible for him to slip past.

"But think of the other fellow," I heard my mother say to him once when he was fuming along in the dusty wake of a slowgoing team, watching for a place that was wide enough for him to pass.

"I do, my dear," he said. "Haven't you ever noticed how quickly I draw away as soon as I am able to get out in front?"

One might think that the automobile, with its superior speed, would have made an instantaneous appeal to him; but the first time he saw one go tearing down Main Street he spoke, not of the speed, but of the dust. And having no mechanical bent whatever, one glance at the working parts of even a simple old one-lunger was enough to arouse in him a distaste from which he never completely recovered. Later on he did buy a car—he had to in self-defence, if he was going to make any use of the public roads and highways. But he never learned to drive, and even after he had owned a car for several years he still believed that the purpose of the radiator was to heat, not to cool, the engine.

With me the case was quite different. I fell in love with the automobile at first sight and became the owner of one back in the days when the general impression was that anybody who tried to drive a road vehicle without a horse in front of it was a legitimate target for public gibes and roadside humor. I was, as a matter of fact, the owner of the second car in town—the first being the property of the proprietor of two sauerkraut factories, who purchased it with the idea that he could skip back and forth from one plant to the other without need for a hitching post and without all the nose-bag service and individual grooming required to keep a horse in proper working order.

As it turned out, the secondhand one-lunger with which he supplanted a good and reliable, if somewhat deliberate, horse proved to have most of the faults he had found with the horse, and in addition it developed a tendency to kick and balk which the horse had never shown. Indeed, the only good word I ever heard him speak of that particular machine was when he said that it was not afraid of the cars—a decided advantage, since both his plants were located on railroad sidings.

My initial motoring venture was likewise a secondhand job, but it was no puny one-lunger. It was a big, powerful, two-cylinder, double-opposed Rambler with a canopy top and a stage entrance to the rear seat. I can't recall whether it was rated at eight or at twelve horsepower, though exactness is hardly required on that point, as the motor never came anywhere near developing either. However, I must admit that it was a wonderful car for a beginner, since there was always something the matter with it.

Another advantage of the Rambler for which I shall

always be grateful is that it brought me into close contact with the pioneer automobile enthusiast of our town, a young bicycle repairman named Tom Hunter. I do not mean to say that without the presence of Hunter the motor car would not eventually have come to us, though I am sure it would have lacked many of the interesting and colorful reverberations lent to it by his mechanical touch. It is no doubt true that the coming of an event, by its very nature, produces the man to cope with it, and without question there was a counterpart of Tom Hunter in every small town in the land.

For centuries the horse had been one of the most essential servants of man. Since primitive days it had been the sole means of individual land transportation. The destiny and the development of the horse had been so closely allied with the destiny and development of our civilization that the problem of separating the two was manifestly impossible without a very considerable wrench—almost as much of a wrench as when a man is separated from a molar.

Perhaps a farsighted man like Ford or Edison may have foreseen the tremendous impact that was in store for both the man and the horse when the motor car attempted to take over. Nowhere was the jolt so severe as in the country town geared to, if not actually built around, the horse and buggy.

Although the incidents related in this volume are without exception drawn from actual occurrences, I have in most cases used fictitious names and have taken certain liberties with both time and place, for which apology is hereby made.

BELLAMY PARTRIDGE

Easton, Conn.
1943

Excuse My Dust

1

Dick Horse

I HAD SEEN TOM HUNTER AROUND AND KNEW who he was, but I had never spoken to him until one afternoon in the summertime when Gid Wilson introduced us. I had gone over to the Brackett Livery and Sales Stables to ask Gid, the head stableman, about the reputation of one of his former hostlers, a shifty-eyed loafer I was planning to use as a witness in a forthcoming lawsuit.

If you ever knew Gid you might think him a strange person to ask about anybody's reputation, since he had so little of his own; but I must say that, even though his friends and hangers-on around the barn were a motley crew who ran all the way from jailbirds to mental incompetents, I found Gid a man of rugged and reliable character.

Gid stood in the doorway as I came up, his feet apart, his hands clasped behind him. Though not a large man he was powerfully built and had long arms that hung down almost to his knees. As a boy I used to wonder if they had been stretched by pulling on the reins of tough-bitted horses. He had a bristling mustache, about the color and quality of a piece of frayed rope, and eyebrows to match, so heavy that they almost hid the pair of twinkling eyes underneath. I had asked him about my witness, and he had given a good report of the fellow's integrity and had warned me that I had better not go into his matrimonial affairs, when suddenly he stopped speaking and squinted his eyes in the direction of a boy who was coming up the long driveway.

"Well, I'll be a son of a gun," he said, a broad grin breaking over his face. "It's young Tom Hunter. Old Everett's boy. I worked there once as hired man when Tom was a little duffer. By damn, how he has growed. Taller'n his old man. Ingenious little cuss, he was, always wantin' me to help him make some'pm. Know old Everett? He's a mean one. I quit the job there three or four years back, because I was afraid that if I stayed I'd murder the old devil. And I ain't the only one—they all quit that way."

As the boy came nearer, Gid stuck out his hand. "Hello, Sliver," he called genially.

Tom grinned, the whiteness of his teeth making a vivid contrast to his sunburned face. "How you been?"

"Fair to middlin'," said Gid. "Guess you know the Counselor, here, don't you?" he added by way of introduction.

Tom nodded bashfully and said, "Hello."

"I used to go to school with your brother George," I said, trying to put him at his ease.

And at this point Gid broke in. "Did you get that field of corn cultivated?"

"How'd you know I was cultivating corn?"

"Oh, I seen you draggin' along there behind the bay mare yeste'day. Looked to me as if you was asleep on your feet."

"Well, you won't see me behind the mare again—or any other horse if I can help it."

· 2 ·

Gid looked at him keenly. "How come?"

"From now on I'm takin' orders from myself."

"Better not let the old man hear you say that."

"What's he got to do with it? I don't live there any more."

"Don't matter where you live, you've gotta take orders from him till you're old enough to vote. Am I right about that, Counselor?"

"I'm afraid that's the law," I said.

Tom looked troubled. "Even if I don't work for him?" he asked.

"If you don't work for him he'll take your wages."

"Can he do that?" Tom swallowed hard and began to dig with the sole of his shoe into a wide crack in the uneven plank floor.

"That's what the law says," muttered Gid. "What'd you do, have a fight with the old man?"

Tom shook his head. "I wouldn't fight with my own father—no matter how much I hate him."

"But you did have trouble," Gid persisted.

"No more trouble than usual. We never could get along."

"I know, I know." Gid gave him a friendly pat on the shoulder, a pat that would have knocked a smaller man off his balance, though it did not shake the sturdy young boy. "Tom, you wouldn't make a farmer in a thousand years. You're worthless around a farm—you and your gosh-darned inventions. But you can't just pull up stakes and walk out. The old devil's got a halter on you till you're of age."

"I didn't walk out—he fired me! Said if I went I needn't come back."

"The old man kicked you out?" Gid's face was beaming.

"That's diff'rent. I'm only a hoss lawyer, but I'd like to bet that you've got the edge on the old slave-driver. Looks to me as if he named his terms and you took 'em up. Don't that make it a deal, Counselor?"

"Sounds like a deal to me," I replied. "There was undoubtedly a meeting of the minds."

"You mean he can't come and get me?"

"You betcher life he can't," muttered Gid.

"And he can't take my wages?"

"Every dollar of 'em—every nickel belongs to you," Gid declared.

Tom ran his hands into his pockets, but drew them quickly out again. "Only of course I ain't got a dollar—or even a nickel, and I got no clothes—just what I got on."

Gid bellowed with laughter. "Well, anyway, you're one of us. You're right up in a class with us hired men! How'd you ever get up the guts to do it?"

"I don't know. Just took a notion, I guess."

Gid pulled slowly at his mustache. "I know all about it. Same way I went. You stand the old varmit's abuse as long as you can, and when the thought of murder becomes sweet to you—then you go."

"Wish I'd brought my clothes."

"When it comes to gettin' away from him clothes ain't important."

"Remember how I brought yours?"

"I ain't forgot."

"Now we'll have to figure out some way to get mine."

"No figgerin' about that. I'll go get 'em for you myself."

Tom shook his head. "You'd have a ruckus with the old man."

"You leave that to me," said Gid. "How much stuff you got out there?"

"Not much. Just my good suit and my shoes and my felt hat. Couple of shirts, too, and a few tools I bought for myself. I'd hate to lose those tools."

"Think your ma would give me the stuff if the old man wasn't around?"

"She might. Used to take my side a little. Much as she dared."

"Uh-huh, I've heard her. But she's afraid of the old stinkpot—and I don't blame her. I got to exercise the black stud tomorrow, and I'll drive over that way. You can't go round lookin' for no job in that rig you got on."

Tom looked down at himself, apparently conscious for the first time that his blue overalls were faded and patched, the sleeves of his coarse workshirt frayed, the clumsy shoes battered and worn. Such things did not matter on the farm; any old duds would do. But here in town it was different, and he began to feel ashamed of his appearance. "Perhaps I shouldn't have come here," he said. "Guess it would have been better if I'd just gone off some place where I'm not known. Then it wouldn't matter how I look."

"Where do you reckon you'll stay tonight?" asked Gid.

"I guess I hadn't thought much about that," Tom lied awkwardly. "I'll have to look around a little and—and find somebody to stay with."

Gid wasn't fooled. "You ain't exactly fixed to do much lookin' around with them clothes on. Why don't you stay here with me and the hosses?"

"That'd be fine, but I wouldn't want to crowd you."

"One more ain't gonna crowd me or the hosses neither. Ever been in this mansion of mine?" Gid led the way.

At the left of the big front door was a fair-sized room partitioned off with matched lumber. When Gid had first taken possession, there had been a single built-in bunk, on which his predecessor had been accustomed to sleep. But Gid tore this out and moved in a double bed, thereby giving rise to a great deal of broad humor and to some scandal, which was not entirely without foundation. It was inescapable that all sorts and conditions of people should visit the livery stable, for though there was a horse and buggy in nearly every backyard in town, there were still people who found it more convenient to hire a horse than to own one. When a woman was seen going into the livery, you assumed that she was going there to hire a horse. And when a woman was seen coming out, the presumption that she had just returned a rig to the stable would not have been illogical. That all persons did not follow this line of reasoning was, as Gid explained, no fault of his. "With three studs and fifty hosses," Gid rambled on, "somebody's gotta sleep in this barn, and if a man sleeps in a barn long enough people get to thinkin' of him as a kind of a stud hoss, I guess."

The room was really more spacious and comfortable than the slant-roofed attic room Tom had occupied at home. And there was a gaiety about the circus posters and horse pictures on the walls that was instantly arresting. The big white iron bedstead at the right of the door was hardly a handsome piece, but it bespoke a certain atmosphere of luxury and somehow carried an inference of hospitality that one hardly expected to find in a stable. The bed was liberally spread with horse blankets and carriage robes, beneath which I could see the outlines of a pair of pillows. A pine-topped table against the wall served in a dual capacity as desk and workbench. There were papers on it, and a pen and bottle of ink. At the left end lay the stud book, with a blotter projecting from between the pages. Shavings clung in the crevice between the wall and the table edge, and a little pile of sawdust on the floor showed where a pine board had been sawed. Aside from this sawdust the place was spotlessly clean.

In front of the desk was a worn kitchen chair with several spindles missing and a wire reinforcement running from leg to leg like a spiderweb. Another larger chair, with arms, stood at the left; and at the right, near the head of the bed, was an armchair fashioned from an old oak whiskey barrel. A monstrosity to look at, this piece was very comfortable to sit in, and it possessed the added luxury of always smelling like aging whiskey.

On a shelf opposite the door stood a battered kitchen clock with the name "Seth Thomas" hand-lettered on the dial and a loud and determined tick that could be heard halfway across the big barn. I could see Tom staring at the clock and I noted at once that the tick was uneven, one interval longer than the other. He knew the clock needed leveling and made a mental note, as he told me afterwards, that he would attend to it before going to bed, for he was sure he could never sleep in the same room with such a lopsided tick. At the left of the desk was a window commanding a view of the large turning space in front of the barn and the driveway beyond. The window on the other side was small and high up from the floor, obviously built for the use of a horse. Heavy curtains made of grain sacking hung beside both windows. They gave the place a finished look, and still one couldn't help wondering at finding curtains in a barn. A stovepipe hole halfway up the outer wall indicated how the room was heated in winter, though the stove itself had been removed and the hole stoppered with an old lard pail.

After looking over the place—which was not entirely un-

familiar to me though I had not seen it in several years—
it occurred to me that the two old friends would like to be
left alone. So I made an excuse of the fact that I had other
witnesses to look up and withdrew. But later on I learned
the details of Tom's break with his family.

It began with Tom Hunter walking along behind the
cultivator, his steps listless, his gaze downcast, his hands
gripped mechanically on the polished handles. He swayed
from side to side as he walked, following the course of least
resistance. Occasionally, when an iron tooth would strike
a stone large enough to heave the cultivator out of the
row, Tom would lurch with it, tearing out a hill or perhaps two or three hills of the corn before he could arouse
himself sufficiently either to stop the horse or to haul the
implement back where it belonged. His father had often
said with feeling that he was the worst farmhand in the
county. But Tom did not mind that; he had no ambition
to be a good farmhand. The monotonous turning of the
furrow or scratching of the cultivator was not for him. He
could not keep his active mind on so dull a routine.

When the cultivator struck a stone Tom never stopped
to heave the obstruction aside, where it would not be
struck again. His mind did not work that way. His attitude was that there would always be stones and the cultivator should be so made as to cope with them. The teeth
could be put on swivels and then any one of them striking
an obstruction could swing around it—wait a minute—
why not a caster action, so they would always swing back
into line once the obstruction had been cleared? One day
when he had found the endless walking tiresome he attached a pair of old wheels to the cultivator, so that he
could ride. But his father soon put an end to this. He

wasn't going to have his farm made a laughingstock by the fool contraptions of that lazy boy—laziness in the Hunter family being an even more detestable curse than brutality or even dishonesty. Not long afterward, however, the disgruntled father found that his son had rigged a pair of cultivators together, with the idea of doing two rows at once. The invention was not perfect by any means. The offset cultivator would occasionally get out of control and cultivate a strip of corn right out of the ground. Still Tom was optimistic. He felt sure that in time he would be able to do a day's work in half a day, so that he could have the afternoon to himself in his workshop back of the corn-crib.

Just the sight of the contraption threw his father into a fit of anger. He came striding over to the place where the boy was at work. "What the devil—what do you think you got there?" he demanded gruffly, muttering still more emphatic words under his breath.

Tom grinned sheepishly. "It's a scheme to do two rows at once."

"What the hell for?"

"I don't know—save time, I guess."

"What you want to save time for? What else you got to do besides cultivatin'?"

Tom never could seem to explain anything to his father. "I don't know. I'd find some'pm to do, I guess."

"You and your damn fool contraptions. You want to kill that mare? She can't pull no such load as that—look at her puff! You'd had her foundered in another hour. Pullin' two cultivators through this heavy soil. You ain't got the sense God give a goose. Go put that mare in the stall and get the Dick horse—and if you know what's good for you, you'll hook him to *one* cultivator and get back to

· 9 ·

work. You needn't think I'm overlookin' all the stuff you plowed up there, neither. You can replant that tonight—after chores."

As soon as Tom's back was turned his father demolished the ingenious yoke the boy had constructed and slammed the pieces down in the corner of the fence. From the kitchen window Tom's mother could see that something was going on. She dried her hands and started to go out, but at the door of the woodshed she met her husband coming in.

"What's he changing horses for at this time of day?" she asked.

"Some more of his damn foolishness. Like to foundered the mare." He picked up the ax and drove it into the chopping block emphatically. "I ain't gonna put up with that fool boy much longer, Ma. Nineteen years old and no more sense than God give a goose."

"What'd he do?"

"Had Mollie pullin' two of them heavy cultivators to once!"

"Well, what's so bad about that?"

"Bad! She couldn't drag 'em, that's all. She was pullin' her guts out. Any fool woulda seen that it was too much for her." He pushed back his hat and wiped the sweat from his brow with a gnarled forefinger. "Why couldn't he have been like George?"

"George certainly is a good worker," she admitted.

"Good? There's no better."

"But he can't fix things like Tom can."

"No, but he can plow a furrow straight as a line and keep it up all day. And when he fetches his horses in they are as dry as when they go out. Did you look at that mare when Tom brung her in?"

· 10 ·

She shook her head. "I didn't notice."

"She was as wet as if she'd been in the creek."

"Tom never was a hand with horses. Can't seem to understand 'em."

"Can't seem to understand no kind of work."

"But he is good at tinkerin'," she said loyally.

Her husband threw up both his hands. "That's the whole damn trouble. It's tinker, tinker, tinker, and always has been. Remember the first thing he ever played with? A bolt and nut. Put it on and took it off a thousand times a day. And you remember the monkey wrench he used to take to bed with him every night?"

She nodded. "Yes, I remember about it."

"How many times do you s'pose he's had that alarm clock apart and put it together again?"

A suspicion of a smile showed at the corners of her mouth, but she quickly concealed it. "A good many times, I guess. But it always runs."

"By God, that's just the trouble. He'd let 'em be if they didn't."

"But you remember how he fixed the pump—in the winter when we couldn't get no help out from town."

"He fixed it all right. He fixed it, but did you ever catch him pumpin' any water for the cattle, unless I stood over him with a club?"

"He fixed the mowin' machine, too."

"Yes, and then run it into a boulder and broke it just as we was startin' the hayin', and I had to pay hired help to get the hay cut while he was waitin' for parts to come. George never broke a machine in his whole life."

"Never mended nuthin', neither."

"Well, you never saw him takin' no clock to pieces—for fun."

"Sometimes you forget, Pa, that Tom's a growin' boy."

"He don't miss no meals."

"Recollect what a sickly baby he was?"

"He's strong enough to walk behind a cultivator, if he'd only take a notion."

"Can you blame anybody for wantin' to make things easier? The boy's got a kind of a genius for makin' things. Remember how he used to close the window on winter mornings without gettin' out of bed?"

"Just like I told you—it's always a way to get outa doin' some'pm. And let me tell you another thing, a farm ain't no place for genius."

"You never can tell. He might invent some'pm."

"Not around here he won't. He'll work or he'll get out. That boy ain't hardly worth his keep. I damn near kicked him off the place today." He broke off speaking and peered out of the window. "Now what! He's comin' back." He stepped over to the door and shouted to Tom, who was bringing old Dick horse back towards the barn. "What's the matter there?"

Tom shook his head but kept on towards the barn. He was moving briskly now.

"What you fetching him back for?" his father shouted as he started across the dooryard. He did not like the look of animation about the boy.

When Tom saw that his father was coming he reined in the horse. "I'm going over to Jim Gates'. Jim just sent a boy over for me."

"Jim Gates?" His father scowled. "How come Jim is sendin' for you?"

"They've had a breakdown over there. They're threshin', you know, and Jim wants me to come over and see if I can fix the engine."

· 12 ·

This was almost too much. His father squinted up his eyes and came close to him. "Are you workin' for Jim, or are you workin' for me?"

A look of anxiety came over Tom's face. "But, Pa, there's fourteen men outa work over there, waitin' for the rig to get mended."

"That's Jim's lookout."

"I been studyin' about those engines. Betcha I can fix it, all right."

"Not today you can't. Take that horse back to the field and go on with your cultivatin'."

Tom struggled to make himself stand up to his father. "You don't understand, Pa—I got to go."

"You'll do as I say."

"But I told 'em I'd go!"

"I don't give a damn what you told 'em. You'll take your orders from me. Now get along with your cultivatin'."

Tom slowly turned the horse and started for the cornfield, but after he had gone a few steps he stopped and looked back. He moved his lips as if to speak, but thought better of it. For a moment he stood looking down at the ground. Then he turned and went on. His father was puzzled by his look. There was something in the expression of the boy's face that he had never seen there before. He couldn't say that it was exactly defiance, but whatever it was it angered the old man, who shouted after the boy as if in answer to something he had said, "Well, if you do go, you needn't come back."

Tom made no answer. He made no sign that he had heard, but drove on to the cornfield and along the row to the place where the cultivators had been left. Here he stopped the horse, hung the reins across its back, and began to unloop the tugs. Suddenly he noticed that his two-cultivator yoke was gone. He looked around for it and soon found it lying broken by the fence where his father had slammed it down. Until this moment he had not been able to decide what he was going to do. Now he knew. A few twisted pieces of wood had made up his mind for him.

He took hold of the reins and clucked to the horse. Dick tossed his head and looked back. His horse sense told him that there was something unorthodox about being driven along the row without some implement dragging behind. He switched his tail and blew through his lips to attract the attention of the boy, whose awkward handling and lack of attentiveness had long been familiar to him.

"You think it's funny, do you, Dick?" said the boy. "Well, you'll think it's a lot funnier in a minute."

At the end of the row Tom stopped the horse and, without turning him, drew the reins forward through the hame rings. He wrapped them several times around the top rail of the fence and tied them securely, so that they would not come loose and be trampled underfoot, for he had a suspicion that Dick horse was going to stand there for a long while. For the first time in his life he put out his hand and patted the animal's neck.

"Good-by, Dick," he said. "Say good-by to the folks for me. You and I were never very good friends, but I don't hold it against you. I guess we didn't see things the same way."

He climbed awkwardly over the fence and, without looking back, started across the fields for the Gates farm.

2

Iron Horse

TOM APPROACHED THE GATES FARM FROM the rear. He had taken off his shoes and waded across the creek, and so arrived long ahead of the messenger who had gone around by the bridge. As Tom walked up the lane from the pasture he became conscious of an unnatural quietness that seemed to have settled over the place. He could see men loading bundles of wheat on a wagon in a distant field, but there was none of the hustle and bustle the countryside had come to expect from a big threshing outfit.

Usually when threshers came they overran the whole place like a farmers' picnic. Helped themselves to fruit and berries, invaded the milk house, took down sections of fence to suit their convenience, and not only poked through the barns but the cellar as well. The stories of their eating abilities were prodigious; and it was not at all unusual for farmers to miss tools, pieces of harness, and other small articles after the outfit had moved on.

These things were in Tom's mind as he slid through the bars at the end of the lane leading up from the pasture, but it was not until he had come around the corner of the hay barn and was in the farmyard itself that he understood the cause of the quiet. Jim Gates had just rolled out a barrel of cider and was tapping it, while the threshing hands lay sprawled in the shade waiting for him to get the spigot installed and in working order. Smart move on Jim's part. He knew how to keep the men from straying.

In the Gates farmyard the buildings were sprawled around a rough quadrangle, about the size of a baseball diamond. In the pitcher's box stood the crippled engine, gaunt and silent, attached by a long belt to the separator, which was standing where second base would have been. Tom had not expected to find so many people around. He had thought only of the job on the engine; and at the sight of such a considerable audience his self-confidence deserted him. He wished he were somewhere else—anywhere else. The stony cornfield that he had left behind him, as a sleeper shakes off a disagreeable dream, did not seem at the moment such an undesirable spot, and even his father's stupid antagonism lost much of its sting. His footsteps lagged, and stage fright was rapidly overcoming him when Gates caught sight of him and waved a welcome. Tom was conscious of the dust-encrusted threshers nudging one another and winking when they discovered that he was supposed to be the mechanic. One clownish fellow made little attempt to conceal his pantomime. He drew down the corners of his mouth and indicated with a wagging thumb that the boss thresher wasn't going to care much for the half-grown sprout brought to his assistance.

Jim Gates dropped his auger and, regardless of the protests of the thirsty threshers who kept reminding him how thirsty they were, led Tom over to the engine, beside which the boss of the outfit, a tall countryman named Mike Kelsey, stood wiping his hands with a piece of oily waste. "The regular engineer is off on a drunk," Jim explained by way of introduction, "and Kelsey here knows how to run it, but he ain't learned how to fix it yet."

Kelsey slowly turned his head and surveyed the new-comer over his shoulder. "You don't mean to tell me this is your—mechanic?"

Jim tried to laugh it off. "Mebbe not a mechanic ex-actly," he said with an attempt at heartiness, "but I ain't never seen nuthin' he couldn't fix."

This brought Kelsey all the way around. "But he's only a kid. It ain't rulable to turn him loose on a big machine like this."

"He ain't troubled with old age," Jim admitted, "but you'll find he's pretty damn good."

The threshers were becoming impatient. "Come on, Jim, come on!" they were calling loudly. "Tap this bar'l first, and then we won't care how long you chin."

Jim motioned to them to pipe down. "All right, all right," he shouted. Then he turned a very serious look on the boss. "Tom's the best we can do," he said with an out-thrust jaw, "and if he can't fix it we'll just have to wait until you can get your engineer sobered up."

"Yeah—and when'll that be? You know how Charley Cosad is."

Jim was still glowering. "You know more about that than I do. But I can tell you one thing—this good weather ain't gonna last forever."

"Prob'ly not." With his dirty waste Kelsey wiped the sweat from his chin. "What makes me so damn mad is that I got nobody to blame but myself. I shoulda stuck to steam. I know a steam engine like the inside of my hat, but this gasoline thing has got me licked." He bent down his pockmarked face and peered at Tom. "Ever work on one of these?" He was so close that Tom could smell the tobacco on his breath, sweet but sickening.

· 17 ·

Tom drew back a little. "Well, they're not exactly new to me. I've seen 'em before, and I know how they work."

"Know all about 'em, hey?" It was a disagreeable challenge.

"Mebbe not all, but I got a good book about 'em—and I know what's in it."

Meanwhile the thresher hands were becoming more urgent with their shouts. "We want cider! We want cider! What the hell, Jim, we want cider!"

Jim was becoming flurried. "I gotta take care of those boys," he said. "Do the best you can, Tom." And he hurried away.

Kelsey slowly fished a plug of tobacco out of his pocket. "So you've read a book about gas engines and now you're ready to tackle one, huh?" He bit savagely at his plug.

"That's right," said Tom agreeably. "The principle ain't very hard to get onto. When you know how they work it's simple."

"Um-m-m, simple." Kelsey contorted his face with the violence of his mastication. "I see what you mean."

Tom thought he meant it. "Just three things," he said. "Intake—ignition—exhaust. That's all there is to it."

"Yeah—that's all—but what comes next?"

"Nothing. Same thing right over again."

"The way you tell it sounds easy enough; but give me steam every time."

"Steam's all right for some things, but it says in the book that a big firebox and boiler is not needed for this kind of a job where you move from one place to another. You don't care if I sorta look it over, do you?"

"Lookin' won't do no hurt, but I don't want you monkeyin' with things. Charley Cosad will have a tough enough time fixin' it when he gets back—damn him!"

"Won't it run at all?" asked Tom. "Or does it just buck and skip?"

The big thresher shook his head. "It's deader'n a smelt. Can't get a poop out of it."

Tom bent over and peered at the motor. "There's a set of rules in my book about finding trouble. They go right along in order, *a-b-c-d*. First you test one thing and if you find it all right you try another."

Kelsey smiled sourly. "Now ain't that nice—they got it down to *a-b-c*."

"Here's luck, boss!" The clownish thresher came up with a Mason jar full of cider.

Kelsey put out one of his grimy hands and wrapped it around the jar. "Don't care if I do." He dropped the tobacco from his mouth and, holding the jar with one hand, drank and offered it to Tom.

"Not now," said Tom. "Join you a little later."

"You mean you ain't got it fixed yet?" asked the clown, retrieving the jar.

Kelsey gave him a not unfriendly shove. "Get the hell outa here, Pete, or we'll never get it agoin'."

"Don't need to hurry on my account. Take your time," muttered Pete with an assortment of profanity, vulgarity, and obscenity run in together. "Take all the blankety-blank time you want to and I'll tell you where to stick it." And he started back for more cider.

With a glance at the congestion around the cider barrel Kelsey shook his head and scowled. "Jim'll have the whole crew drunk if we don't get this thing agoin'. Now what about all this *a-b-c* business? Is there an'thing to it?"

Tom searched his memory. "First you look to see if there is fuel (*a*) in the tank and (*b*) at the carbureter."

"(c) and then what?" There was a sarcastic edge on the thresher's voice.

"You test the sparkplugs for current."

"(d), (e), (f), (g). But how the hell do you do it?"

"Just lay the plug on the cylinder casting and turn the engine over until it sparks."

The big thresher wavered. "You almost sound as if you know what you're talkin' about. I got half a mind to let you try it." He stopped and glanced again at the group around the cider barrel.

"I suppose you've tested your dry cells," said Tom.

"Not me," said Kelsey. "Mebbe Charley did."

"I don't suppose you've got an ammeter?"

"God, boy, if I knew what one of them things was do you think I'd be yellin' for help?"

Tom smiled. "It's a little round thing like a watch, with a wire hangin' to it."

Kelsey slowly shook his head. "Might be one in the tool-box. Charley's got some funny stuff in there." He stood pointing with his finger at the toolbox when a burst of raucous laughter came from the group at the cider barrel. It was the laughter that did the business. "All right," he muttered, "you can go on with your *a-b-c* stuff. Only don't take nuthin' apart that you can't put together again. And listen, I'm gonna walk over there by the boys. They'll be a little more careful if they see me around. Just holler if you need me."

Half-a-dozen jars of cider were proffered to the boss as he sauntered over into the shade of the apple tree under which the barrel had been set up. He declined them all on the plea that he had just taken a fresh chaw of tobacco. Didn't want to waste a good chaw. He told them that he was makin' the kid a little nervous by watchin' him and he thought he'd better leave the youngster alone. "It's rulable to give him a chance to fix it if he can," Kelsey went on, "because if he can't make it go we'll be up against a lay-off until Charley can wind up his spree and get back on the job, or until a man can come from the factory."

The prospects of a lay-off made the men a little less cheerful, but the arrival of Jim Gates with a dishpan full of doughnuts occupied their attention for a time, while Jim and Kelsey were discussing the eventualities and Tom was struggling through the various steps of his *a, b* and *c*.

Suddenly there came a cough from the engine, followed by a labored wheezing. Then came a louder cough. The wheezing accelerated, and the spokes of the flywheels disappeared as if they had been wiped away. This outburst of speed was of short duration, however, and the engine began to heave and falter. Tom grabbed hurriedly at this and that trying to give it more gas, and when he finally found the right adjustment the machine swung into its customary stride and went humming along as if nothing had happened. The farmyard came to life like an enchanted village in a fairy tale. While Kelsey went striding over to throw the belt from an idler pulley to the power shaft, the members of the crew rose up from the grass like a swarm of locusts, drained their jars at a gulp, and started for their stations, jamming on their hats as they went and knotting their sweaty bandannas around their thick necks.

The belt swung and swayed as it took up the load. With a mighty shudder the separator came to life. The slats of the carrier began to move. Wheels turned, beaters pounded, gears hummed, and soon the separator had attained its working speed and was putting out its usual deafening roar. Feeders shoved the golden stalks across the glistening apron, great clouds of dust and chaff arose, wheat straws started floating out of the stacker, and a thin trickle of grain came pouring from the spout. Once more Jim Gates began to figure his harvest in terms of bushels.

As soon as Kelsey was satisfied that the engine was really going to run he took Tom by the arm and led him a little aside to ask what had caused the trouble. Embarrassingly enough, Tom did not know. When he had found (a) that there was plenty of gasoline in the tank, he had (b) drained the carbureter and had found both water and sediment, which he had flushed out. But as he came to (c) and was testing the connections he found so many of them loose that he lost track of them, and it was while he was turning over the engine to test them with the spark that the initial charge had ignited and startled him nearly out of his wits. Just what he had done that had made it go he never could be quite sure.

"I guess there wasn't much the matter with it," he shouted above the din of the machinery. "If you'd fussed around a little more you'd have found it yourself."

"Yeah, but what was it?"

Tom wasn't going to admit that he didn't know. "Oh, it was a little bit of everything." He waved his hands indefinitely.

Kelsey laid a large rugged hand on his arm. "Listen, feller," he said, "I didn't mean no harm when I said you was a kid."

"Of course not."

"It was just that you looked so damn young, and this breakdown was so damn serious I just couldn't figger you'd be able to handle it. I didn't mean to make you sore."

Tom shook his head with an exaggerated negative. "I wasn't sore about that."

"Well, I didn't mean nuthin' about the book, neither," the big thresher struggled on. "Lots of folks has learned things out of a book. I just meant I never could learn nuthin' out of 'em. A book is like a stick of dynamite—it's all right if you know how to use it. Now listen, I'm willin' to pay you for what you done, but it's rulable I should know what it is, so if it happens again I'll know how to fix it myself." He turned to Gates, who had just joined them. "Am I right, Jim?"

Gates squinted up his face with serious consideration. "I don't rightly know," he said; "but what you're askin' don't sound unreasonable to me."

"I ain't holding anything out on him," shouted Tom. "I'd explain it to him if I could." It was the shouting that made it difficult. Tom felt sure that if he could have spoken in a rational tone he could have satisfied them both with very little difficulty; but he found it hard to explain a thing at the top of his lungs, especially a thing that he didn't quite understand himself.

By this time Kelsey was scowling. "What do you mean you can't explain it to me? You mean I don't know enough? Is that what you're gettin' at?"

"No—that's not it at all." Tom was rapidly reaching the point of desperation. There was just no sense in trying to explain everything that he had done. It might have been the dirt in the carbureter and it might not. It might have been one connection and it might have been another. Nearly every little nut on the dry cells had been loose and the trouble might have been caused by any one of them. A large, dusty, sunburned ear was held in front of him for an answer, and he didn't know what to say. Then suddenly an idea came to him. "I'll show you," he shouted.

Tom walked over to the engine and pointed at the most conspicuous connection in sight, the wire attached to the sparkplug. "That's the one right there! *It was loose!*"

The big thresher grinned with satisfaction. Here was something that he could put his finger on—and did. The resulting flash threw him back like a blow on the chin.

"See—!" Tom shouted in his ear. "Plenty of current there now, but you've got to keep it tight!"

Kelsey nodded as he examined the end of his finger. "I'll watch it," he said. "Much obliged. Gates'll settle with you. Be sure to tell 'im where you're gonna be—I might need you again."

Gates nodded and walked away with Tom. On the further side of the house, where the clatter of the machines was muted, the farmer drew a wallet from his hip pocket and asked Tom how much. But Tom waved him aside and no amount of argument could change him. Gates explained that it was not *his* breakdown and that the cost of it would come out of Kelsey, but Tom still shook his head. He hadn't come there to work for Kelsey, but just to do Gates a little neighborly turn, such as any fellow would do for a friend; and besides, he explained, he had been hankering for some time to get his hands on a gas engine. Even when Gates admitted that the boy had probably saved his wheat crop and that a man from the factory would have cost at least twenty or thirty dollars, Tom still refused to listen.

He finally settled for a glass of cider. And when Gates offered to have one of the boys hook up a horse and take him home Tom insisted that he had an errand off across the fields in the other direction that could best be done on foot. Tom had pursued his errand for a mile or two before the thought came to him that his total assets were his pocket knife and a dollar watch. He could easily have had five dollars or even ten from Jim Gates, but he was glad he hadn't asked for it. He would have been ashamed to take money for the pleasure of getting his hands on that engine. By the leather thong he used as a watch chain he pulled out his timepiece. A glance at it told him that in a couple of hours somebody would have to go for the cows. He smiled as he thought that this time he wouldn't go. He enjoyed the mental prospect of his father calling "Co' boss, co' boss!" and then going after the laggards with a stick. And it would take the old man quite a while to do the milking alone. Tom wondered if Dick horse was still standing tied to the fence, and what his mother would say when she found that her younger son had left home.

3

Horse Barn

As he walked along the road he thought of the dull, monotonous miles he had plodded along behind a lurching cultivator or a swerving plow, and he was suddenly elated at the thought that never again would he take a step behind any horse-drawn farm implement. From now on he would follow his own free will. He could do as he damn pleased. He could go and he could come without a word to anybody. Never again would he be told when to go to bed and when to get up.

At just that moment a disturbing thought obtruded—where would he go to bed? He couldn't go to the Woodpecker Inn, because he had no money. He had no close friends in town, no relatives there with whom he could stay until he got a job. His only relative anywhere around was his brother George. George was older, quite a little older. They never got along very well. But after all, they were brothers, and weren't brothers supposed to help each other? He could drop in on George and tell him the news. George himself had quit home, so he'd understand. Perhaps George would ask him to stay for a few days until he could find himself a job. It wasn't far to George's—only a mile or so out of his way—and he felt that he ought to take the chance.

As he came over the hill he could see George working

in the field—cultivating. It would have to be cultivating. Just the thought of it depressed him. His footsteps lagged. He sat down under a tree to think things over. As he sat there George passed so near that Tom could hear his directions to the horse. "Steady there, Dolly. Who-o-oa. Get around there. Easy, girl—easy! Lift up there! You know better than to step on a tug."

He was hidden from George by a screen of fence line shrubbery, but he knew what was going on in the field as well as if he could see. From far across the field he could hear George's wife yelling at the children. She brought a new element into the situation. He had forgotten all about her. Never liked her. She was too shrill, too ready to put in her oar. She'd have something cutting to say when Tom explained that he had quit home. Perhaps it would be better for him to make his explanation to George before going to the house, and then George could tell his wife whatever was necessary. Why wasn't this a good place to explain to George, here at the end of the field, far from the house?

Tom stood up and went quickly over to the shrubbery, where he stopped and listened. He could hear no sound from the field, but he felt sure that George had turned and was resting his horse. Perhaps he had better look. He parted the branches gently and leaned over to peer through just as George chirped to the horse and started back along the return row. George passed within a few paces, but he was looking neither to the right nor the left. When George was cultivating, he cultivated. He seldom raised his eyes from the task in hand. He was a worker, George was. The idea of a short cut never entered his mind. Never in his life had he thought of a way to make a task easier. He did not want things easier. All he wanted was to get them done, and the way to get things done was by work. Steady work. Good work.

When Tom heard the cultivator start he quickly drew back, not wishing to be caught spying upon his brother. After he was sure that George had passed he again parted the bushes and peered through. He could see George's back plainly, but somehow it did not look like George's back—it looked more like his father's. There was the same grim rounding of the shoulders, the same determined crook in the arms as he gripped the handles of the cultivator, the same awkward, rocking gait. But it was not just the physical similarity. Tom had always known that they looked alike. It was something stronger, deeper, a sort of spiritual identity.

Tom leaned his elbows on the fence and thought about it. With George getting farther and farther away all the time Tom's notion began to seem silly to him, the confusing of one with the other. George was all right, a little stupid and slow-witted perhaps, but he wasn't mean. That was where he differed from his father. The old man had a mean streak in him. Always did have. Tom smiled. He could smile about it, now that he was through with the old man. A faint clank against a stone told him that George must be coming again. Back and forth. Back and forth. Same old thing, over and over again. That was what made farming so damn monotonous. This time he would catch George coming up the row. He would step out and meet him face to face. Then there'd be no question of his being spied on. But he'd better look and see where George was. George was closer than he thought—and even from the front he bore a disagreeably close resemblance to the old man. Tom stood and watched him come, but for some reason he could not bring himself to speak. And George

· 29 ·

went by to the end of the row, where he turned his horse and stopped awhile to breathe him. Presently he went off across the field again, and Tom had not accosted him. Three times George came and each time Tom let him go by. He couldn't speak, he couldn't bring himself to ask anything of a person who looked so much like his father.

As he retraced his steps and once more started for town, Tom guessed he was in a kind of a jam. He did not doubt for a moment that he would be able to find a job—and it wouldn't be farm work either. From now on he would do the kind of work he wanted to . . . but there was still that little matter of eating, and it wouldn't do any harm if he had a roof over his head at night. However, he was determined he never would return to the farm again, not even to get his clothes and the tools that belonged to him. He felt pretty sure his mother would send his clothes to him by one of the neighbors. She had made it a practice to send the hired men's belongings after them when they went away in a huff, usually stalking out of a field too mad even to remember their clothes. Tom smiled when he thought of something Gid Wilson had said when Tom took his clothes to the livery barn after Gid had quit. "The old son of a gun may take his hired help out to the farm in a wagon, but he always manages to make 'em leave under their own power."

Tom was still smiling about it when he turned into the driveway leading to the livery stable, the day he had found me there talking with Gid. As Tom told me the story afterwards, he liked everything about Gid's room except the smell. It reeked of horse and of the accompanying odor of liniment and leather. He wondered, a little dubiously, how he would be able to sleep in such an overpowering aroma, and he saw nothing humorous in the thought that he had run away from one horse to spend the night in a barn with fifty.

The question of eating was something that he had not dared to think about; but Gid soon brought it up when he allowed that he'd fetch some supper over from the lunchroom and they'd eat in. He was expecting rigs back at any minute and did not want to be away when they came. Being the guest and without funds, there was nothing for Tom to do but to acquiesce. So he volunteered to tend barn while Gid stepped across the street for refreshments. Tom had just finished leveling the clock—a little improvement of which Gid never was aware—when a rig came in. He at once assumed the duties of stableboy, and by the time that Gid returned with a newspaper package of supper and a tin pail of coffee, Tom had checked the arrival on the blackboard and had the nag unharnessed and in its stall.

"How'd you know which stall?" asked Gid.

"I didn't," Tom admitted. "I just let the horse pick his own stall."

Gid chuckled. "That hoss'll do it, but there's some of 'em that won't."

Tom washed his hands thoroughly before eating, but the horse smell came through with every mouthful. It was not sufficient, however, to dampen the ardor of his lusty young appetite; but never again could Tom bring himself to say that he was hungry enough to eat a horse. Another rig checked in just as they had finished eating, and by nightfall all the horses except one were in their stalls. For the next two hours Tom sat in the barrel chair at peace with all the world. He was relaxed and contented. There was none of the antagonism that he always felt in his father's presence. His mental state was like that of a man just out of jail; the worst was over, and the future couldn't be anything but bright.

He wanted to talk freely, to pour out all his hopes and ambitions and aspirations, but somehow he could not get them into words. He made one false start after another, groping, stammering, reaching first one way and then another without conveying to Gid any intelligible idea of what he was driving at. Gradually the impulse to pour out his heart subsided, and under the not unfriendly guidance of the down-to-earth stableman the future was resolved from a rosy dream into the very practical problem of earning a living.

"Reckon you ain't never worked for cash money, have you?" asked Gid.

"Guess that's right."

"Never need money around a farm. Three meals a day come on the table without your even askin' for 'em. Place to sleep, clothes to wear, room enough to turn around in. If you just want to keep alive, that's about all you need. But most of us wanta do more'n just keepin' alive, and if you do you gotta pay for it. It's gonna be different with you from now on—you gotta pay for everything you get. Reckon you can earn a livin'?"

"I reckon I can."

"Doin' what?"

"Well, anything but farm work. I'll starve before I'll ever work on a farm again."

Gid laughed. "I guess you got a bellyful of farmin'. But what else can you do?"

"I don't know why I can't work in a shop. I'm extra good with tools."

"What shop?"

"Any of 'em—carriage factory, plow works, sprayer shop."

"You wanta be a factory hand and stand beside a machine all your life?"

"But I gotta start somewhere."

"I know," said Gid, "but what's the matter with a clean job?" When Tom made no reply Gid did not press the question. "Well, anyway," he said, "you'll never get a job as a machinist in that farm rig you got on. I'll fetch your clothes tomorrow, and then we'll see what happens. Right now I'm fallin' asleep in my chair. Why don't you get into bed, and I'll kick off my boots and lay down beside you and snooze along till the nag comes in."

Gid went out and hooked a heavy rope across the big doorway and hung a lighted lantern on a peg outside the door. When he came back he found that Tom had taken off his shoes and was stretched out on top of the bed. He caught the point at once—the boy wouldn't get into bed until he did. Gid smiled; the kid was all right. He pulled off his boots and stretched out beside him. Not a word was said, and soon Gid was snoring. Tom couldn't sleep. The excitement of the day was too much for him, and he found the barn a very noisy place at night. The horses stamped and whickered, and they clomped and grunted as they lay down and got up. And he had never realized before how much noise just the mastication of a forkful of hay could make when it was multiplied by fifty. But that was not the worst of it, for the fumes of the stable came in upon him like a cloud of poison gas. At last, however, he fell off to sleep. The next thing he knew Gid was shaking him.

"Wake up, boy!" he was saying in a guarded whisper.

"We gotta get outa here and go up and sleep in the hay!"

Tom rose up on one elbow, blinking and rubbing his eyes. "Up in the hay?"

"That's right. Grab yourself a horse blanket."

"But we got to wait for that horse to come in."

"The horse is in."

"You—you mean I slept through it?"

"That's right. Now grab yourself a blanket and come with me."

"But, Gid, why do we have to go up in the hay?"

"Can't explain now," muttered Gid. "Grab yourself a blanket and come along."

With a blanket over his arm and his shoes flapping loosely on his feet, Tom followed the stableman back through the darkness to the stairway. Somehow he managed to feel his way up the stairs without falling. In the haymow the two spread out their blankets and lay down. As before, Gid was snoring almost immediately, but Tom was wide awake. He kept wondering how it had happened that Gid had gone off to sleep without telling him why they had to move. He could think of only one good reason—that somebody else had to have the use of the room. But who? Who else around there was as important as Gid?

The sounds from the horses were more muffled up here, and there was a welcome dilution of the odor from the stalls. The smell of the hay reminded him of the farm and, though it was not unpleasant, there was a constant rustling from underneath the blanket. He had an idea that the rustling was caused by the bending of the brittle stalks of grass from the weight of his body, and he reasoned that if he could lie perfectly still for a long enough time the rustling would stop. So for a while he lay perfectly motionless, but the rustling went on. He tried holding his breath, but the rustling still continued. It was not that the sound was unpleasant or annoying. What bothered him was the persistence; he simply could not get away from that whispering sound. He turned and twisted and rolled, he sat up and he lay back again—and the whispering of the hay went on without the slightest interruption. Horses stamped and tramped and shifted about; they snorted and blew and blubbered with their lips; they pawed and sniffed and coughed. Tom heard these things. He took pains to hear them, he listened for them and tried to keep his attention on them. But all the time, whether he was listening or not, he could not help hearing that unceasing whispering of the hay. Finally out of sheer exhaustion he fell asleep.

When they woke up in the morning Tom kept expecting Gid to explain why they had been routed out of their bed and driven into the haymow; but Gid said nothing at all about it. Tom never quite understood whether this was intentional or just an oversight. However, as it turned out, Tom was able to draw his own conclusions, for when he went into Gid's room that morning he found the place heavily scented with something very different from the ordinary fragrance of the horse barn. It was reeking with perfume, which, to Tom's mind, could mean only one thing—a woman.

4

Stud Horse

ℐT WAS ONLY A LITTLE AFTER SIX IN THE morning when Tom walked out of the big barn and strolled slowly towards the main street of the town. He had expected to help with the morning chores and stable work, but Gid wouldn't have it. Wouldn't be any help to him, he said. Stable hands were hired to do that work and they wouldn't thank Tom for horning in on their job. As for the three studs, Gid forbade him to go near them. He explained with picturesque profanity that they were as jealous and as notional as old maids.

"We keep their doors locked," he said, "and we don't let nobody in there but a lady horse. Why don't you take yourself for a walk while I give them their breakfast in bed?"

Tom strolled off to the other end of the barns and eventually made up his mind to go out and look over the town. At this early hour few people were stirring when he reached the street. It was to a large extent a two-story town. The Inn and some of the more recent buildings had found the ambition to go up another story, though it was commonly believed that, while people would climb the extra flight for lodge night or other purely social purposes, they certainly would not do it for business reasons. With peculiar satisfaction Tom ran his eye up to the top of these three-story skyscrapers. They really were something to be proud of. He had admired them before, but now that this was to be his own home town he savored for the first time the tang of civic pride. He walked over to the curb and stood with one foot on the stone stepping-block. The old town certainly looked good to him.

Cobb, the freckle-faced porter, who had just come out on the front porch of the Inn with a bucket of steaming suds and a broom, looked up at the sky and yawned. Then he dipped his broom and began scrubbing listlessly at the steps. In front of his harness shop, across from the Inn, Brad Cowan was sweeping away what looked like whittlings on the sidewalk. Tom shook his head. Just taking a stick of wood to pieces with a knife was a pastime in which he had never indulged. He wondered what Brad was thinking of the shavings that he was sweeping into the street, and how many bales the shavings would have made through the years if they had all been saved. He watched the harness maker put away his broom and take up a feather duster, with which he proceeded to brush off the slightly dilapidated wooden horse used as a sign to advertise his business.

"Hi, Brad!" he heard Cobb call from across the street. "Have you fed the hoss his oats?"

Brad nodded. For years he had been answering banter about that horse. "He's had all he can hold," he replied patiently.

"Frank, there, is waitin' for you to clean out his stall."

Brad was not amused, but he turned to see how Frank Decker had received the sally. Frank, a gloomy fellow in brown jeans trundling a wheelbarrow up the road, paid not the slightest attention. As expressionless as if he had not heard, Frank plodded along until he came to a spot where a horse, evidently a well-fed horse, had been standing the evening before. Here he set down his barrow and took up his shovel and broom.

"If you'd do that, Brad," shouted Cobb, "mebbe you'd have as good a garden as Frank."

At that moment Old Tick, the innkeeper, stepped out on the porch in his shirt sleeves and carpet slippers, every one of his 256 pounds quivering with irritation. Cobb's dawdling and his talkativeness were a great trial to the short-tempered innkeeper. Old Tick would often foam up like a Seidlitz powder just at the sight of his porter doing nothing.

"Jees Cri!" he screamed in his high-pitched voice. "Ain't you got them steps cleaned yet? You been out here long enough to mop off the whole goddamed town! And what the hell you yellin' around for at this time of day? You wanta wake up every goddamed guest we got in the goddamed house?"

Cobb very calmly dipped his mop in the suds. "I was just talkin' to Brad. And besides, we ain't got no guests in the house."

Old Tick waved his paper menacingly. "Well, by the Jees Cri, if you don't let that mop do your talkin' for you and get them goddam steps done in a hurry, I'll fire you outa this place on your goddam ear!" He shook the newspaper menacingly at the porter and, still glaring back at him, slowly shuffled into the lobby.

Utterly impervious to all this bickering, Frank Decker went on about his business. At the hitching rail in front of the post office he made a rich haul. There was a glint in his eye, Tom thought, like that of a miner spying a nugget, though there was no acceleration in the tempo of his movements. A few well-aimed scoops of his shovel and he moved along. When the barrow was filled he started for home, swaying as he walked. As Tom watched him he was thinking of ways to improve the wheelbarrow.

His flow of ideas was interrupted by the appearance of an emaciated man jingling a ring of keys in his hand, to which he kept time as he walked. Tom did not know the fellow's name, though he recognized him as the clerk on his way to open the post office. He watched the thin man unlock the door and gather up the night letters which had come through the slot. Soon afterwards he heard the rapid thumping of the cancellation hammer as the clerk neatly obliterated the face of Mr. Washington from each stamp and at the same time impressed a blurred postmark of the office of origin on each envelope.

More people were on the street now. Big iron keys turned in locks and store doors began to swing open. Tom noticed the hardware man putting out buckets and garden tools for display; then a stepladder and a wooden wash-tub, and finally a stack of nested baskets still in the crate. Meanwhile the grocers were sweeping out the rubble from last night's business, and piling their outdoor display stands with fruits and vegetables. The clothing store shoved out two battered dummies showing what the well-dressed lay figure would be wearing for the rest of the summer.

Tom looked down the street, past the bank corner, past the Inn, far beyond the cluster of stores which made up the business section of the town. His gaze ran along the stately avenue of trees which formed a shady archway the full length of residential Main Street.

He ran his eyes over the wide green lawns lying before the best houses in town. Tom took a certain pride in these houses, though he had never been inside any of them.

Whether he ever would be or not was something that had not yet occurred to him. Across the grass on the north side he could see the impressive mansion of Morton Towner, the only stone house on the street. There was something about a stone house that overawed him; he didn't know quite what it was.

On the other side he caught a glimpse of the wide veranda of the Andy Brackett house, white through the shrubbery. As he looked, he saw the tall form of the owner come down the steps, pause, light a cigar, glance at the sky, and start up the street with vigorous, morning strides. All his life Tom had known who Andy Brackett was. Not to know who he was in this town would be like not knowing who Teddy Roosevelt was in Washington. Tom never had spoken to Andy Brackett. He had no idea that Andy knew who he was or even that he existed. This was because he was not familiar with the nature of the small-town political leader, who makes it his business to know everybody who is or who may become a voter.

A smile came over Tom's face as he stood watching Andy. "My host of the night before," he thought. "Of course he doesn't know it, and probably wouldn't give the matter a second thought if he did. But, after all, it's something to be even the barn guest of the most important citizen in town on a fellow's first night away from home."

He watched idly as Andy picked up his morning paper from a bench in front of the drug and stationery store and walked along the street towards his office, reading it as he went. After Andy had gone inside Tom strolled slowly over to the bandstand perched in the fork of the road at the end of the town. As yet no stores had crowded west of the fork, and the ornate circular bandstand stood like a battered sentinel at the end of his beat. The flag staff on the pointed roof was leaning slightly, its halyards gone, all but a frayed piece of rope which hung motionless in the quiet of the summer morning. Through the sagging door, which stood slightly ajar, Tom could see an open stairway leading to the loft from which local musicians dispensed spirited band music Saturday nights throughout the summer.

He passed to the other side of the street and walked slowly down to the post office corner, where he leaned against one of the recently installed telephone poles and watched old Joe Spears open up his general store. Biggest store in town. Probably the best. Tom had traded the eggs there many times, and over and over again he had heard his father say that Joe was the only storekeeper in town who could count eggs. Other merchants unlocked their establishments. Drowsily the town rubbed the sleep out of its eyes and got ready for another day.

Many of the storekeepers came to business in buggies with safe old horses that looked as if they would stand at the hitching rail half a day without any trace of uneasiness or impatience. But Tom imagined they would be ready to go home when midday approached, for by that time they would be feeling the need of a drink of water and a measure of oats.

There was a little more style to the arrival of Morton Towner. He wore gloves and came in a phaeton drawn by a black horse as portly as himself. Tom watched with interest and some amusement as Mr. Towner, who always dressed in grey, eased himself slowly from the low step of his phaeton to the curb and, accompanied only by his gold-headed cane, walked with a burdened look to the door of his bank, which stood on the corner across from the post office. There was about him none of the easy cameraderie that prevailed among the other merchants of the town, no salutes, no cheerful greetings. He spoke to nobody but went straight to the keyhole and inserted the key which, unlike the keys of ordinary stores, was small and flat and shiny. After he had the key in the lock, and with his hand still on it, Mr. Towner raised his eyes and glanced first to the right, down Chestnut Street towards the railroad station, then to the left, down the full sweep of Main Street. After this he quickly turned the key and stepped inside.

Tom was so intent on watching the banker that he failed to see a bicycle rapidly approaching on a diagonal line from the other side of the street, and when suddenly it whizzed by missing him by no more than an inch or two, he gave a startled jump followed instantly by a surge of indignation. He didn't care if Asa Parker was the youngest county clerk in the state, he had no business to be slamming by people as close as that. As Tom turned to glare after the bicycle he saw Asa Parker swing skilfully from the seat and bring the machine to a standstill. He did not bother to lean it against the building, but hurriedly dropped it on its side on the pavement and strode into the post office. The precise workmanship, the beautiful finish of the piece of machinery caught Tom's attention. No chain—it must be one of the new bevel drives—a Columbia chainless. He had never seen one before.

Inside the post office he could hear Asa in heated altercation with the clerk. "Quit your blasted back talk and open up that bag. This is state business—it's got to go to the comptroller!"

"And I tell you this is gover'ment business," shouted the clerk. "You can't delay the U. S. mail!"

"Who wants to delay it? All I want to do is get an important letter into it."

"That mail is closed and it's gonna stay closed." The clerk slammed the locked bag down on the table for emphasis.

"Now listen to me, Mister Smart Aleck, you're not the postmaster of this town, you're just a dumb clerk. You're not even civil service and you can be fired out on your ear any time the postmaster takes it into his head—and I'll see that he does take it into his head!"

The sound of the voices was plainly audible on the street. People stopped, looked in to see what it was all about, and began to draw nearer so as not to miss anything. Then Andy Brackett pushed through the crowd and laid his hand on Asa's shoulder. "What's going on here?" he asked quietly.

Asa forced a smile. "Just a little difference of opinion," he said, trying to hide all trace of belligerency. "I was askin' Jess to open up the mail long enough to get in an important piece of state business that's got to go out this morning, and Jess was showing his usual concern for the convenience of the public that hires him."

By this time Jess, too, was putting on a great show of affability. "I was just explainin' to Asa that my instructions are to close the mail at seven-thirty, and when I get it closed I ain't got no right to open it again. I was gonna tell him he'd have to give it to Fred and have him put it on the train."

"And I was trying to tell Jess that I didn't have time to wait for Fred," said Asa.

Fred appeared in the doorway, a sturdy young fellow who flagged the crossing when he was not carrying the mail. "Who's takin' my name in vain?" he asked with a grin.

It was Andy Brackett who answered him. "Asa has a letter for you to put on the train."

Fred held out his hand for it. "Sure," he said. "Sure; let me have it."

Nobody paid any attention to the gawky boy in faded overalls who stood leaning against the telephone pole, but Tom was not missing any of it. He saw the look of triumph on the clerk's face as Asa turned and walked out of the door with Andy Brackett. He heard what Andy

Brackett was saying to Asa after the onlookers had scattered and Asa had retrieved his chainless from the sidewalk.

"You don't want to rub their fur the wrong way," Andy was telling Asa. "That will never get you anywhere."

"Of course not—but that fellow—"

Andy cut him off with the wave of an emphatic hand. "His vote's as good as anybody's."

Tom watched them go slowly along, Asa pushing his bicycle, and Andy Brackett gesticulating with his cigar. He admired the way Andy Brackett had put an end to the disturbance—hardly had to do a thing, just his presence there was enough to shut up the wranglers. He could see that both were ashamed to be caught at it, especially Parker.

For some reason Tom found Parker's faultless attire offensive. The creases in his pants, the lack of wrinkles in the trim double-breasted coat of grey flannel, and worst of all, the corner of a handkerchief perking up out of his breast pocket. Tom could stand the necktie—nearly everybody wore one of those, though he couldn't see the use—but he could not quite stomach the corner of that handkerchief.

Opposite the bandstand Asa Parker stood and talked with Andy for a few moments. Now he was laughing and in a fine mood. Andy finished his cigar and threw it down. He tramped on it as he started across the road towards his own place of business. Asa Parker swung onto his bicycle and swept down the sidewalk with an effortless rush, passing the overalled nobody leaning against the pole without so much as raising his eyes.

After Asa had gone by, Tom turned slowly around to watch him. But several other bicycles were moving about the streets, and by the time that he had found Asa again he saw that the youngest county clerk in the state had dismounted and was just catching up with a girl. She was a tall girl, almost as tall as Asa, and though she was wearing a sailor hat he could see that she had yellow hair. Tom did not know who she was. So far as he knew he had never seen her before, but he certainly liked the way she carried herself. She was as graceful as the mast of a ship.

As Tom watched the two they turned into the Brackett place. Asa leaned his bicycle against a tree while the girl walked slowly towards the house. Tom saw him hurry to catch up with her—and then the shrubbery shut off his view. He watched for a while, hoping that the girl might reappear from the house, but during the next half hour the only person he saw around the Brackett place was an old man cutting the lawn. Then he caught a glimpse of Asa Parker, who came hurriedly out and made a flying leap to the seat of his bicycle. At the same moment the whistle of the westbound train sounded to the east of the town.

Tom smiled. So the county clerk had to tear himself away and go to business. He could make the train all right —of that Tom was quite sure; and without knowing why, he kept hoping that Asa wouldn't miss it.

People had been passing frequently as Tom stood by his telephone pole. Some of them he had looked at and some he hadn't. Nobody had paid any attention to him. A farm boy lolling against a post or hitching rail was too ordinary a sight to arouse any curiosity. A new hitching post or a strange horse would have been much more likely to awaken an interest on the part of citizens. Then suddenly a passing pedestrian penetrated his protective anonymity in a way that would not have startled him any more if his name had been called aloud. It was a woman who had gone by without his looking at her at all, and it was not until she was a step or two beyond him that he caught the fragrance of a perfume that was traveling right along with her. It was a familiar perfume—a significant perfume—for it was the perfume that he had detected in Gid's room that morning.

Tom quickly turned and looked after her. Somehow he had expected that kind of woman to be beautiful, but from the back he found her very ordinary to look at. She had dark hair, she had hips, she was small in the middle. He had been able to get no farther than this when she went into a store and was lost from sight. But he was so curious to see what she looked like from the front that he kept his eyes glued to the door. When a few minutes later she emerged and came towards him he was surprised and not a little disappointed to discover that aside from a tight-fitting dress which showed her shape to an almost indecent advantage, she was not much to look at.

She had a long nose, a bad complexion, and crooked teeth. She was, he was forced to admit to himself, an improvement on old Kate Vandenburg, long one of the town's debatable characters; but there was no denying that she was a homely woman.

On going back to the barn Tom found that Gid had already driven off with Hambletonian Boy. The stable hands did not know just where he had gone or when he would be back, though one of them volunteered the information that when he took a stud out for exercise he usually was gone about an hour. Tom would have liked to go into Gid's room and do his waiting in one of the easy chairs, but he was afraid the stable hands would think him presuming. So he sat down on a wooden bench outside the door and hoped that nobody would notice him, but almost immediately an old fellow he had seen in the barn came out and sat down beside him.

"Waitin' for somebody?" he asked.

Tom nodded. "Waiting for Gid."

"You a friend of his?"

Tom felt that somehow he must justify his presence there at the barn. "Gid used to work for us," he said. "I'm kinda stayin' with him just now."

"Single man, I take it?"

"Well, I ain't married, if that's what you mean."

The old fellow glanced around to be sure he was not being overheard by any of the stablemen, then he turned a wizened face very close to Tom's ear. "Lemme give you a bit of advice—never marry a cold wife."

Tom blinked at the man, wondering if he could be in earnest. He wasn't quite sure what was meant by a cold wife, but from the gleam in the faded blue eyes Tom had an idea that there must be something off-color about it. "I'm not thinking about getting married," he mumbled.

"Nobody does. That's just the trouble. You don't think much about it before—but you think a lot about it afterward, especially if you do get a cold wife."

Tom tried to drop the subject. "I don't even know what a cold wife is," he said.

"Well, you're very lucky," the old fellow said and proceeded with very evident relish to launch himself into an animated discussion of the matter. He had not gone very far before he discovered that Tom had very little comprehension of what he was talking about. Suddenly he stopped and eyed Tom keenly. "You're a farm boy," he said, "you must be well acquainted with cows."

Tom nodded. "I know too much about cows."

"All right, then you must know what a slinker is."

"Everybody knows that."

"Don't want to visit her husband, does she?"

Tom shook his head. "That's just the trouble."

"There you are—that's exactly what I'm talking about."

At just this moment a clatter of hoofs was heard in the driveway. To Tom's relief it was Gid bringing in Hambletonian Boy.

5

Horse Auction

HAMBLETONIAN BOY CAME PRANCING into the barn with an impressive pounding of hoofs on the plank floor. He had found the drive very stimulating and was tossing his handsome head and whinnying with the joy of living. Gid brought him to a standstill and handed down to Tom a large package wrapped in newspaper. His mother had been willing enough to deliver the clothes to Gid, but she had shaken her head over the tools. She didn't know which tools belonged to Tom, and she was not any too sure that her husband would want the tools taken away. Tom was sorry not to get the tools, but he said it was all right, and immediately went into Gid's office to change his clothes.

That afternoon he went out to look for a job. Gid noticed that he was pretty quiet after he returned, but he did not annoy him with questions. He knew that when Tom was ready to talk he'd talk. The next morning before Tom started out, Gid pressed a five-dollar bill into his hand. "You'll never have no luck lookin' for a job unless you got money in your pocket," he said. "You can pay it back after you get work."

Tom was reluctant to take the money. He said it was a lot to owe to anybody, especially when you didn't have a job. But Gid was insistent. He said an empty purse was the worst hoodoo a man could have when he was looking for a job. Not that Gid really believed in hoodoos, but he was a man of varied experiences. He had been through his ups and downs and never in his life had he been more than a few jumps ahead of the wolf. There had been times when he had been literally without a dime, and he knew that there was nothing so depressing to the spirit as that feeling of utter destitution. It wasn't the money itself that was important—it was the thought that you did not have any, that you were completely worthless; and a man who feels that he is worthless is not a very convincing applicant for a job.

The possession of the money was not without its effect on Tom. His spirits rose perceptibly after he had it in his pocket. Gid advised him to carry it where he could get at it easily and to touch it with his fingers whenever he was talking with an employer about a job. The idea was probably sound enough, but unfortunately times were poor and instead of hiring men most of the shops were letting them go. Tom's spirits were sagging a little when he came home after his first full day of job hunting. He had looked over some very interesting machinery, and had had some good talks with some of the mechanics, but he had not heard of an opening anywhere.

Tom offered to return the money, saying that he was afraid it wasn't going to work, but Gid rejected the offer with some emphasis. The chief trouble, he said, was that Tom had not spent any of it, and he intimated that if Tom wanted to take him to supper over at Fred's Lunchroom it might bring a change of luck. Gid felt that the boy's self-respect needed a little bolstering up, and he knew from his own experience that nothing is quite so good for the soul as buying another fellow a meal.

The supper for both of them made a big hole in a fifty-cent piece, but when Gid saw the change in Tom he felt that the money was well invested. The boy cheered up and began to take an interest in life once more. The next morning he started off full of optimism and ambition, but when he came home at night his feathers were dragging. He had exhausted the possibilities of the town; there was nowhere else to look.

Gid knew Tom was defeated when he saw him coming in the driveway. He waited for the boy in the big door-way of the barn. "Any luck?" he asked.

Tom shook his head and without a word went into Gid's quarters. Gid found something to do in a distant part of the barns and kept away from the boy. After about an hour had passed he went noisily up to the door. When he opened the door he found Tom sitting in the barrel chair. Gid took pains not to look at him, but walked over and shuffled among the papers on the desk as if hunting for something.

"Wanta watch the barn while I go over to Fred's for a bite? I'm expectin' a couple of rigs any time now, and I want somebody here to take care of 'em." Gid apparently found what he was looking for and put it in his pocket.

Tom stood up. "Sure. I'll take care of things."

"I won't be gone long," Gid threw back over his shoulder as he went out the door. "And as soon as I get back you can go."

Gid took his time about eating. He did not return until he had seen both rigs come in and had given Tom time to take care of them. He'd probably have to do the work over again himself, but he didn't want the kid to feel that he was useless. It was not until after Tom had been out to supper that Gid really took him in hand. He called the youngster into his office and made him remove his best shoes, which must have been torturing his feet after a day of walking on sidewalks and cement floors. Then he started in without any introductory matter and questioned him bluntly about everything that had happened during the day. It was the same old story, lots of interesting talk but no job.

"Well," said Gid, after he had heard it all, "you won't be goin' out tomorrow."

Tom looked puzzled. "Why not?"

"Because I got you a job—a one-day job. You're gonna be clerk at the auction."

"The hell you say! I wouldn't know how," Tom protested.

"You can write, can't you? And you can add up a colyum of figgers and make change, can't you?"

"Well, yes, I can do that."

Gid removed the battered slouch hat, without which Tom would hardly have known him, and threw it on the bed. He ran his big, knobby hands over his small, bullet-shaped head. "Yes, sir, Tommy, these auctions have growed to be famous all over the county. We bill 'em in every town, and if the weather looks reliable, folks come drivin' in from a good many miles away. I guess I don't hafta tell you that Andy's one of the biggest hoss men in this part of the state. Been in the business for years. He's got a name that means some'pm. And if we get a good day you'll see one of the biggest hoss sales of the year.

"And another thing," Gid brought out roundly, "it ain't gonna hurt you none to be settin' up there as clerk with half the township standin' around here lookin' on. You're a damn lucky boy to get the chance."

Tom nodded, though not with any great enthusiasm.

"Then it's settled—we can count on you?" said Gid.

"I'll do the best I can."

Gid walked outside, limping slightly from a horse kick that had damaged his kneecap a dozen years before. He gazed up at the night and allowed that there was no bad weather anywhere in sight. And he was right about it, for the day of the auction was perfect.

I remember that sale distinctly. Gid had told me that young Hunter was being tried out as clerk, and when in passing I saw the huge crowd that had been attracted I pushed my way in to see how he was getting along. I had never attended a horse auction before, so I looked over the affair with some curiosity and not a little interest. The auctioneer stood on a little railed platform that had been installed near one end of the big stable yard. The sale had already begun when I arrived, and the auctioneer, a small man with a big voice, was rattling off his musical chant with effortless ease, gesticulating at this bidder or that with a little willow wand he held in his hand. At the word *"Sold!"* he would slap the little wand on the rail of the platform, and then toss it into the air and catch it. No hammer for him—this was not that kind of auction. For a sheriff's sale, yes, the hammer was just the thing. But these horses were not going under the hammer; there was nothing compulsory about their being sold—it was just a question of competitive bidding.

Gid and the other stablemen brought out the horses one at a time. They were paraded up and down in a roped enclosure in front of the auctioneer's stand for all to see. The spirited horses were kept well in hand, but the old plugs were made to appear as skittish as possible. Gid had a way with spirited horses. He talked to them almost constantly in a low tone, and he must have spoken their language, for they seldom became excited when he was in charge.

The old plugs were exhibited by Wally, a colored stableboy who could make a great variety of cluckings, chirpings, twitterings, smackings, and other sounds with his lips and tongue. Only a deaf horse could have failed to be startled and perhaps prettily enlivened by the succession of sounds which emanated from the magic lips of this coal-black stableboy. A horse never knew what was coming from him next. It might be the hum of a bumblebee or the loud and sudden clacking of a locust. It might be a pop like the opening of a bottle or the unexpected hiss of a steam engine. Wally was a good entertainer and popular with the crowd. Everybody got ready for a laugh when he brought out a horse, and usually the horses he showed brought good prices.

Sometimes bidders would insist on being allowed to run their hands over a horse's legs in quest of splints and spavins. Sometimes they wanted to look into the hoofs for cracks or under the hocks for scratches. And, almost without exception, when a horse was led up to the stand his teeth were exposed for all to see. Not every man can read a horse's teeth, but those who think they can have great faith in them as an indication of age.

Tom sat at a little table below the auctioneer. It was his job to get down the name of the buyer and the horse, and to make a note of the price. At the end of the sale I watched a great crowd of the buyers come surging up around him, each clamoring to be waited on first. He was quick about catching the names, his figures were accurate, and he treated everybody with a boyish good nature that kept the crowd from becoming irritated. What if he was a little awkward about counting the bills, never having handled any large sums of money before? He was careful, and there never were any arguments over his change. Andy Brackett, hovering around the place arranging for notes and credits, did not miss any of this. Usually after an auction he had to spend an hour or two untangling the mistakes of his clerk, but this time there was nothing to untangle.

"The kid's smarter than he looks," Andy remarked to me. "Dumb looks and weasel brains. It's a good combination—if it should turn out the kid has them."

"Where did you get hold of him?" I asked, just to see what he would say.

Andy smiled. "He's a friend of Gid's—if you know what that means. Gid used to work for his father. Perhaps you've heard him sound off about the old man."

At that point Gid motioned to Andy from the door of the barn. Andy nodded, and a moment later disappeared into the barn with Gid and a man I did not know.

From his table where he was finishing his accounts Tom watched them go. The auctioneer had already left, but quite a crowd of men were still lingering around, probably for want of a better place to go, and for the pleasure they seemed to derive from talking horse. Occasionally a name came floating over to me—Lou Dillon, Bud Doble, Maud S. The colored stableboy, Wally, was tidying up the place with a big barn broom while some of the other men were pulling the stakes and preparing to move away the platform on which the auctioneer had done a good day's work.

I could see Tom watching the Negro boy and turned to look at him myself. It occurred to me that Tom had probably never seen many colored persons and was there-

· 56 ·

fore looking this boy over with a good deal of interest. He was a fine Negroid type with a broad nose and thick projecting lips which, as I was looking at them, suddenly cracked open with a fine display of ivory. At the same time his eyes lit up, blinking rapidly. But it was not until the cap was snatched deferentially from the woolly head that I turned to see what might be the cause of the stableboy's delighted grin.

It was Lucy Brackett, Andy's niece, a tall youngster about eighteen who lived with the Bracketts. She had gone to stay with them as a child on the death of her father and mother, and though never formally adopted had been brought up as if she were their own flesh and blood. Andy worshiped her, and while he lavished on her all the affection of an indulgent parent he had somehow not succeeded in spoiling her. She was a handsome child who always managed to dress in such a way as to make the most of her dazzlingly yellow hair—a tribute to her aunt, no doubt, who took her to the right places for her clothes. And she looked even lovelier than usual when she smiled at Wally and asked:

"Is Uncle Andy anywhere around?"

At the sound of her voice every man in the place turned to look—every man, that is, except old Fly Marvin, and Fly was stone deaf. I happened to look at Tom Hunter, and I must say that he had the appearance of a man in a daze. It occurred to me that he had never been so close to a beautiful woman before and was completely bowled over.

Wally, greatly honored at being singled out from those present—all of them white men—extended his grin another notch. "He shore is, Miss Lucy." But before he could go any farther Gid came hurrying out of the barn. He, too, had heard her voice.

Gid touched his hat (a concession he rarely made to any person, male or female), but he did not call her "Miss." To Gid she had been since childhood the "Skipper." He had given her the nickname when he was teaching her to ride her first pony, and had never called her anything else. "Why, Skipper, he's sellin' a nag in there," Gid said with a flirt of his thumb, "but the deal must be about over, for I just seen 'em passin' some dough. I'll call him if you're in a hurry, but he'll be here in a minute anyway."

Lucy shook her head. "You needn't do that, Gid. I know how he is when there's an auction, and I'm in no great hurry anyway."

Her glance roved curiously over the auctioneer's stand, and I realized that sooner or later it was going to reach young Hunter. He realized it, too, and by the time she had found him he was bending over his papers as if weighing some knotty problem and was making motions, doubtless unnecessary motions, with his pencil. And even through the heavy tan on his face I could see that he was blushing furiously. A moment later Andy came striding up.

"Well, Lucy," he said, quite obviously glad to see her, "you're too late for the auction—just sold the last horse."

"Did you get good prices?" she asked with a smile.

"Extra good. There was a lot of competitive bidding. Once or twice I thought I heard Gid's voice from back there in the barn when the bidding would slow up."

Gid denied this. "Not that I wouldn't do it," he explained, "but I didn't need to. There wasn't a nag that didn't sell for more than it was worth."

"In that case," said Lucy, "perhaps you can spare me twenty-five cents. I came away from the house without a penny, and I want to buy something."

Andy smiled and produced a handful of change. "You're letting me off easy," he said. "Take whatever you want."

Lucy saw me and greeted me with a wave of the hand as Andy was leading her off down the driveway, his narrow-brim grey derby hat cocked slightly to one side. I could see Tom watching her, and after she and Andy had passed out of sight he gathered up his papers and went into the barn. Just as he was entering the door I saw old Ike Meeker catch him by the arm.

"Don't forget what I tole you the other day," said Ike. "Never marry a cold wife!"

Tom angrily yanked his arm free. "I don't know what you're talking about."

"Oh, yes, you do—I just seen you lookin' at that girl."

I could see Tom's fist doubling up, but he did not use it. Instead he turned his back and strode into Gid's office.

6

One-Horse Town

I RAN INTO ANDY LATER THAT SAME EVENING. He was in a mellow mood and invited me into his office for a smoke and a talk. We drew chairs out on the little back porch which overlooked the horse pasture and sat down to enjoy the summer twilight. Andy removed his grey derby hat and hung it on his knee.

"Was there ever a prettier sight," he mused, "than horses grazing on the rolling green turf of that pasture? What a picture it would make."

It was a gracious sight. Twenty acres of velvety grass nibbled down like a lawn and framed by a border of tall, almost majestic trees. Andy had been particular about those trees. He had eliminated, year by year, every one that developed a propensity to lean or showed any tendency towards distortion or disease. He preferred the elms to the maples, but he had spared a goodly number of maples because of their freedom from blight and pest.

The auction, Andy said, had gone much better than he had dared to hope. He had moved out some plugs that he had been feeding altogether too long, and he had received on the whole the highest auction prices in a couple of years. Recently the general tendency had been downward. He blamed the influx of western horses for this. For some reason the western stock raisers sent only the cheaper grades east. He wondered why this was. Certainly there were plenty of good horses in the west. He had seen them himself. Perhaps they were trying to improve their stock by consistently shipping out the culls. Mustangs were all right for saddle ponies, but they did not take kindly either to the carriage or the plow. They were tough little rascals, but they were mean. What they lacked was breeding. They had none of the character and nobility of the Morgans, Hambletonians, Schuylers, and some of the other fine eastern strains.

We spoke about politics, and Andy again expressed his regret that I didn't take more of an interest. He had spoken to me about it several times, since Father was now leaving most of the political work to him. He also mentioned Tom Hunter in passing, remarking that he was taking the boy into his office.

"If he's as good every day as he was today, we'll get along all right," he said.

We sat and smoked until the night began to gather, and as I rose to leave, Andy said he would walk along with me. He locked the door and pocketed the key, and we started out. With the crowd already gathered for the Saturday night band concert his progress down the street was a succession of greetings, for he knew everybody. He knew even the horses, calling many of them by name. We had just reached the crosswalk where I was to leave him and had paused for a moment to say good night, when suddenly he caught my arm.

"I almost forgot something," he said. "Lucy wanted me to ask you to drop in a little later. Some of the young folks are going to be around, and there might be some fun."

I was just saying that I would stop by after I had

finished a little work at the office, when he interrupted me.

"Excuse me if I tear myself away, but there's a fellow just tying in and I want to catch him before he's lost in the crowd. See you later." And he was off.

Just out of curiosity I stood and watched him. He did not have far to go to catch his man, who proved to be old Everett Hunter.

"Hello, Mr. Hunter," I heard him say as he extended his hand.

Hunter threw a quick glance at him and went right on tying his horse. If he made any answer at all I did not hear it, and he did not seem to see the friendly hand.

"I see you've still got Mollie." Andy Brackett placed his hand on top of the post as if that was what he had intended in the first place.

"Certainly I've got her. What'd you expect?"

Andy was plainly annoyed by the surly answer, but he was not easily deviated from what he had set out to do and he chose to overlook the incivility. "I've got a customer who's looking for about that kind of a horse—is she for sale?"

"Don't want to sell her."

This would have been a good place for Andy to say that he was sorry, or that it looked like rain, and pass on. But he was evidently determined not to be brushed aside too easily by the asperity of a churlish countryman, for he made a further effort to get the old fellow in a more agreeable mood. "Well," he said genially, "I may not be able to buy your horse, but I've got some good news for you about your son." Andy was grinning in his most ingratiating manner, secure in his belief that any father would want to hear good news about his son, and he was quite obviously taken by surprise when the old man turned on him with a growl.

"Did I ask you for any news?"

Startled completely out of his air of genial banter, Andy began stammering on the defensive. "I—I guess you don't understand what I mean."

"When I want any news from you I'll ask you for it," muttered Hunter.

Andy began to bristle. "All I'm trying to tell you is that I'm giving young Tom a job—I've hired him."

Old Hunter raised the palm of his hand as if to ward off any further words. Muttering profanity, he shoved past Andy, shouldered his way into the crowd and disappeared, leaving Andy standing there with one hand still on the top of the hitching post. Andy quickly pulled himself together. He reached out and patted the horse on the nose. "Well, Mollie," he said, for the benefit of anyone who might have observed his predicament, "I guess he doesn't want to sell you, so I might as well be going on."

As I pushed slowly through the crowd on the way to my office I noticed that every post and tie-rail along Main Street was occupied, and even around the corner on Church Street not a space was to be found large enough to accommodate a horse. Everything in the township that would run on wheels was there that night, and the sidewalks were jammed with farmers, their wives, and their children, all looking slightly ill at ease in their best clothes, but full of animation and bent on having a good time. The street vendors were busy, the air reeking with the fragrance of their gasoline torches and their popping corn, and as the people stood around waiting for the music to begin they munched their popcorn from greasy fingers or cracked their peanuts with an appetizing sound.

As soon as they could get away, the men sneaked off to have a glass of beer, and that was usually the last the women saw of them until it was time to go home. There were baskets of eggs and crocks of butter in the wagons, but there was no hurry about these, as the trading went on all the evening. Sticky-faced children with licorice or lollypops in their hands dodged round my feet, and I was really glad for the sanctuary of the office in the comparative quiet of the side street. However, I had been there only a few moments when Gid came limping in.

"Well, what do you know!" he bellowed as he dropped heavily into a chair. "Andy's offered the kid a steady job!"

"So Andy told me."

"He did? Tell you an'thing else?"

"Not a thing. Why?"

"Well, I'm a little bothered by the way Tom's actin'. I don't know whether he's gonna take the job or not."

I don't know what Gid thought I could do about it, but he went on and told me about the discussion they had had.

Naturally Gid was elated over the offer. "Well, by damn!" he cried. "And after you was turned down by every dirty old machine shop in town. Boy, you've landed on your feet!"

Apparently Tom did not think so. "But, Gid, it's office work," he protested.

"Yes, sir!" Gid jerked his head approvingly. "The kind of work a banker does."

Tom scowled. "Well, who wants to be a banker?"

"Everybody!" answered Gid with enthusiasm. "Nobody works in a machine shop from choice; greasy overalls, and blue hammer-welts on your thumbnails. Boy, you'll go to work every day in your good clothes."

"And a necktie," muttered Tom.

"All right, and a necktie," Gid conceded in a good-humored bellow. "I don't know where you farm boys git the idea there's an'thing crim'nal about a necktie."

Tom pointed at the open throat of the stableman's shirt. "You don't wear one."

"Not when I'm workin'. How could I, with horses slobberin' over me most of the time? Good God, youngster, you thinkin' of refusin' a good job because you gotta wear a necktie?"

"That's not what I meant."

"Listen here, kid, you don't know how lucky you are. If Andy Brackett takes you under his wing—you're made. Lookit what he's done for Asa Parker. Asa was nuthin' but a young kid in town clerkin' in a store when Andy took holt of him. He likes to grab a young feller he can shove out in front. Lookit where Asa is now. Good job, fine salary, right in line for promotion. You'll see 'im in the Assembly inside of a coupla years—and if he lives, he'll never stop short of the State Senate. You mark my word. And let me tell you some'pm else—Andy'll do the same thing for you."

Tom looked a little alarmed. "You think he would?"

"Think it? I damn well know it! You've heard about the lunkhead who fell down the hole—and came out with a dress suit on and fifteen dollars in his pocket?"

"No." Tom shook his head. "What about him?"

"That's you. You go in to hand the boss a roll of bills that belongs to him—and the son of a gun gives you a good job. Say, what's he gonna pay you?"

"He said he'd start me at fifteen dollars."

"Oh, boy! Now ain't that better'n followin' a cultivator?"

Tom stood up and began to walk around motioning with his hands. "Gid," he said, "if I could only explain to you—if I could only make you understand—"

Gid jumped up and clapped him jovially on the shoulder. "I know what you mean, old boy. You just can't say it. You got the wind knocked out of your sails."

"I guess that's right." Tom ran his fingers through his hair. "I'm hungry. That's what's the matter with me. I'll go get something to eat and then I'll talk to you some more."

I did not give Gid any encouragement about being able to help, but after he had left I started out to see if I could find Tom Hunter. I thought it might be amusing to hear his version of the talk with Gid, and I had an idea that he would be found in Fred's Lunchroom getting something to eat. He had been there but had gone, and Fred felt sure I could find him down at the "justice court" where they had Charley Cosad up on a "drunk and disorderly" charge.

"Charley's been painting the town red for a couple of weeks," said Fred. "Finally got to be so much of a nuisance that even the saloonkeepers began to yell for mercy."

I went on down to court and reached there just as the justice was imposing sentence. "Nuthin' like crackin' stones to sober a man up," he said, "and I'll give you ninety days on the county rock pile to recover from this late indiscretion. Court's adjourned."

I could see Tom standing in the rear, his face clearly visible above the heads of the people in front of him, and as the crowd broke up I went over to speak to him. He smiled when he saw me, then shook his head seriously.

"A fellow can break a lot of stone in ninety days," he said. "That's a long stretch. Did you catch his name?"

"I know him," I said. "His name is Charley Cosad."

He blinked at me for a moment. "Not Mike Kelsey's engineer?"

"Yes, that's the same man."

For a few moments he stared off into space and I could see that he was cogitating about something. Then he turned to me and said, "Well, I've got a long way to go, and I guess I'd better get started."

It did not occur to me at the time that he was going to walk the six miles over to Mike Kelsey's place to see if he could get Charley's job. But that is exactly what he did. And since he was anxious to get started, I had no further talk with him that night.

After parting with young Hunter at the door of the Town Hall, I started down the street in the direction of Andy Brackett's house. I had gone only a short distance before I was almost entirely freed of the band concert crowd, which seldom strolled far away from the lighted windows of the stores and markets. It was darker here in the residential district. Lights showed in the windows of the houses, but they were back from the street and many of them were screened by vines and shrubbery; and though there was by this time a street light at every crossing, the blocks were long and the swinging incandescent lamps were far apart.

Voices from the verandas on either side of the street were plainly audible as I went along. Horse-drawn vehicles kept passing up and down the street, most of them moving at a moderate pace, though occasionally a reckless youth bent on impressing some girl with his skill and dash as a horseman would go speeding past at a smart clip.

I could see the light gleaming on several bicycles leaning against the porch as I turned into the Brackett place. None of these, I knew, belonged to Lucy. She had told me herself that, although she was crazy to have one and could ride as well as any of the girls, she had not been able to bring her uncle around to her way of thinking.

All the young people in the neighborhood seemed to be gathered there. Some were inside, grouped around the piano singing college songs, and a few were on the veranda, swaying gently back and forth in the hammock or crowding into the porch swing, which was then a great novelty. These harmless diversions seeming somewhat juvenile to a young professional man, I gravitated towards the other end of the veranda where Roscoe Towner, the son and partner of our leading banker, sat talking with Andy Brackett. Andy made room for me and offered me my choice of cigarettes or cigars. Roscoe was just back from his class reunion at New Haven, and as I came up he was explaining to Andy that the motor-driven vehicle was no longer known as the horseless carriage.

"Almost anything is better than 'horseless carriage,'" said Andy, "but why did they call it that in the first place?"

"Because it was a horseless carriage in the beginning. The first one to run in this country was made by mounting a motor under the seat of a buggy. And there was a man in Michigan who put out one of the buggy-type machines with a life-size model of a horse's head attached to the front of the dashboard."

"What was that for?" asked Andy.

"To keep from frightening the horses."

Andy chuckled. "You could hardly call that one horse-less."

"What's the new name, Roscoe?" I asked. "Anything other than automobile."

"Well," said Roscoe, "that word is all right, but it always provokes an argument, because no two people pro-

nounce it the same way. Some put the accent on the first syllable, some on the last, and some in the middle. It's a lot safer to say 'motor car' and be done with it."

"But let me ask you something else," said Andy. "What's the difference between an automobile and a Lo-comobile?"

Roscoe laughed, sparingly as always, before he explained that the difference was about the same as that between a horse and a sawhorse. "The Locomobile," he said, "is just a make of car."

"Roscoe has just had quite a trip," Andy explained. "He drove in a horseless motor car all the way from New Haven to Albany."

Not much encouragement was needed to get Roscoe to give a full account of the trip, which was replete with breakdowns, tire trouble, inability to obtain fuel, and the frightening of horses on narrow roads. One or the other of the driving-chains came off every few miles, and if they went for two hours without a flat tire they thought they were very lucky. They pushed the car up hills, pried it out of mudholes, and dragged a small tree behind like the tail of a kite to assist in braking on some of the steep downgrades.

"Were you ever lost?" asked Andy.

Roscoe laughed. "Practically all the time."

Andy had listened to the voyager's narrative with close attention, and when Roscoe had finished he said thoughtfully, "Roscoe, you've had a chance to study the motor vehicle at first hand. What's your opinion of it? Do you think it will ever reach the point where it will supplant the horse?"

"Never!" said Roscoe emphatically. "It will never supplant the horse any more than the bicycle has supplanted the horse. And I'll tell you why—the motor car is adapted to sport, not utility, and it never can be adapted to utility."

This was evidently the answer Andy had been wanting to hear. "Why do you say that?" he asked eagerly.

"In the first place, it's not reliable enough," said Roscoe. "Of course they may be able to fix the mechanical part of it in time; but the moment the motor car rolls off the city pavement, it's a fish out of water. And it's hardly likely that just to make the going easy for a rich

· 70 ·

man's toy the roads of this country are going to be turned into pavements. Think what that would cost!"

Andy shook his head. "It would bankrupt the nation," he said.

"But there is still another reason why the motor vehicle can never compete with the horse—it's too expensive. Who is going to pay from one to five thousand dollars for a machine to take the place of an animal that can be bought for one or two hundred?"

"Roscoe," said Andy slowly, "I think you're right—no machine can ever supplant the horse."

7

Horse Thief

Aʟᴡᴀʏs ᴀ ᴅɪsᴛɪɴɢᴜɪsʜᴇᴅ ᴛʜᴏʀᴏᴜɢʜꜰᴀʀᴇ, East Main Street was never quite so impressive as on Sunday morning. Then it really came into its own and for an hour or two became the most active and important artery of the town. Until ten o'clock the street would be unusually quiet, for the milkman was about the only person abroad. No shouting of newspapers disturbed the morning calm, for there was no Sunday delivery; and those who were worldly enough to desire the news were put to the trouble of calling at the drugstore between twelve and one, since the druggist was a regular attendant at church. And even during that brief period of activity the shades of the drugstore were never raised, and though a brisk business might be going on inside, the illusion was rigorously maintained that the establishment was closed for the day.

Few people had any occasion to venture out on Sunday morning for matters unrelated to their spiritual welfare, so most of them lingered over their breakfast eggs and coffee cups, or found small domestic tasks to occupy their time. But when on the stroke of ten the church bells sounded the first of their solemn reminders the street began to show signs of life.

Men in their shirt sleeves and Sunday pants walked out

on the porch to take a look at the weather. Women, too, came out and looked up and down the street. This was more or less instinctive; it was like dipping fingers in the water before getting into the tub. What the women really wanted was to get the feel of the day. If it felt a certain way it meant a certain hat, a certain parasol, or a particular fan. This first bell was also the starting gun for churchgoers who had some distance to walk, and almost before the clangorous echoes had died out of the sky little family groups would begin to emerge from the houses and start for the Methodist church at the other end of the town, or the Baptist church over beyond the railroad station. There must be no haste about their progress; they must move with seemly moderation. To hurry to their devotions would have been regarded as undignified if not mildly disrespectful of the day.

At about this hour the carriages from the country would begin to make their appearance. These usually drove up and disgorged their passengers on a cut-stone landing designed for the purpose at one end of the church steps. The driver then proceeded around towards the rear of the church to his shed, if he was foresighted enough to be a shed-holder. Otherwise he tried to find an unoccupied hitching post along the street and not too far away.

Though the country folk were not noted for their piety, they found churchgoing a quiescent form of pastime, and the social life it provided distinctly agreeable. So there was ordinarily a good turnout of the farm population. It was not until the sounding of the ten-twenty bell, however, that East Main Street put on its all-out performance. People came pouring out of their houses as if they had been standing in line just inside the door waiting for the tap of the bell. For the next ten minutes the thoroughfare was thronged—and then, as suddenly as it had filled, it became empty and was once more as quiet as when the milkman had first begun his rounds.

It was during one of these quiet periods of the Sunday morning after my talk with Roscoe Towner and Andy Brackett, when I walked out of our house and started up the street. Being only a wayfarer I did not move with the solemn precision of a worshipper. I was bent upon the strictly personal errand of buying a newspaper, and since I wanted to get past the church before the service was out I was stepping right along. But I had somehow miscalculated the time, for I had gone only about half the distance to the grim red-brick edifice when I saw the doors swing open and the congregation come pouring out.

I immediately slackened my pace, not wishing to hurry through the leisurely worshippers, who paused on the church steps and on the sidewalk in front of the church for the customary social amenities before starting for home and the overwhelming dinner that was about to come out of the oven. As it happened, however, not a member of that congregation was to be on time for that particular Sunday dinner.

Among the churchgoers was a well-to-do farmer named Simeon Webster. Simeon had purchased from Andy Brackett only a short time before a matched pair of high-steppers of which he was proud to the point of vainglory. This was the first time he had driven them to church, and all through the service he had tried to keep one ear open to assure himself that the horses were quiet and well-behaved. Once he heard muffled sounds that seemed to be coming from the direction of the sheds, and would have gone out to investigate had the parson not been in the midst of a rather long-drawn-out prayer. As Simeon listened he heard a vehicle moving in the driveway outside and wondered idly who could be coming or going at such an unseemly hour. But since he heard no signs of a disturbing nature, he took it for granted that all was well with his animals and forced himself to turn his attention to the service.

Seated near the back, he was among the first to emerge from the building, and he went straight to the shed where he had left his team. To his astonishment he found that the doors, which he had shut and padlocked, were wide open, and his team and carriage were gone. Simeon's first thought was of the Horsethief Protective Association of which Andy Brackett was the head and in which a number of his fellow worshippers were active members. He accordingly ran back to the church entrance shouting in a frenzy that his horses had been stolen and calling for the members of the Association to rally to his aid.

While still some distance down the street I heard the shouting, and though I could not distinguish the words, recognized the sound as a hue and cry for aid and instinctively quickened my pace. I could see people running about as I hurried along, little knots forming and re-forming. Persons came hastily out of the church doors and disappeared in the direction of the sheds. When suddenly the church bell began to ring with a wild and hurried clamor, I instintively thought of fire though I could see no smoke or flame. I had almost reached the church property when the ringing stopped and Andy Brackett in a long-tailed coat and white vest mounted the church steps and waved his hands for silence.

"This way, members of the Horsethief Protective Association!" he shouted. "All members step this way—*please!* There's no time to lose—there's been a horsethief in our midst. While we were sitting quietly in this church engaged in the worship of Almighty God, Simeon Webster's team has been stolen right out from under our noses! The horsethief has less than an hour's start. If we can get after him right away we'll catch him. The posse will form on Main Street and leave from the post office corner in just fifteen minutes. All members who can be notified must be there at twelve-fifteen and ready to go. Ride your fastest horse, strap on your guns, and we'll bring back that horsethief dead or alive!"

As he waved his hands with a gesture of hasty dismissal the members of the Association shouted in angry approval and scattered in all directions.

News travels rapidly in a small town and practically all the inhabitants were on hand to see the start of the posse. Riders had already begun to gather by the time I had reached the center of the town. Among them were a dozen different kinds of saddles and side arms. Some men were in overalls and some in sweaters. One or two were still wearing their best shoes and their Sunday pants. Men will start off to war with a joke on their lips, but when they go after a horsethief they are grim and wordless.

At exactly twelve-fifteen Andy Brackett came thundering up on a black thoroughbred stallion. He had on hardworn riding breeches and a flannel shirt, and I could not help having the feeling that he was dressed for the part, which none of the others was. Behind Andy came Gid, wrestling with a buckskin mustang, known to be the meanest and toughest horse in the barn. Not belonging to the Association I was not in the saddle, though I thought at the time that it might be fun to go along. Asa Parker was there, mounted on what he called his "polo pony" with an English saddle fitted with open stirrups which seemed to me to be too high for comfort. He was not in the main group of riders but had drawn his horse over near the sidewalk where he was talking with Lucy Brackett, Zelda Harper and some of the other girls.

Andy was all business. He began to tell the men off in pairs. "You two go south. Keep west of the lake. If you haven't picked up the trail by the time you reach the end of the lake, divide. One go west and one east. And keep asking questions of everybody you see." They nodded. "All right, get going."

One pair he sent east, and another north, but the main

body of the posse went west with the intention of spreading out like a fan and covering all the main roads. For from the reports that had begun to come in the horse-thief had gone west driving the whole length of Main Street at a very leisurely pace which had attracted no attention at all until after the news of the theft had begun to get around. Nobody had reported seeing the team after it had left the village limits traveling in a westerly direction, but the riders did not doubt that they would pick up plenty of clues as they went along.

The crowd cheered as the riders thundered off in a cloud of dust, and then most of them remembered the Sunday dinner and started for home. I remembered my newspaper and was just coming out of the drugstore with it tucked under my arm when I saw Tom Hunter talking with a thickset little fellow that I recognized as the Green Pack Peddler. This peddler was a curious, though by no means unusual product of the horse-and-buggy days, who used to travel around the country on foot tugging on his shoulder a big green pack containing notions and novelties. The variety of his stock was astonishing; he could produce from it almost any small article the householder might call for. We children used to have a field day whenever he came to our house. His visits were almost like receiving a personal call from a five-and-ten-cent store. Everybody called him Sol, but I don't think anybody, with the possible exception of my father, knew his last name.

Father had a great deal of respect for the little peddler and used to say that he knew more about what was going on in our part of the world than the Pinkerton Detective Agency. I was a little surprised to find Tom on familiar terms with the itinerant, until it developed that the Hunter place was one of his regular overnight stops.

"But, Sol," I said banteringly, "I thought it was your boast that you stopped wherever the night happened to overtake you."

Sol chuckled. "That iss right. But usu'lly the night overtake me in some place where I want to be. Don't you call that luck?"

"Peddler's luck," I said.

As I made a move to go along Tom detained me. "If you're not in a hurry, I want to talk to you."

"Then I don't keep you," the peddler said quickly. "But when you see Gid, tell him I haf left a Hello for him." And he started down the street.

"So he's a friend of Gid's, too?" I asked.

Tom nodded. "They're old pals. I walked all the way in from Mike Kelsey's to see Gid and got here just in time to miss him. You see, I went out to Mike's last night after I left you. I wanted to see if I could get Charley's job. Well, I got it all right, but it left me in a kind of a funny fix, because Andy Brackett had already offered me a job, and Gid thought I ought to take it—I guess he thought I had taken it, kind of—and I wanted to put myself right with them, you know. And now they're both gone, and I don't know what to do. You're a lawyer, and maybe you can tell me."

"Why don't you leave a note for them," I suggested.

"You think a note would be all right?" he asked.

"Of course. What else can you do?"

"I don't suppose you know how long they're going to be gone?"

I shook my head. "Nobody knows. They may be gone two or three days."

He smiled. "I couldn't wait that long. I have to go to work tomorrow morning. I wish I knew what to say in a note—it's a kind of a hard thing to explain. I don't want Gid to feel that I've let him down. I got a suspicion that he had to work pretty hard to get Andy to offer me that job."

"Perhaps so," I said. "Gid wouldn't hesitate to do it."

"I don't want to hurt Gid's feelings—he's my best friend."

Being a little curious to know why he preferred the heavy work with a threshing outfit to the comparatively easy work of an office job, I finally asked him.

"That's hard to answer," he said. "I tried to explain it to Gid last night, but I couldn't seem to do it. I know what it is myself, but it doesn't make sense to anybody else. If I get into office work, I'll never get out of it, and I don't want to spend the rest of my life with a lead pencil over my ear."

"Then you're interested in something else?"

"That's what's making the trouble."

"Do you want to tell me what it is?"

"Machinery—mechanics—I want to make things—invent things."

"That's perfectly understandable," I said. "I think you've done the right thing. You got this job yourself with Mike Kelsey. It's what you like, and I think you ought to take it."

"I wish I could say it to Gid like that."

"But why can't you?"

"Maybe I could if you'd help me."

"And what about Andy?"

"Oh, I don't care so much about Andy. We'll let Gid explain it to him. But I don't want Gid to think I don't appreciate what he's tried to do for me. You—you wouldn't want to help me with that—that letter to Gid, I suppose?"

"Well, it's a rather personal matter," I said. "I don't know that I can help you a great deal, but I'll give you the benefit of my advice—such as it is."

We went around to Gid's office in the stable, and after a long talk he took a pencil and wrote:

Gid:
Office work is not my stuff. I'm no good for it. So I took a job as engineer with Mike Kelsey. I stopped to tell you about it so you could explain to Andy. Got here just as the posse was starting and thought it was not a very good time to talk business. I hope the buckskin does not spill you. Thanks for everything. I will never forget how you helped me. Sol sends you a Hello.
Your friend Tom.

"Do you think I ought to tell him I'm taking my clothes?" he asked.

"Perhaps you had better, so he won't think they've been stolen."

He picked up the pencil and added:

I'm taking my clothes. Again thanks for everything.

He left the note on Gid's desk, wrapped up his clothes in a newspaper, and started on his long walk to Kelsey's; but just as we reached the street we could see a solitary horseman approaching from the west, obviously one of the posse.

"Wonder what he's coming back for," said Tom.

"He could be coming back to say they've found the trail."

But there was no such luck. It was only a crestfallen posse member whose horse had thrown a shoe and gone lame.

"Why do you suppose they didn't use the telephone or the telegraph to send out an alarm?" Tom asked.

"Perhaps they did; but there's no Sunday service in most of the little towns, you know. And if the thief is smart he'll keep away from the towns where a warning of that kind would be of any use."

"What'll you bet that team hasn't been broken up into two single rigs?"

"It probably has."

"What'll you bet those two horses are not pretty close to twenty miles apart right this minute?"

"I don't think it's unlikely."

"What'll you bet both nags haven't had their white feet painted over black?"

"I wouldn't bet a nickel on that."

"Then what's the use of all this posse business?"

I shook my head. "I guess it's just to put the fear of God into any other horsethieves that might be around."

"It wouldn't bother me if they should steal every horse in town," he said with a grin. "From now on I'm an engine man." And with a word of thanks to me for helping him he tucked his bundle of clothes under his arm and started down the street.

Riders began to trickle in that night. Some came through town and others went directly to their homes. They were still coming in Monday morning, bedraggled and weary. Most of them had the smell of liquor on their breath and some were drunk with nothing more than exhaustion. Andy and Gid were the last to return. Andy hated to admit defeat and had kept going long after his good sense should have told him to go back. Asa Parker was home just after dark on Sunday night. Asa said his horse had gone lame, but Gid always insisted that Asa had come back because he had a date with a girl.

Andy's stallion came in travel-stained and disheveled, but bearing himself with the distinction of a gladiator who had met the test of the arena. Gid's buckskin returned as he had started, mean and cantankerous. He had no distinction when he had started and certainly none when he came back. Nor was he too tired to aim a kick at the first stableman who approached him. Gid unsaddled and turned him into the paddock, and after rolling a few times the mustang had energy enough to leap to his feet and pick a spirited fight with a new horse that had arrived while he was away. It was not until Andy had been home for twenty-four hours that he remembered his new clerk and asked if anybody had seen him. Nobody had, and Andy went to the barn to inquire of Gid.

"Seen anything of young Hunter?" he asked.

"Nope."

"Wonder if he's been around while we were gone."

"Couldn't tell you."

"Know where I can find him?"

"Nope."

This economy of words on Gid's part did not escape Andy's attention. Ordinarily the stableman's answer to any question was fairly certain to be verbose if not voluminous. And to have him answering in curt monosyllables was enough to make Andy suspicious that there was more here than met the eye. "I know you're holding out, Gid," he said. "Go ahead, let's have it."

Gid did not raise his eyes but continued with what he

was doing. "Guess the kid musta got tired of waitin' for you," he muttered. "He's took another job."

"Another job!" Andy glared at him. "What is it?"

"Engineer."

"For what?"

"Mike Kelsey's threshin' outfit."

"Um-m-m—that must be what old Hunter was trying to tell me Saturday night, but the old codger was in such a state that I couldn't make out what he was saying."

"Yeah—Tom took Charley Cosad's place when Charley got sent up."

"Well, I guess they're both right where they belong." And without another word Andy turned and went out.

8

Runaway

T OM HUNTER FINISHED HIS SEASON WITH
Mike Kelsey at what was still called the Captain Jenks
farm, though the Captain had been dead for several years.
It had been a good season. Crops were heavy and the
weather unusually favorable for threshing. Of course
there had been an occasional thunderstorm, but the serious fall rains had held off until the important grain-
threshing had been finished. And Kelsey remarked more
than once that he never had a season where the rain had
been so accommodating about coming after a job was
done and while they were on the move to the place where
they were going to start the next one.

Kelsey lost no time in hiring the boy when told that
Charley Cosad's spree was ending with a sojourn at the
county rock pile. He had put up with a lot of Charley's
nonsense, he said, for the simple reason that good engineers were hard to get. Naturally he wanted to shade
Tom's pay somewhat. He couldn't be expected to pay a
mere boy—good as he was—the same wages he had given a
licensed engineer. That would hardly be rulable. "Rulable" was Mike Kelsey's test for all business transactions.
If a demand was rulable he would give in with good
grace, as good grace as the situation required. But let
Mike get the idea that there was any question about the

rulability of a matter and he would fight it with every-thing he had.

Charley Cosad's license was for steam, and though it was framed and fastened to the side of the toolbox where it looked official and important, it was in truth no more than a hangover from the days when all traction engines were steam powered. Tom was well aware of this; he knew that no license was required to operate a gas engine, but he preferred to make no issue of it. The job was what he wanted. Pay was secondary.

"I don't see how I can possibly pay you more than twelve dollars a week," Kelsey put out as a feeler, after pretty thoroughly airing his views on the rulability of this and that.

"And found?" asked Tom. "You know I don't live at home any more."

"Well, yes. I think that would be rulable. Why not? I got plenty of room at my place."

And so Tom took the job. Gid exploded with some angry profanity when he received Tom's note. He had hoped the other job was all settled, and he was disgusted with the boy for kicking over the traces the minute his back was turned. What he couldn't understand was how anybody could refuse a gentleman's position and take instead a filthy job as wet-nurse to the stinkin' old gas engine of a gang of threshers. He was still sputtering when he came in to tell me about it, and he kept repeating that everything would have been all right if he had not gone off with the posse; and in the same breath he would swear that he would never recommend any son of a so-andso for another job. It was not until Gid heard about the pay, news of which was brought to him within a week or two, that he began to look at the situation as something more than juvenile damfoolishness. The three dollars less a week set him to thinking. He didn't agree with the boy; but he had to admit that the kid knew what he wanted and was not afraid to go after it—even if he had to take less money and step on Andy Brackett's toes to boot.

Tom knew nothing of all this. He thought that his letter to Gid had made an adequate explanation of the situation, and he threw himself into the job with the Kelsey outfit and enjoyed every minute of it. He studied the big stuttering engine until he knew it as well as the inside of his hand. He learned all its moods and peculiarities, its likes and its dislikes. He found that it ran better when its nose was slightly depressed, and though he was never able to prove to himself that this was a matter of better circulation of water or improved carburetion, he always tried to place the engine on a stance with a down-hill slant. He went back to it after hours to pet and polish it. If he was not oiling and adjusting he was taking things apart on the pretense that they needed cleaning, when they really needed nothing at all and he just wanted to satisfy his curiosity as to how they were made.

Mike Kelsey took a liking to the boy, and towards the end of the season—not early enough to cost him a great deal, and as Mike figured it, not too late to give the youngster the idea that his services were being appreciated and properly rewarded—he gave the lad a three-dollar raise. It seemed to Mike that he had never had a more satisfactory hand on any of his machines. The kid was always around and was just as good Monday morning as he was Saturday night. The whole outfit missed Charley Cosad's Monday morning hangovers, which had served to start the week with some rough but good-natured humor. Kelsey, however, was glad to be done with them, for the Monday breakdowns and stoppages had been traditional ever since Charley had joined the outfit. Another advantage of a steady man on the engine was that no watching was required and Mike was left free to get out and work with the men; and since he was a prodigious worker they had to stay on their toes to keep up with him. Mike could not remember a season since he had gone over to gas when he had run up such big tally sheets as he had that summer.

He tried in a nice way to nail Tom down for the following season, but the boy would not make any promises. As Tom explained it to me, he did not want to seem ungrateful, for he felt that Mike had done him a great favor in giving so inexperienced a fellow a chance at Charley's job. But it did seem to him that he could not afford to come back to a job from which there was nothing more for him to learn. He felt that he had mastered the single-cylinder engine and he was ambitious to move on to the multiple type, such as they had begun to use in the horseless carriages, with two and even four cylinders. His imagination had been greatly stirred at the sight of a sleek red machine that had passed the threshing outfit on the road. They had seen it coming and had pulled off to one side and waited for it to pass. A dyed-in-the-wool miracle could have moved him no more deeply. He kept talking about it until the others began to guy him, and even after that he was so absent-minded that, for the first and only time while he was with the Kelsey outfit, he let an oil cup run dry and was aroused from his reveries by the squeak of a bearing.

Tom kept imagining that the great clumsy juggernaut he was steering was a horseless carriage. In his mind he translated the two miles an hour of grinding lurching progress on the broad iron rims into the swift graceful gliding of the roadster which must, he was sure, have been making all of fifteen miles an hour. He swerved his mount as he thundered along, dodging stones no larger than walnuts, which ordinarily he would have crushed into powder or pressed far down into the earth; and he straddled puddles which he could have rolled out as flat as a bit of baker's dough.

His serpentine course was not entirely lost on Kelsey who finally climbed down from his perch on the separator to ask if anything had gone wrong with the steering gear.

Tom gave him a look of surprise. "Not that I've noticed," he said. "I guess she's all right."

"But you've had her all over the road," Kelsey insisted. "I thought mebbe you couldn't hold her."

Tom kept his eyes straight ahead and hoped he wasn't blushing. "I can hold her all right. Little rough back there. I was trying to see if I could make it smoother by dodging the bumps."

Kelsey shook his head. "You don't have to do that. She'll run over practically anything. Makes her tracks look funny to see 'em wanderin' all around."

"All right," said Tom. "I'll hold her on the line. We don't want her tracks to look funny, do we?"

Kelsey went back to his perch, and from that time on Tom saw to it that the separator was taken over all the best bumps in the road. But that night a trim red roadster kept skimming through his dreams, and for days the vision of it was often with him. After the rest of the crew was paid off, Tom went with Kelsey to help put the equipment into winter quarters; and though during previous winters the engine had stood uncovered in a shed, Tom insisted this time on smearing it with grease and covering it with a tarpaulin. Kelsey must have thought this was foolishness, but he let the boy go through with it.

"So you kinda like the old girl, eh?" he asked.

Tom nodded. "She's a good machine."

"But you don't want to make a date with her for next summer?"

"Not so far ahead of time. I may be doing something else by then."

"All right. Let's hook up a nag and I'll take you to town. Be funny to you, ridin' behind a horse, I guess."

"That's right, I haven't had a whiff of horse smell all summer. But listen, I'm not going into town just yet. I want to stop off and see my folks, and if you'll take me as far as the Bannister bridge I'll cut cross-lots over the hill and save you a couple of miles of driving."

Tom would have found the distance a little shorter if he had approached the house from the rear, but after giving the matter some thought as he went along, he decided that wasn't quite the thing to do. He didn't want to come upon the family when they weren't expecting him. To appear suddenly in their midst seemed a little too familiar for one who had left under the circumstances he had. The right way, he thought, was to come down the road where he could be seen long before he came to the house; and then, just to make sure, he could slam the front gate when he went into the yard. And then what? Should he walk right in as if nothing had happened? Or would it be better to knock—like a stranger? Perhaps it would be better yet to step up to the door and call inside, "Hello there! Anybody home?" Then if they did not want to see him they needn't answer, and he would turn and walk away. As it happened, he encountered none of these difficulties, for his mother saw him coming down the road and was on the side porch to meet him.

He didn't kiss her. He hadn't kissed her in years. She asked him to come in and he went. The chair where he used to sit was there in the kitchen and he sat down on it. His mother asked him where he was staying and how he was getting along, and he told her about his work with Mike Kelsey.

"Does it pay pretty good?" she asked. "Can you live on it?"

"Live on it? I saved practically every cent! And the best part is that it's my kind of work. Just what I like."

She nodded. "Machines would suit you. You never did like horses."

"Horses are all right, but I don't like the smell."

"You mean to say there ain't no smell to gasoline?"

He smiled. "That's a smell I like."

Tom kept listening for his father and wondering what the old man would do when he came in and found him there. He could hear noises from the barn and imagined that his father was out there doing the chores. He kept hoping that his mother would say something about it, but she had evidently made up her mind not to, so he took the bull by the horns.

"How's Pa?" he asked.

"He's doin' pretty good."

"How will he like it when he finds me here?"

She glanced uneasily out of the door. "I been wonderin'."

"I can hear him out in the barn," said Tom.

"That ain't your pa—that's Pete Wagner, the hired man. Pa's gone to town. Took a load of logs to the sawmill. Needs some boards to mend the cowshed."

"Which sawmill?"

"The one over acrost the railroad tracks—Gridley's I guess it is."

"He ought to have a power saw," said Tom. "Then he could cut up his own logs."

She threw up her hands. "Don't tell *him* that!"

Tom smiled. "I won't. When you expecting him back?"

She glanced at the clock. "Shoulda been here before this. I declare, I don't know what's keepin' him. 'Tain't like him to leave Pete with all the chores to do, and supper's already cookin'. Be ready in another fifteen minutes. You're gonna stay, I s'pose, and eat some'pm with us?"

"Oh, I don't believe I better. Got to get into town. Just thought I'd stop and say hello—and pick up my tools. I'm going to need 'em."

"I'd of give 'em to Gid that time, only I didn't know which ones they was. I didn't want your pa to see him anyway. I was afraid of trouble between 'em."

"Are my tools in the workshop where I left 'em?" asked Tom, standing up.

"Likely as not. Don't know where else they'd be."

"I'll go out and gather 'em up before Pa comes. Then if he don't take kindly to my bein' here I can clear right out."

"Now promise me, Tom, that you won't have no words with him."

"I don't know why you say that—I never did argue with him much."

Again she glanced at the clock. "Better go get them tools."

Tom went to the tool house and spent half an hour hunting up his tools, which he found badly scattered. Finally he succeeded in getting them together and wrapped them in an old piece of burlap. When he returned to the house he saw that his mother had laid out a plate of supper for him on the kitchen table.

"I don't know where your father can be," she said, "but this supper ain't gonna keep much longer, and you might as well eat while it's good."

"What about the hired man?"

"He'll come in when he's ready. We won't wait for him."

Tom guessed that she wanted him to eat and get out of the way before his father came, so he sat down and addressed himself to the supper with relish. His mother walked over on the other side of the room where she could look out the window and get a view of the road. He felt sure that she would tell him the moment his father came in sight. At first Tom began to eat rapidly, so that he would not have to go away hungry if his father should fly into a rage at seeing him there; but after the edge had been removed from his appetite he began to take more time with his eating. His mother did not sit down with him, and as he ate she stood quietly looking out of the window. She turned when he pushed back his chair and stood up.

"I declare I don't know what's keepin' him," she said. "It ain't like him to be so late."

Pete Wagner came in for a basin of hot water, which he took to the bench outside the kitchen door. He nodded to Tom without any idea who he was, and then rolled up his sleeves and went about his washing.

"Peter, are you ready to eat?" Tom's mother asked.

The hired man splashed the water over his face. "Been ready for the last coupla hours," he said in a muffled tone.

"All right," she said, "come in when you're through there. We ain't gonna wait for Pa. I'll spoon your supper right up." She took one last glance out of the window and stepped over to the stove where she began to fill a plate for the hired man. It was while she was standing at the stove that they all heard the hoofbeats of horses.

"There he comes now!" she said. "But listen to them horses—ain't they runnin'?"

She dropped her spoon and ran to the window, but she was too late to get a glimpse of the fast-moving animals which by now were in front of the house and no longer visible from the kitchen window on that side. But a moment later they came thundering into the driveway and skidded to a stop before the closed doors of the horse barn. They were still fastened together by a tangle of harness, but the wagon was gone, severed from them as cleanly and as completely as if it had been swept away by the stroke of a giant cleaver.

Pete ran out and caught the horses by their bridles, and Tom, with a feeling of terrible apprehension, began to examine the tugs, the reins, and the other dangling ends of harness, to see whether they had been cut or broken. Then he noticed a wound high up on the rump of the nigh horse.

His mother came panting up behind him. "What do you think?" she asked.

"I don't know what to think," he answered with a half-hearted attempt at evasion.

"Well, I do! It was the railroad."

Tom turned and looked at her. Her face was drawn up into a series of little wrinkles from which her eyes glowed sharply. "What makes you think so?" he asked.

"I don't just think—I know. Something tells me!"

"But what makes you think it wasn't a runaway?"

"Those horses run away? Never!"

"They were running plenty when they came home."

"But look at that cut—way up there on the flank. No horse was ever cut like that in a runaway. Pa's dead—I know he's dead—now what we gonna do?"

"I'll hitch up Dick horse and go back and look for him. It may not be as bad as you think."

"You ain't got to talk soft to me. I'll go right along with you. It'll be dark before we can get to that crossin', and we'll need a lantern. I'll go get one while you're hitchin' up. We'll leave Peter to tend to the team and look after things."

They found a crowd around the crossing, but the body had been taken to the undertaking parlors.

That is the story as Tom told it to me when he came in to get his father's will. I was alone in the office at the time, and I was not sure that his father had made a will. But when I took the bundle of wills from the safe I found his father's almost on the top. It had been made within a week of the time that Tom had left home, and only a glance was needed to show me that everything was left to George, subject to the life use of the testator's wife, Matilda. Tom's name wasn't even mentioned. I put the will in an envelope, hoping that he would take it home before opening it. But he didn't. He drew it right out and began to read it. When I saw what he was doing I retired to the other room to give him a little privacy for the jolt that I felt sure was coming. But I had been there only a few moments when he appeared in the doorway with a smile on his face.

"Do you know what's in it?" he said.

I nodded. "I read it when I took it out of the safe. My father must have drawn it. I don't know how it happened that he never mentioned it to me."

"Oh, that's all right," he said. "I just want to tell you that it suits me right down to the ground. It leaves me free to do just what I want to."

As it turned out, Tom was not quite as free as he thought he was going to be, for George was tied up with an ironclad lease which held him where he was until the end of his term, and Tom had to go back home to stay with his mother and run the farm until George was ready to take over. It must have been a bitter pill to swallow, for it set him back almost a year, but he went without a word of complaint and remained there until George and his family were ready to move in. Gid, who went over to see him occasionally, had some wonderful stories to tell about Tom's mechanical hay stoker which fed the livestock automatically, a non-spill milk stool and pail-holder that a cow could not kick over, a calf-feeding device that a heifer couldn't tell from her mother, and an automatic tail to switch flies off the animals while they were in the stalls. How much of this was God's truth and how much was Gid's fabrication I never could be quite sure.

9
Horses—Horses—Horses

I HAD SEEN TOM OCCASIONALLY DURING THIS period of agricultural pinch-hitting. Even though he was receiving nothing from his father's estate, there were certain papers that had to be signed by him because of his relationship. And when finally George and his family were able to move in with his mother, Tom promptly resumed his career. He walked into town one morning with a roll of tools wrapped in burlap under his arm and came up to me as I was standing in front of the Town Hall awaiting the arrival of some witnesses in a justice court case.

"Going over to your office pretty soon?" he asked. "I want to have a little talk with you."

"I expect to be busy here for a couple of hours," I said. "I've got a lawsuit to try."

"That'll suit me all right," he said. "I'll look around town a little bit and see you later." He ran his eyes slowly up and down the street. "Horses—horses—horses—" he mumbled. "It's a horse world. The machine will have a tough tussle when it comes to knocking out old oat-eater."

"Do you think it will succeed?" I asked.

"Well, why not? The machine's got everything in its favor."

I smiled. "All except one thing—you can make a horse go."

"Don't you worry about that," he said with a laugh. "When they get the machine right it will go—and go plenty."

Just then my witnesses arrived and I started inside, but I reminded him that I would be at my office at eleven. I was not so long in finishing my trial as I had expected, and when I came out I found Tom on his knees on the sidewalk with his tool kit spread out before him. He was mending a bicycle for a lad who had had a slight encounter with a fractious horse and had received the worst of it. He was too much engrossed in what he was doing to see me as I went past, but soon after I had reached the office he came in all aglow over an idea that had come to him. He wanted to open a bicycle repair shop.

"Can you imagine a town of this size that hasn't got one?" he asked excitedly. "Four blacksmith shops, and another one up in the west end, and not a single place where you can get a bicycle fixed."

"How much of an investment will it take?"

"Don't know yet."

"Well, how much capital can you put your hands on?"

"Don't know that either. I got all the money I earned when I was working for Kelsey. He used to deposit it for me every little while and bring me a certificate of deposit."

"If it's in Towner's bank all you've got to do is go over there and ask about it. They keep a special account of certificate holders."

"I might as well find out about it," he said.

For a time we sat and discussed the project, but since

neither of us knew much about it we did not make a great deal of progress. Finally he tucked his roll of tools under his arm and started for the bank. When he came back about an hour later he had Gid and the Green Pack Peddler with him.

"What's this crazy idea of yours for startin' this boy in the bicycle bus'ness?" Gid shouted as he came in the door. He always shouted when he was enthusiastic either for or against a thing.

I began to laugh. "What's crazy about it?" I demanded. "Fifty or a hundred bicycles in this town and nobody to take care of them."

"What's the matter with our blacksmith shops? Those fellows are good mechanics."

"They're all right with anything that you can hammer out on the anvil, but would you trust one of them to mend your watch?"

Gid did not even hear what I said. "All the damn things are good for is to frighten horses. Every time I go out with a stud I have a narrow escape. One of 'em goes shootin' by right under my nose, and the stud tries to set down in my lap. One of these days the big feller's gonna make it—and then you can all stand around and say, 'Don't Gid look natcheral!' "

"Did you find out about your money?" I asked, turning to Tom.

"Yes, I did," he replied. "I haven't got quite as much as I thought I had."

"Do you think you can borrow any money?"

Tom shook his head. "I'm afraid not. I tried that on Mr. Towner."

"What!" bellowed Gid. "You asked that old bastard to loan you money?"

Tom shrugged. "Well, that's what he's there for, isn't it?"

The peddler reached over and touched Tom on the arm. "Go ahead and tell about it," he said. "I see if I can keep Gid under control."

"There's not much to tell," said Tom. "When I first went in I could see Roscoe sitting on a high stool behind the counter. He was bending over a big red leather book and running his finger down the page as if he was adding up a column. But he wasn't really adding anything, and I'll tell you how I know—his finger kept right on going when he looked up to see who it was that had come in. Old Mr. Towner didn't even look up until I'd been standing at the counter quite a while. And then those steely grey eyes of his bored right through me. He didn't know me at first, but when I told him about the certificates of deposit he remembered who I was. I explained that I had left the certificates at home, but was considering a business deal and wanted to know how much they amounted to.

"He opened up a big book and told me what the total was right away, and then he asked me if I needed any business advice. When I said I was thinking of going into business, he opened up that little gate and invited me into his private office. You ought to have seen him shake that head of white hair when I told him I wanted to start a bicycle repair shop. He didn't leave me in doubt for a minute. His answer was No—in a single two-letter word. He said a young man starting out in life should stick to established lines of trade and not go running off after every silly fad that came along. He gave me quite a lecture, telling me how fads go up and fads go down, but established lines go on forever. He says that the bicycle business is already going to pieces; that the factories are in financial trouble and are trying to sell out to the motor car people. He said it in a nice way, you know."

"You mean like fatherly advice, iss it?" asked the peddler.

"That's right—just telling me for my own good."

The peddler smiled. "And did he suggest other business to you?"

"Well," said Tom, "he tried to interest me in a sawmill that he said had come to the bank on the settlement of an estate and could be sold to the right man at a very attractive figure."

Sol sat up straight in his chair. "Would that, by some chance, be the Eagle Mill?"

"Yes," said Tom. "That's the very place. How'd you know?"

The peddler's round moonlike face was wreathed in smiles. "I just heppen to remember he tried to sell me mortgage on that mill—it must be ten years ago—and when I look into matter, what do I find? Even then water has failed. And here after all this time, with water getting scarcer and scarcer, he iss still trying to sell the property as going concern. What answer did you say?"

"I told him I didn't want a sawmill at any price. But I certainly am surprised to think he would try to sell me something worthless. I thought he was a gentleman."

"You are right," Sol assured him. "He iss in every inch gentleman, but also he iss first-class rascal. I have known him many years. Charm he has, but no conscience."

Gid was enjoying this. He had long hated Morton Towner, and now he added with some enthusiasm that the banker was a damned old bastard.

"He iss nothing of the sort," declared Sol indignantly.

· 101 ·

"There iss no question, not even little one, about the regularity of his birth. If there iss, in this country, such a thing as aristocracy—he iss it. If you say he iss grasping, to that I agree. His greedy nature has done more to keep back this town than all the tight-fisted taxpayers and retired farmers who ever lived in it. In his position, before things heppen he knows it, and soon as he knows it he go out and get options. Why did Northern Central put station two miles out of town? Because Towner held key to every suitable site for station, and his price was impossible. Through the years I haf known him, he has so many fectories driven off you could hardly count them."

"Maybe the old bastard don't want factories in town," suggested Gid.

"That iss right. Factories would bring other banks and other troubles. With things as they are he is satisfied." He waved a pudgy finger at Gid. "And there iss others. Your very excellent employer, Andy Brackett, what about him? Does he want a change? Iss he progressive?"

"Hey, listen," Gid protested. "He's the first man in this town to sign any paper for a good cause."

"Tell me this," said the peddler. "Who was to blame that cinder path for bicycles was killed?"

"Well—now—listen," said Gid. "Who the hell wants to make it any easier for bicycles? I wouldn't care if there was never another one brought into the world. And let me tell you some'pm—old Towner's right; they're on their way out."

"Where do you get figure for that?" demanded the peddler.

"I'll tell you where I got 'em—I got 'em from the canopy-top wagon. A while back everybody wanted one —and after they all got one, what happened? Nobody wanted one. Today you couldn't give one of them away."

The peddler shook his round head emphatically. "You are misinformed, my friend Gid. The bicycle iss multiply like rabbits. A craze it iss, but useful craze. The bicycle iss quick—it can tire any horse. But it must be repaired and adjusted if it iss to run good."

"Then you're on my side, Sol?" said Tom. "You think a repair shop would do all right."

Sol nodded with owl-like gravity. "My humble opinion it iss, that after centuries of horse the world iss now on wheels; and I do not belief it will go back any more to four legs."

Gid leaned over and whacked Tom on the shoulder. "Don't let him kid you, boy. No amount of them little spindly wheels will ever throw old Dobbin to the crows."

The peddler slowly shook his head. "So it was, your grandfather speak of flail and tallow candle. So it was, your father speak of scythe and kerosene lamp. Progress iss funny thing—never does it get along so fast as when you give it fight."

"Do you think that's going to be true of motor cars?" asked Tom.

"The perfect example it iss." Now the peddler was gesticulating with both hands. "At first it iss joke—people poke fun at it. Then it iss dangerous—somebody gets in front of it. After this it iss too fast—somebody goes ten, fifteen miles an hour in Central Park, and the motor vehicle iss prohibited from all parks. Then what heppens? Great public clamor. People who never even smell horseless carriage protest to high heaven. The papers iss full of it, and authorities cannot hold off the uproar— the law iss changed. Horseless carriage iss a joke no longer. A vehicle it iss—with rights."

"Not around here it ain't," growled Gid. "Here in God's country it's just a damn nuisance."

Sol smiled. "Once again you are misinformed, my friend. The law duss not use the words you speak. I have read it in paper only. The Counselor will correct mistakes. A motor vehicle iss vehicle propelled by something not muscle and not running on rails. Iss it that I am right?"

I turned to the law. "The words are 'power other than muscular.'"

"Then it says nothing about a damn nuisance?"

"Not that I can find."

"Don't be so damn legal," muttered Gid. "Your words may be printed in the books, but I'm tellin' you what folks are sayin'."

The peddler smiled. "Then they are saying wrong. The motor vehicle iss good—much better than the bicycle. Bicycle is muscular power, but with motor car it iss motor that does the pooshing. Bicycle it iss nice, but rider keeps thinking how much nicer if he had little engine to do the work."

"That's right," said Tom. "The first time I ever saw a bicycle I thought how much better an engine would drive it than a pair of feet."

"When the muscle iss tired—horse or man—it must stop; but with motor power," Sol was making circular motions with his hands, "you pour in more gasoline and keep going." He turned to Tom. "To start with bicycle iss good. Then, as the motor vehicle comes along—if it does come along—you be ready for it."

"You—you—you think my idea's all right then?" asked Tom eagerly.

With a pudgy finger the peddler pointed at the burlap roll lying on the floor. "What iss that bundle?"

Tom poked it with his foot. "That's my tools."

"It iss enough for start in business, no?"

"In a small way, yes." Tom grinned.

Sol rolled out of his chair and started for the door. "Bring it along, and come with me."

"Where are we going?"

"To see if we find a hole in the wall—for shop."

"But, Sol—I haven't got money enough."

The peddler raised his hand to put an end to that kind of talk. "I will take care of that." He glanced at Gid. "But not here. Our business affairs we should not discuss in presence of one who iss not sympathetic."

Gid leaned back in his chair and laughed quietly. "You can both go plumb to hell for all I care. But if I ever meet either one of you ridin' on one of them damn push-pedal nuisances—I'll ride you down, law or no law. And lemme tell you some'pm, Tom, he's a Democrat and it'll pay you to watch him."

Gid waited around until after the others had gone. Then he said to me, "Listen, Counselor, I wouldn't want it to get around or nuthin' like that, but if the kid is short of money you can count on me for a coupla hunderd if you'll keep your trap shut and never tell where you got it."

"That's nice of you, Gid," I said. "Of course I don't know how much money he's got, but it shouldn't take a great deal."

"But if he's gonna get himself lined up so's he can take care of a hossless buggy, he's gotta have some room."

I was ready to agree with that.

"Guess we don't hafta worry, though," said Gid. "Sol'll

take care of him, and that little feller's smarter than both of us put together."

With that Gid went out, and I heard no more from any of them until late in the afternoon, when Tom dropped in to say that he had not yet been able to find a suitable place. "But," he added, "I've got the money in the bank to start me in business."

According to Tom's account, the meeting between the peddler and Morton Towner must have been entertaining. Sol, as Tom told it, walked into the bank with a check in his hands, saying, "I want to deposit this to the credit of Tom Hunter."

Mr. Towner looked at the check on both sides, pursed his lips and softly whistled a bar of *Yankee Doodle*. "My friend the peddler," he said solemnly, "I don't doubt that your check is good, but your sense of humor is such that I will have to ask Mr. Hunter to wait a few days for it to clear."

Sol laughed softly. "Such a memory—and at your age."

"So we are to have a new business concern in town," said Towner.

The peddler looked the banker straight in the eye. "What gave you such idea as that?"

"Why, only this morning I was urging Mr. Hunter to start a bicycle repair shop." Mr. Towner was in a very jocular mood.

"So he was telling me," replied the peddler gravely. "By the way, you don't know of somebody who wants to buy a sawmill, no?"

Mr. Towner leaned slowly over the counter. "West of the Mississippi River they shoot men for less than that," he said.

10

Blue Grass

IT WAS AT JUST ABOUT THIS TIME THAT I caught up with Lucy Brackett on the street one day. As I walked along with her, bicycles kept whizzing past, and I remembered the campaign she was waging to get her uncle to buy one for her. Andy was in a peculiar position. He was ordinarily a hard man to convince against his will, and he was probably the worst enemy of the bicycle in town. On the other hand he was very fond of Lucy and found it hard to refuse anything she asked. But when I inquired how her campaign was progressing, she sadly shook her head.

"I'm afraid I'll never have one now," she said, and she told me what had happened only a day or two before, when she had tried to bring the question to an issue.

The showdown had occurred in the big dining room at the Brackett home, probably the most elegant room in town devoted exclusively to eating. The furniture in it was massive, with large spaces between the pieces. The room was just as it had been left to Andy by his father. Even the china fruit on the sideboard and the game pictures on the walls were the same. Aunt Harriett shifted these around occasionally at house-cleaning time, but they were so much a part of the room that she never thought of taking any of them away and substituting something else. Double doors opened invitingly from the great central corridor which bisected the house, and more double doors gave into the front parlor. Even the French windows looking out on a wide veranda were double.

Of a morning the dining room was a cheerful place with the bright sunlight streaming in through the French windows, though at midday it was not so bright, and by eventide it had become dull, perhaps a little gloomy, in spite of the lights from a somewhat elaborate chandelier.

Andy was seldom expansive at the evening meal. He felt no urge to linger over the empty coffee cups or the heavy damask linen. But at breakfast it was quite a different matter. This was the one time of day when he was likely to let himself go. There was something about the sunlight, or perhaps it was the big breakfast, which loosened his tongue. Neither Lucy nor Aunt Harriett was unaware of this morning expansiveness, and if either one had any important favor to ask, she was pretty sure to bring it up at the breakfast table.

As Lucy told me the story, she could hear her uncle's voice as she was coming down the broad walnut staircase. He seemed to be in fine fettle, and it occurred to her that this might be a good time to see if she couldn't settle the question about the bicycle. So far she had not had much success with the project, but she was not discouraged. Uncle Andy's resistance was something that usually gave way by degrees if she had perseverance enough to wear him down.

"It's the intimate contact with people; that's what makes life worth living in a small town," she could hear him saying, and at once guessed that Aunt Harriett had brought up her project of a couple of weeks in New York for shopping and some amusements.

He stopped as Lucy appeared in the doorway, and ran his eyes over her—as he would run his eyes over a horse, she thought. "Good morning, my dear. How sweet you are looking this morning." It was his usual formula.

"Good morning, Uncle Andy and Aunt Harriett." Lucy walked around to the farther side of the long table and sat down in her place.

"I was just speaking of the advantages of the small town."

Lucy smiled as she cut an orange in two and attacked one of the halves with a sharp-pointed spoon marked "Souvenir of Pasadena." "I guessed as much," she said.

Andy speared a triangle of ham with his fork. "Of course, you appreciate that it is something that will bear repeating at frequent intervals."

"But why repeat it to those who are already converted?" asked Lucy with a smile.

"Well, you women keep getting the idea that the social life in the cities is just a little better than it is in the small town, and I tell you it isn't so. Where would you find any finer people than there are right in this town? Old established families—been here for a hundred years or better. Got something back of 'em."

"The people here are nice enough," Aunt Harriett admitted, "but what I'm saying is that there are nice people in the city, too."

"Oh, the city people are all right," Andy conceded a little grudgingly. "What I object to is that they have no individual existence. They're herded around like cattle. They all wear the same things—do the same things—think the same things. Can't you understand that the life they live erases the individual instead of developing him? It's not the kind of life that turns out big men."

"But they have big men in the cities," Harriett protested.

"Of course they have," Andy agreed heartily, and then went on to qualify not quite so heartily, "but you'll find that most of them got their start in a small town."

"But, Uncle Andy," said Lucy, "I thought—I had an idea—what I mean is—isn't every small town anxious to grow larger? Isn't that so?"

Uncle Andy took a rather long sip at his coffee cup. "The answer to that is, Yes and no. The small towns don't want to go back, of course. Naturally they want to go ahead, a little. But, Lucy, it would be the greatest catastrophe this country could undergo if all the small towns should grow up to be big as New York or Chicago, or even as big as Boston."

"I think it would be pretty nice," said Lucy banteringly.

"But, my dear girl," cried Andy, "don't you see that we would have dried up our best source of really great men, and we'd have nobody capable of running the country in case of a big emergency. You know as well as I do that Washington, and Jefferson, and Abe Lincoln were all small-town boys. They're the men who made this country great, and if we're going to keep it great we've got to keep breeding more of the same kind."

"It seems to me," said Harriett, "that I've heard of a couple of gentlemen named Adams who had quite a little to do with the founding of our country, and who happened to come from Boston."

Andy smiled. "You know better than that," he said. "Or you ought to, for you and I visited the Adams house on our honeymoon, and it's in Quincy, my dear, not in Boston. And Quincy was probably no more than a four corners when the Adams family lived there."

"But we visited some President's house in Boston, I am sure," Harriett insisted. "I remember it distinctly. Could it have been John Hancock?"

"John Hancock may have been a great insurance man, my dear, but he never was President."

Having fairly well cleared up the point he had been laboring, Andy turned to Lucy. "Well, young lady, what's on your mind this beautiful morning?"

Lucy smiled. "Do you really want to know?"

"Of course I do," he assured her heartily.

She was a little timid about coming out with it, but she finally nerved herself up and said, "If you really do want to know, Uncle Andy, I was thinking about—that bicycle."

Andy managed to smile, but there was little mirth in it. "I suppose I ought to be glad that you haven't set your heart on one of those motor-buggy things; but after all, this bicycle craze is bad enough."

"It isn't a craze, Uncle Andy," Lucy protested. "It's really nothing more than a very jolly pastime, and it gets you around from one place to another in just no time at all."

Andy looked troubled. "In a way this is just the sort of thing we've been talking about. The thing that gives the small town its vitality is that by its very isolation it is protected from the succession of crazy whims that sweep over the cities. Now look at the phonograph, for instance. A little while ago it was all the rage. Everybody wanted a phonograph; but where are they today? They're in the candy stores, the billiard parlors, the soda-pop stands, where they want to make a noise to attract the trade. And do you know where this wonderful machine that reproduces the human voice will be next year? It'll be on the junk pile. Why? Because it's useless."

"The bicycle isn't useless," said Lucy. "It's really very handy."

"But did you ever stop to think why it is people buy a bicycle?"

"I don't have to think—I know it's because they're such fun to ride."

"No, I mean the real reason. The bicycle is largely bought as a substitute for the horse by people who for one reason or another feel that they can't afford to buy a horse. For instance, what does a Columbia bicycle cost?"

Lucy thought for a moment. "Asa paid one hundred and fifty for his chainless."

"What did Roscoe Towner pay for his Stearns?"

"About the same."

"And that female bicycle of Carrie Sayles—know what that cost?"

"Carrie told me it cost one hundred and twenty-five."

"Well, there you are, my dear—the top is one hundred and a half. And how much of a horse—a real horse, a thoroughbred, say—do you think you could get for a hundred and a half?"

Lucy shook her head. "I'm afraid it wouldn't go very far towards the kind of thoroughbreds you buy."

"Such a nag as that thoroughbred of Patterson's, for instance?"

Lucy knew every thoroughbred in the county. "You mean Blue Grass?"

Andy nodded. "Wouldn't you say that Blue Grass is worth as much as any four bicycles in town?" Andy watched her keenly as he put the question.

Lucy was puzzled by his expression as she answered

slowly, "I should think that would be about right." As she spoke she intercepted an exchange of glances between her aunt and uncle. He had asked her something and had received an affirmative answer.

"Well, my dear," Andy began, smiling largely, "we had not intended to tell you this until your birthday; but since this talk about bicycles has come up, we've decided not to hold back the news any longer. You are to have a present that is better than all four of the bicycles we were speaking of—Blue Grass is yours."

Even as Lucy was telling me the story her voice failed her. Spots of color appeared in her cheeks and her eyes flashed.

"And they've really bought him for you?"

She nodded.

"When are you to have him?"

"On my birthday."

"And aren't you delighted?" I asked.

"No, I'm not delighted at all!" she said angrily. "All I wanted was a bicycle."

"Is that what you said to them?"

She shook her head. "I behaved as the well brought-up young girl is supposed to behave. I said it was too much, that I could not let them do it."

"But since they had done it?" I suggested.

"Exactly!" she said. After a moment she added with a smile, "And all I wanted was a bicycle."

11

Repair Shop

EOPLE CALLED IT THE WEST HILL, THOUGH
it really wasn't much of a grade. Leaving the business section at the fork there by the bandstand, Main Street went
down a little, across a stone bridge, and then gently up all
the way to the cemetery. The only time that hill ever
stopped anybody was the winter's night when it was iced
by the firebug to keep Old Ocean and the other fire appa-
ratus from spoiling an incendiary blaze that was illuminating half the township.

Commerce, in the guise of a carriage factory, a reposi-
tory, and one or two miscellaneous enterprises, straggled
down from the fork but stopped abruptly on the farther
bank of the creek with a blacksmith shop and a rugged
building called the Stone Mill. Beyond the bridge property values were down because nobody wanted to go that
far from the center of things. But Tom thought he had
better investigate, for Sol had insisted that the shop must
be on Main Street, and there were no vacancies on the
other side of the bridge. The only space he had been able
to find was a tumble-down shed behind one of the stores,
and he did not want his shop to be behind anything.

Tom knew that putting up a place of his own was entirely out of the question, but still he derived a certain
melancholy satisfaction from playing with the idea. He

walked part way up the west hill, across the street, and into a vacant, grass-grown lot. He selected the spot where he would have liked the building to be. It should face the road, with large double doors that could be left invitingly open like those of a blacksmith shop. Then people could wheel their bicycles right inside or even ride them in. Sol had seen bicycle repair shops in the city, and he insisted that space must be left at the front for a display room. Workbenches, he said, could be tucked away anywhere at all, but goods must be displayed at the front—either the proprietor's goods that he was offering for sale, or customers' machines that had come in for repair.

Having located the front doors Tom thought it would be fun to lay out roughly the outlines of the building that he would like to have sometime—off in the distant future. He located the workbench and marked the spot with twigs. Then he paced off the rest of the building and put stones at the corners. He was so occupied with his fancy that he did not notice the approach of Vacy Boyden until the old fellow was standing in the open doors of the shop-to-be.

Vacy had what he thought was a very good reason for being interested in what Tom was doing—the land belonged to him. He had owned it for twenty years. He had bought the land for two reasons, he used to explain. To begin with, it was right in the line of business growth—if there ever was any on this side of the creek—and in the next place, it was the only space where the cemetery could expand. Mighty pretty view of that cemetery from here, and there wasn't much doubt in Vacy's mind that the cemetery was going to expand eventually, whether the town did or not. Tom was the only person, Vacy said, who had ever had the sense to show any interest in the property except the tax collector, and that worthy servant of the people showed an interest only once a year. So Vacy suddenly turned on Tom and asked him what kind of a proposition he was figuring on making.

Caught more or less unawares, Tom fenced for a while; and then broke down and confessed the truth—feeling that he had been guilty of a very silly performance. He was somewhat surprised to find that Vacy didn't think it silly at all. It was Vacy's attitude that you more or less had to see a thing before you could do it, and after the two had discussed the possibilities for a while he suggested that what Tom needed was not a new building but an old one, and he mentioned a vacant barn that could be bought for twenty-five dollars.

"You can rent a little piece of ground from me," he said, "and if you put your own building on it you can fix it up any way you want it."

Tom was puzzled. "My building on your land?" he asked. "Is that practical, or even possible?"

It was at this point in the negotiations that Vacy suggested they should come up and talk it over with my father. But, as was usual at this time, my father was not there, so they talked it over with me. This discussion led to the most complicated lease that I had ever been called upon to draw. The consideration, I might explain, was only four dollars a month, but the lease must have required between fifteen hundred and two thousand words to cover all the manifold provisions that were insisted upon by one party or the other.

The barn was bought. It was hauled to the new location for five dollars. And when the foundation was ready Vacy called in his neighbors for a barn-raising, and literally lifted the building into place. At the conclusion of the affair Vacy produced a keg of cider and Tom set out a box of cigars—the first he had ever bought.

When Tom had first come back to town after the death of his father he had lodged with Gid and had taken all his meals at Fred's Lunchroom; but by this time he was living at Mrs. Bannister's on East Main Street. Mrs. Bannister's was in no sense of the word a boarding house. No, indeed. She would no sooner have thought of putting a sign in her front window than she would of hanging her wash on the front porch. But because of certain unfortunate circumstances, into which there is no need to go, Mrs. Bannister found it necessary to augment her income and could think of no better way to do it than "taking in" some of the schoolteachers.

For a year or more she had three; then one was taken sick and had to give up her job and go back home, which left Mrs. Bannister with only two, and a vacancy. The new teacher lived at home, and the vacancy continued for so long that it was threatening to become permanent when Tom Hunter came along. Mrs. Bannister had always insisted that she would never have a male boarder, but the long vacancy must have modified her views; for when, at Tom's request, I stepped across the street—she lived almost opposite our house—to tell her that Tom was looking for a place to stay, she quickly reversed herself and decided to take him in.

Meanwhile Tom had been rebuilding what he was now calling his "horseless barn" into a well-arranged machine shop with a small showroom in front, and in the rear an office that could easily be converted into living quarters. Once he had started on the rear room he became quite interested in it, constructing a built-in bunk which let down from the wall, hinged tables, and a number of other ingenious arrangements for making life convenient.

Business began to trickle in as soon as the shop was opened. A punctured tire, a sprung wheel, a broken chain, and after a little, worn sprockets and loose bearings to replace. The work was simple enough, though for a while his inexperience caused him some slight difficulty. His first trouble was with the ball bearings. The tiny shot-like spheres would slip out of his fingers and roll across the floor, dropping through cracks into inaccessible hiding-places. One or two jobs had to be held up while he sent away for new balls to replace the lost ones.

But he soon devised a foolproof method for the handling of these tiny bearings; he would fill the race with cupgrease and press the balls deep into the grease to hold them as he was adjusting the cone to the proper pressure.

And after spending hours digging hardened cement from the rims, on removing the tires for repairs, he found a way of melting the cement by running a little trickle of gasoline over it and touching a match to it. This enabled him to soften all the cement at once, so that the tire could be snapped back on the rim in a matter of seconds. When he went to board on East Main Street Tom had hoped that he would meet all the people who lived in the neighborhood; but as time passed he found that he was not meeting very many of them, and he was seeing very little of the ones he did meet. He had been particularly anxious to become acquainted with Lucy Brackett, but for some reason she seemed to be the most inaccessible of all. Sooner or later the bicyclists were almost certain to come to him. Most of the younger people with whom he had an acquaintance had been met in that way. He had occasionally seen Lucy on a bicycle, but she had never come near his shop, not even to have the tires filled with the automatic pump that had attracted most of the others. He kept wondering why this was so, and one day he asked Gid about it.

Gid chuckled. "I can answer that for you in damn few words," he said. "The Skipper ain't got no bike." For a few moments he sat laughing softly to himself. "She's about the only gal in this town with any hoss sense, I guess. She wouldn't take one of the damn things as a gift."

"I appreciate your loyalty to your four-footed friends," said Tom with a smile, "but I've seen her riding a bicycle —more than once."

Gid shook his head. "Must have belonged to somebody else. A lot of them young cacks have got 'em. Likely she just borrowed one to go some place in a hurry. You know what Andy give her for her birthday, don't you?"

Tom shook his head.

"Blue Grass."

A vague look came into Tom's eyes. "What is it?"

Gid was disgusted. "Ain't you never heard of Blue Grass?"

"Isn't it something that grows in Kentucky?"

"Why, you poor bicycle wet-nurse, Blue Grass is the finest thoroughbred hunter in this part of the state."

"Hunter—?"

"That's what I said—a cross-country hoss that can take water-jumps and fences like a bird. Do you mean to tell me you never even seen the Skipper on hossback?"

"Not that I know of."

"Well, if you ever seen her on a hoss—you'd know it. She goes out in the mornin'. About six o'clock. Mostly she goes alone, but sometimes Andy goes with her. Once in a while it's young Parker. Not often, though—Asa don't like to get up that early."

"I'm always up by that time," said Tom. "It's a wonder I never saw her."

Gid shook his head. "She don't go out your way. Mostly she rides along the creek. Andy's got a bridle path down there across his flats. Goes clear through to the lower road. Bars from one field to the next if you want to use 'em, and fences to go over if you don't."

"I'd like to have a look at that horse," said Tom. "Where do you keep him?"

"We don't. She keeps him in the barn down there back of the big house."

Tom knew where that bridle path was. You turned downstream just before coming to the bridge by the Grist Mill. He had walked the full length of the path on Sunday afternoons more than once. The shade of the overhanging willows had invited him, and the soft turf of the meadow grass had felt grateful under his feet. A sign which said that no trespassing was allowed had not escaped his attention, but he regarded it as being addressed only to people on horseback. Walking along the banks of the creek, either with or without a fishpole, had been a local custom so long that more than a mere painted sign was needed to keep people out.

As Tom went down the street on the way home to supper he kept thinking of Lucy sailing over the whitewashed bars on Blue Grass. What a sight it must be. He couldn't keep it out of his mind. Not that he particularly wanted to; and still he was a little surprised at himself for taking such an interest in a horse. If he had pursued the thought a little further he must have come to the conclusion that, with anybody else as jockey, he would scarcely have raised an eyelash to see the most famous horse in the world; but he never went quite that far.

At Mrs. Bannister's boarding house Tom found the most comfortable home he had ever known. The two schoolteachers were safe old ladies in their thirties. They carried a certain air of authority, and still he was not afraid to dispute with them on subjects that he understood. The only trouble with the teachers was that they were more interested in other people's private affairs than they were in the mechanical progress of the world.

Tom had been reading a newspaper account of how Wilbur Wright had remained in the air for a minute and forty seconds, and he wanted to talk about it. But the teachers weren't interested. They couldn't see why people wanted to fly, and they could think of much more interesting ways of getting killed, if that was what the Wright brothers wanted. Miss Peters said that a good Columbia bicycle was as near flying as she would care to get. On the other hand Miss Morehouse, who was a bit on the plump side and who shunned anything which smacked of exercise, ventured to say that she would take a chance on riding in a horseless carriage if they would ever get them so that they would run. This gave Tom a chance to air some of the knowledge of the motor car.

Judging by what I knew of those teachers, they must have become quite weary from time to time of the young man's talk. No doubt they felt that there was, after all, something in the world beside science. Miss Peters, who taught Latin and Greek and dabbled in ancient mythology, was fairly well versed in the campaigns of Julius Caesar. If Tom could have explained to her that the pieces of something or other fitted together like the shields in a *testudo* she would have understood perfectly. But Tom knew no more about a *testudo* than Miss Peters knew about a torsion rod or a toggle joint. Miss Morehouse was a little more science minded. She taught algebra and geometry and was really good at advanced arithmetic, though she admitted one day that she had never heard of a slide rule, and she was politely skeptical of anything that would make a mathematical computation without the use of the human brain.

Tom never forced his talk upon them. He was perfectly content to sit in silence as he ate the very excellent food Mrs. Bannister placed upon the table, and to confine himself to the weather and the likelihood that Mr. Robert Peary, then on an early trip to the Arctic, would ever reach the Pole. Tom spent his evenings at his own shop among his tools and drawings and gadgets. He never tarried in the Bannister sitting room after a meal, though Mrs. Bannister and the teachers had from time to time invited him to sit and learn how to play cards. They were really in need of a fourth and were disappointed to find that he took no interest whatever in any of the amusements they had to offer.

Nor did he join in the small talk they loved to indulge in about other people's affairs. In fact, they found his silence on such occasions so sternly disapproving that they tried to do the best of their gossiping when he was not around. Tom was not long in discovering this. More than once he sensed a petering out of animated discussions when he appeared in the door of the dining room, and he said to himself a little grimly that he was glad they understood. One of these interrupted conversations, however, had left the ladies in such a fluttery state that he felt sure that their talk had concerned something that they particularly did not want him to hear.

The fragments he had overheard from the hallway had not at the moment sounded important. It was the significant tone of voice that had attracted his attention. He tried later to remember what they were saying, but could recall only a few words.

"You mean divided skirts, of course?" Miss Morehouse had exclaimed with an inflection which had denoted that this was not what was meant at all.

"I mean nothing of the sort," Miss Peters had said shrilly. "I mean trousers, or to be more explicit, *pants,* if you will. No more modesty than a circus performer. Now wouldn't you think . . ." Miss Peters, who was facing the door, cut herself off sharply. "Oh-ho-ho! Here's Mr. Hunter." It was the "view halloo." "How are you today? Nice weather we're having." This was followed by a great fluttering and twittering by the others to cover up their tracks.

Tom kept thinking about it on his way back to the shop. There had been nothing more about clothes during all the rest of the meal. Not that he was interested in clothes, though he did wonder why those old maids were concerned over the modesty of a circus performer. As he came up to his shop he found old Ike Meeker occupying the bench he had built for the convenience of waiting customers.

"You don't mind my settin' here a spell, do you?" the old fellow asked.

"Not at all," said Tom, "only you'll find more shade a couple of hours from now."

"I ain't afraid of the sun—had to go somewheres. Gid got mad at me and I thought I better git out. Dunno as I ever seen Gid flare up like he done today. He was what you'd call peeved and no mistake."

Tom unlocked the doors and swung them open. "What

was the matter with Gid?" he asked without interest, just making talk.

"I don't know why he was so danged upset," said Meeker. "I just happened to tell him that the whole dang town was scandalized by them britches Lucy Brackett's been wearin' on horseback."

Tom glared at him. "Britches, did you say?"

"That's exactly what I said. From what I hear tell, they're newfangled ridin'-pants, only they're pretty tight around the laigs—and around the seat, too, for that matter! You oughta hear what my wife says. But I say, oh, boy, what an eyeful!"

Tom turned and walked into the shop. So that was it. That was what those teachers were shrilling about in such bloodthirsty tones when he appeared in the doorway.

Meeker followed him inside. "That Lucy don't look to me like she'd be a cold one—not like my wife. My wife has got more ways of throwin' cold water on me than you ever heared of. Ever since we been married, if it ain't one excuse it's another, and every time I so much as touch a finger to her she jumps like I'd pricked her with a pin, and I wanta tell you a feller just can't make love to a woman who jumps like that. 'Tain't possible. Makin' love is some'pm that's gotta be done with delicacy—like makin' a good cherry pie."

By this time Tom had grabbed hold of a bent fender and was hammering on it lustily, making so much noise he could not hear any more of what the old fellow said. For a while Meeker tried to get started every time the hammering stopped, but at last he gave up and went away.

Tom was disappointed. For some time he had been intending to take a a bicycle ride down the road some nice morning around six o'clock to see Lucy ride. He especially wanted to see her taking the jumps on her new horse; but after the talk he had heard, he began to waver. He did not want people to believe that he was moving in for a closer view of Lucy in the much-discussed garments. Anything she wanted to wear was all right with him. But he did not want to get the reputation of being a Paul Pry, and most of all he did not want Lucy to get the idea that he would come down there just to stare at her. For a day or two he wavered, and then he made up his mind not to be influenced in any way by the malicious talk of a couple of old maid schoolteachers and Ike Meeker.

The next morning as the town clock was booming out the hour of six in a cracked metallic voice, he rolled out of Mrs. Bannister's dooryard and started in the direction of the Grist Mill road. As he reached the foot of the hill and coasted out on the bottom land he began searching the meadow for a rider. The view down across the fields was unobstructed, but he could detect nothing that appeared to be moving. So intent was he upon the distant scene that he did not notice how far along the road he had gone, until suddenly the gate to the bridle path loomed up before him and he realized that he had reached the end of his beat. If he went on his view of the meadows would be cut off by the trees along the banks of the stream. On the impulse of the moment he dismounted and quickly drew the key from the master link of the chain, thus providing a visual imitation of a serious breakdown for any possible passer-by. His alibi being thus secured, he again turned his attention to the bridle path, and far down across the meadow he discerned a figure on horseback.

Watching closely he saw the horse go soaring over a fence, the rider leaning slightly forward with elbows raised—she was riding astride. His first impression was that the horse was out of control, but he knew almost immediately that this was not so, for the rider slackened pace after the first jump, crossed the field at a more moderate pace, and speeded up as she approached the second. One after another Lucy took the jumps, her yellow hair blown by the wind, her cheeks red, her eyes shining, her body swaying in unison with the movements of her magnificent mount. Now she was in the third meadow—now in the second—and now in the first and charging head on at the gate directly in front of the place where Tom, chain in hand, stood gripping the handle bar of his bicycle.

If only he had remained motionless, if he had pretended that he was part of the landscape, all might have been well. But in his anxiety to keep from spoiling the jump Tom attempted to shove the bicycle off to one side at the exact moment when the head of the leaping hunter came over the top rail of the fence. Naturally the horse shied and landed off balance. It stumbled to its knees, but instantly recovered and started for home in a panic—though by this time Lucy had been pitched off and had landed in a sitting posture almost at Tom's feet.

She had no more than landed before she was up again and screaming angrily into Tom's face.

"Why did you do anything so stupid!"

Still feeling for the breath that had gone out of him Tom gasped out, "Wh-wh-what did I do?"

She shook her crop in his face. "You fool—you threw him off his stride—you might have broken that horse's legs!"

Nothing so annoyed Tom as being yelled at, and in a flash his quick temper had let go. "Damn the horse's legs!"

he hurled back at her. "What about your own—are you hurt?"

She raised her crop as if to strike him. "Don't let that horse get away—he mustn't go home like that! Stop him! Catch him—" Then she noticed the bicycle chain in his

hand and let out a moan. "Oh, it's broken! What can I ever do!"

Tom shoved the machine into her hands. "Here—hang onto this and I'll fix it." He dropped to his knees and in what looked to Lucy like a single motion snapped on the chain. In another motion he snatched the machine out of her hands with a suddenness that almost took her with it. Then she saw him make a flying leap into the saddle and go spinning up the road in pursuit of the horse.

By the time that Tom had drawn up on the big bay, the animal was becoming winded and had begun to slow down. And once he had succeeded in heading the horse, Tom began to crowd the big fellow towards the side of the road. Suddenly the thoroughbred spied an open gate and dashed through it—and then Tom had him.

He closed the gate and walked slowly up to the horse, talking to him in the soothing tones he had heard Gid use when handling fractious horses. He patted the horse's shoulder, then his neck, and after that he very gently took hold of the bridle. Without making any attempt to mount, he led the panting animal down the road in the direction of the trim figure that was hurrying towards him, waving a riding crop.

This was when Tom took his first real look at Lucy. He did not know whether he would ever have another such chance—and he did not miss a thing. It was a moment that he would long remember.

"How did you catch him?" she asked as he handed over the bridle.

"He sorta stopped and waited for me, I guess."

She straightened out the bridle and stepped around to the horse's side. "Would you mind giving me a knee up?" Not a word of thanks. Not even a smile.

He could feel his face getting red as he replied, "I guess I don't know what you mean."

"Put your foot right there." She pointed with the crop. "Bend your knee a little and I'll show you."

As he bent his knee she touched her left toe to it, leaped lightly up, swung her right leg over the saddle, and was off in a shower of gravel.

12

Horseless Buggy

I DON'T KNOW WHAT IT WAS THAT AROUSED my interest in the motor car. Certainly it was not any remarkable performance on the part of Dorlon's one-cylinder Rambler. The non-performance of that car should have been a portent and a warning to any person who might have a suspicion that the motor car would ever amount to anything. It was almost never seen in motion. The first half-a-dozen times I saw that vehicle it was standing disabled somewhere in the roadway. I am told that it came into town under its own power. But that is hearsay; and hearsay, as anybody knows, is a species of evidence given no credence whatever by the courts.

Just how that car made the thirty-three miles from Rochester, I don't pretend to know, but I have my suspicions. It was in front of Dorlon's house one morning when the town woke up—and even then it was standing still. A little later in the day it was standing still in front of the Inn—not over by the curb, but right in the middle of the street. Mr. Dorlon, with his good clothes on, was hovering over it. The good clothes were somewhat unusual for a working day, and it occurred to me that Mr. Dorlon had an idea that a little more was expected of him now that he had become an automobile owner.

It must be admitted that Mr. Dorlon was giving a good

account of himself. He was opening this or closing that, or throwing on or off a little switch on the dashboard. Occasionally he would step over to the side of the machine and engage a crank, with which he would make a few turns. Then he would remove the crank and go around the car and shut all the things he had opened, or open all the things he had shut. And after that he would try the crank again. By the time I arrived Mr. Dorlon already had a large audience, and as long as I stayed it kept getting larger. It was, on the whole, an attentive and admiring audience. Many of the people there had never had a good look at a horseless buggy before and did not wish to miss the opportunity. The helpful audiences, with suggestions shouted by some anonymous member well back in the crowd, were to come later.

In the position of latecomer I found myself on the perimeter of the crowd and unable to watch developments as I would have liked. While looking around I happened to catch sight of the shirt sleeves and carpet slippers of Old Tick, who was standing on the veranda of the Inn, his elbows resting on the high balustrade, watching proceedings in the street. Since the veranda looked like a very desirable vantage point I went over and joined him, arriving just at the moment when Mr. Dorlon was taking one of his occasional turns at the crank.

"Jees Cri!" Old Tick let out explosively as I came up beside him. "Does the goddam thing run by clockwork?"

"Hardly," I said, not knowing whether he was in earnest or in one of his witty moods.

"Then what in hell is he windin' it for?" he demanded, and I could see that he was very much in earnest. "You know there is such a thing as breakin' a mainspring. Broke one myself once." He tapped the vest pocket in which he

· 130 ·

carried his large silver watch, as thick as a man's wrist. "Wound the goddam thing up too tight and it went off with a whizz like a rattlesnake. Cost me a dollar to get a new one—as well as scarin' me out of two dollars' worth of wits. How can he keep windin' it like that? He musta broke a mainspring. You can only wind anything so fur—and after that you can't wind it another goddam twist."

From the veranda I could get a very comprehensive view of Mr. Dorlon's new machine. It was dark green in color and had a wheelbase of about six feet. The part in front of the dash stood some four feet off the ground and had a hinged cover which could be lifted up. Inside was the gasoline tank of three gallons' capacity, and a reservoir to hold the supply of water for the radiator. There were two seats, both facing the dashboard in this particular car—though in other cars that I had seen, there were rear seats facing towards the back. It seemed to me at the time that this back-to-back arrangement was very cosy; and certainly it must have been an aid to conversation, which was very likely to be impeded by the noise of the machinery.

The rear seat of Mr. Dorlon's car, a removable part called a tonneau (from the French word meaning tun or cask), could be taken off or put on very simply, with the aid of no more than two or three able-bodied and cooperative neighbors. Access to the tonneau was through a door at the rear, though I cannot now recall that I ever saw anybody occupying the seats of it.

This car was a distinct departure from the buggy, being both longer and lower. It was more on the order of a buckboard, though the wheels were much smaller than those of any buckboard I ever saw and were mounted with inflated tires. These wheels were sturdy, like the wheels of a well-built wheelbarrow, which they quite closely resembled. The steering wheel or "controller" was located in front of the driver's seat at the right, within easy reach of the whip socket, had a whip socket been necessary. Indeed on some of the early Packard cars, one of which was owned in Geneva, the bodies, built by a carriage manufacturer, were equipped with whip sockets. These, I am told, came in very handy for carrying a cane or an umbrella, though for some reason they were discontinued on the later models.

By keeping up the appearance of doing something, Mr. Dorlon managed to hold his audience until the arrival of Tom Hunter, who eventually came sauntering down the street in response to a message dispatched to him by Mr. Dorlon. Tom was carrying under his arm a roll of tools wrapped in a piece of burlap. The crowd fell back to admit him, then closed in behind him as the waters of the Red Sea are said to have closed in behind the Children of Israel after their celebrated crossing.

When Tom had penetrated the inner circle he stopped and looked over the vehicle. "Good-looking wagon," he said to Mr. Dorlon. "What's the matter with it?"

Mr. Dorlon shook his head. "I can't make it go."

"How'd it get here?"

"Oh, it ran all right until it got here."

"Where from?" asked Tom.

"In front of my house."

"Drive it yourself?"

"Sure. I know how to drive. The fellow I bought it from showed me how yesterday."

"How'd you get it started?"

"Just like he told me. I pushed over the little handle on the dash, and I cocked that lever up there on the wheel. Then I put the crank in this hole around on the side, and after I turned it around a few times the thing started."

"But what stopped it?" asked Tom.

"That's what I don't know. All of a sudden it give a couple of kicks, and then it passed out."

Old Tick nudged me. "Jees Cri!" he squeaked. "It give a cough just like a dyin' hog. I didn't know the goddam things could cough."

Tom removed the cover from a little box on the dash and poked something with his finger. "Vibrator sounds all right," he said. He went over the connections of the dry cells, tested the compression with the crank, and was just raising the front cover to look into the gasoline tank when Mike Kelsey drove past.

"Hi, Tom!" he called out in friendly greeting from his perch on the seat of a farm wagon. "Give her the old *a-b-c!*"

With a wave of the hand Tom answered, "That's just what I'm doing." A moment later he turned to Mr. Dorlon. "Got a measuring stick?"

"What for?"

"I want to see if you've got any gasoline."

"Certainly there's gasoline. It wouldn't have started if it didn't have gasoline."

Tom removed the cap and stuck one of his long fingers into the tank. When he pulled it out it was dripping. "That's funny," he said. "You got plenty in the tank and still there doesn't seem to be any in the carbureter. Is there a gasoline cut-off?"

Mr. Dorlon scratched his head. "Seems to me that fellow said there was, when he shut off the car last night.

But he couldn't have turned it, or the motor wouldn't have started this morning."

"Don't be too sure," said Tom. "There might have been just enough in the pipes to give you a start and run you a block or two." Suddenly he drew his head out of the front part of the car and poked it down underneath. Then I saw him running his fingers along a little copper pipe. After a few moments he stood up and lifted one of the seat-cushions. "Ah, here it is," he said, "and it's shut off."

He gave it a turn, snapped on the switch, cranked the engine—and Mr. Dorlon drove on. He went all the way to his upper factory, a distance of nearly a mile, without further trouble. But I saw him later that day stalled in front of the Presbyterian church. The following day he broke down in front of the cider mill and was there half the afternoon before he could get started again. But his favorite place for breaking down seemed to be in front of the cemetery. Somehow he managed to stall there two or three times every day. It may have been that the long climb was too much for the car, and it may have been something else, for Mr. Dorlon confided to me that it had broken down in front of other cemeteries. Eventually this inability to go past a cemetery began to get under Mr. Dorlon's skin, and he admitted to me privately that he had regarded very seriously the possibility that he was being given a premonition. It struck him as particularly significant that these cemetery breakdowns occurred only when he was driving the car, never when his son was driving—in fact, never when anybody else was driving.

Mr. Dorlon came around to our office and made his will. He began to go to church assiduously, twice every Sunday, and he never missed the Thursday night prayer meeting. I was told that he made very long and very earnest prayers, though I never had the pleasure of hearing any of his uneasy supplications. But if the temperamental one-lunger was possessed of evangelical powers while in the hands of the father, it had a worldly influence when in the hands of the son; for when he had a breakdown it was usually in front of a saloon or while he was passing a particularly tough roadhouse.

I had my first automobile ride with young Stew Dorlon. We had the temerity to set out for a neighboring village one evening with the intention of calling on a couple of girls. The car ran perfectly until we were three or four miles out of town, when the high-gear clutch-band burned out its lining and we had to continue on low. This was more than the low-gear clutch-band could take, and after laboring along for half a mile further, that too refused to function. With the two forward speeds disabled we had nothing left but the reverse, so we ran backwards all the way home, passing along Main Street in the early evening when most of the inhabitants were sitting on their front verandas.

Tom Hunter relined the clutch-bands and soon had the car in its normal condition again. But I never was able to reestablish friendly relations with that girl. She thought I had broken my date and had gone out with some other girl, and she had too much pride to take that kind of treatment even from a young professional man who had his name painted on the door of a law office.

My second automobile ride was also with Stew. This time we got caught in a sudden thunderstorm, and the car bogged down in a treacherous mudhole while we were trying to reach the shelter of a farm barn about half a mile away. We went the rest of the way on foot and I ruined a pair of white flannel trousers, which shrank until they were almost up to my knees; and what was worse, I completely wrecked a new, wide-brimmed straw hat for which I had sent all the way to New York. I was not so concerned about the pants, which I had already worn for two or three seasons; but that wide-brimmed straw hat, enviously known to my fellows as the "cow's breakfast," was brand new and had a brim that was just a little wider than any other hat in town.

You might think that with such a disastrous start, my motoring career would have been over even before it had begun. But no, only a few days after the adventure that had ended in the destruction of the cow's breakfast, I went to Tom Hunter and arranged to have him go with me to Rochester in quest of a good secondhand car. I couldn't afford a new one, which at that time would have cost me almost fifteen hundred dollars. But I had heard that a good two-cylinder job was to be had for around eight hundred, and I had made up my mind that if this were so I must certainly have one. I had seen these two-cylinder jobs go thundering through the town with the driver in gauntlets and goggles, tooting the horn and crowding on the power.

I am very much afraid, however, that it was not entirely the craving to handle this immense speed and power that was burning me up, though I will admit that it was a contributing factor. From this distant view I am pretty well convinced that the mysterious females occupying the tonneau must have had something to do with it. It was the fashion at the time for the men to ride in the front seat, which was then regarded as more hazardous, and to tuck the ladies away in a place of safety in the tonneau. Here they covered themselves from chin to toe with linen dusters and veiled their faces like the houris of a Turkish harem. These veils, usually of gay colors, were tied under the chin, with the ends fluttering far back over the shoulders, and gave a carnival touch to passing traffic which has been entirely lost since the coming of the closed car.

Together Tom and I combed Rochester. I think we saw every secondhand car in the city, and eventually the choice narrowed down to an Elmore at $500 and a two-cylinder, canopy-top Rambler at $850. Personally I liked the Elmore—it was a much better color, a brilliant scarlet, whereas the Rambler was a muddy green. I could just see myself flying around the country in that red Elmore with the long streamers of harmonizing veils fluttering out behind. But Tom shattered my dreams with the statement that if I should buy that Elmore I would probably do no more flying around than Mr. Dorlon was doing with his old one-lung job, and that I might be more than a match for the Dorlon car in the matter of breakdowns.

"The trouble is that it's a two-cycle motor," he said.

That did not mean a thing to me, but I felt that I had to look wise. "Only two?" I said. "That doesn't seem like very many to me. How many cycles has the Rambler got?"

"Four."

I made a quick computation and figured that the Elmore was asking $250 per cycle while the Rambler was asking only $212. "The Rambler's the better buy."

Tom smiled when he heard how I had arrived at my conclusion. We had bought the Rambler and were on the way home before he explained to me the difference between a four-cycle and a two-cycle motor.

"To make an engine run," he said, "four things are necessary—suck in gas, compress it, explode it, blow out the smoke. A four-cycle engine gives a complete piston stroke to each job. There's your four cycles. A two-cycle engine crowds two of those jobs into each piston stroke. Naturally it doesn't make a clean job. The functions come so close together they get mixed up. The idea is fine, it's economical, it cuts out lost motion, it performs all four functions on a single revolution of the crankshaft. The only trouble is that in a small engine nobody's ever been able to make it work."

We were about halfway home when Tom began sniffing the air suspiciously. "Do you smell something burning?" he asked.

I shook my head. "I don't smell anything that I didn't smell when we started out."

"Well, I do," said Tom, "and I guess we'd better stop and take a look."

It is just as well that we did, for we found the whole underpart of the car in flames. We put out the fire by throwing sand on it, and then Tom went under to see if he could discover the cause. He found an accumulation of oil and grease in the big sheet iron drip pan that hung underneath the engine, and he also found an oily rag that had been partly consumed by the fire. We had no more trouble except a puncture or two and reached home in time for supper, having covered the entire thirty-three miles in less than three hours.

We parked the car in front of our house, and as Tom was leaving to go over to Mrs. Bannister's he reminded me to write to the Secretary of State in Albany and send two dollars as a license fee.

"Will they send me a number?" I asked, anxious to have something to hang on my new motor vehicle.

"They'll send you a little brass seal like a dog tax number, but you'll have to get your own tag to hang on the back of the machine."

"Anything else?"

Tom smiled. "Well, there's an operator's license, but that doesn't cost anything and they'll send it to you without your even asking for it."

13

*D*ust

FATHER DID NOT WANT MY CAR KEPT IN THE same barn with the horses, so I hired a shed for it over near the coal yard. I was glad of this, in a way, as it gave me more freedom about using my time for dusting and polishing and oiling. The hours I spent on that automobile, and the others which were to follow it, if diligently devoted to any profession whatever would undoubtedly have placed me near the top. My only excuse is that I enjoyed working around a car—and still do.

I was over at the shed fairly early the next morning, wiping off the dust of that long journey down from Rochester, when old Ike Meeker came along. Ike said he was in a hurry, but he stopped long enough to admire my car and to tell me the somewhat disturbing news that Mr. Dorlon had broken his arm that morning while cranking his.

"What," I exclaimed, "that old one-lunger!"

Ike nodded. "Tom Hunter says it's got a kick like a mule. Say," he added, "you gonna start up this machine pretty soon?"

I said I was, and Ike began to look for a place to sit down.

"I thought you were in a hurry," I said.

"I was," Ike said with a smile, "but I ain't no more.

Guess I'll stick around and see how you make out. You might want somebody to go for the doctor."

The same uneasy thought had occurred to me, and the more I considered it the more uneasy I became. I lingered over my dusting and polishing for a long time in the hope that Ike would get tired of waiting and go on. But I was finally convinced that Ike was the kind who does not tire of waiting, the kind who knows how to do nothing and do it well; and the longer I fussed around, the more comfortable he made himself. I could see that I was fighting a losing battle, so I thought I would have to try something else.

"I don't suppose you know what time it is?" I said, holding up my hands which were too smeared with brass polish to get into my watch pocket.

Ike slowly shook his head. "I never know what time it is—except when I get hungry."

With some show of reluctance I wiped off my hands. Then after a quick glance at my watch I began to gather up my cleaning cloths and tuck them away. "I'll have to go back to the house and clean up," I said. "I can't go to the office looking like this."

I went away and left Ike sitting where he was. How long he may have remained there I have no idea, for after I had washed my hands I went directly to the office without returning to the shed. I felt sure that he would go home to dinner, and I think he did, for when I went to the shed with Tom Hunter in mid-afternoon Ike was nowhere to be seen. I had changed my mind about driving to the office that morning and had decided that it might be the better part of valor to take a cranking and a driving lesson from Tom before trusting myself out on the road. As it turned out, it is just as well that I did, for I found that there were a number of starting precautions that I had forgotten.

Tom insisted that I must go through the motions several times, and then, just to be on the safe side, he wrote out a list and tacked it on the wall of the shed. He also insisted that I should be the one to handle the crank, saying that the only way to get over being afraid of it was to get used to it. He had me start the engine and stop it at least half-a-dozen times before we backed out of the shed—and he made me do the backing. As soon as we were on the road I headed for the country, intending to keep to the byways where few conveyances were likely to be met. But Tom vetoed that plan and kept me on the main-traveled roads. His idea was that I might just as well get used to meeting teams, since I was going to meet plenty of them every time I went out in the car.

It was with some nervousness that I spied the first horse-drawn vehicle in the offing. I immediately reached for the horn and began to honk, but after I had given only two or three blasts he stopped me.

"That man knows you're coming," he said, "and so does his horse. And he's probably feeling irritated with you because you are holding to the middle of the road and blowing for him to get out of the way."

"But that isn't what I meant," I explained. "I just wanted to call his attention to the fact that an automobile was coming."

"Of course," said Tom, "but the odds are that he saw you long before you saw him. Just remember that these horse people aren't going to like you anyway, and you must go out of your way to encourage their goodwill."

"Don't you worry about me," I said. "I'll turn out before I get to him."

"That isn't enough," Tom insisted. "You should turn out long before you get to him and throttle the car down, and turn 'way out so as to spare him all the dust you can. Whoa!" he called out suddenly. "There goes his hand— you've got to stop the car."

I had already turned out as far as I could, and when I stopped the car the fenders were almost over to the fence line. But the horse was prancing and dancing and threatening to back up. For a few moments the driver tried unsuccessfully to make the animal go past, and then he again raised his hand.

"What's that for?" I asked.

"It means he wants you to turn off the motor," said Tom.

I snorted. "That farmer's got his nerve. If I should shut off the motor I'd have to get out and crank, and I'm not going to do it."

"Of course you know it's the law, but if you don't want to do it—I can't make you."

Without another word I bent over and cut the switch. We repeated that experience half-a-dozen times in an afternoon's drive, and when I reached home I felt that I was a seasoned driver. I never took another lesson from that day to this, though I have been learning things about the intricacies of automobile driving ever since.

To people accustomed only to the modern, dustless road it is hard to give an adequate account of the dust of those early days of the motor car. For centuries the horse-drawn vehicle had been raising a fair amount of dust from the dirt roads during dry weather, though in all this time there never was enough of it to constitute a problem sufficiently urgent to require a drastic public solution. Towns used to sprinkle their streets with water once or twice a day, though the horses drawing the sprinkling carts stirred up almost as much dust as they laid. Outside the towns and cities, nothing whatever was done to cope with the dust nuisance. Roads had always been dusty, and the agricultural population had reason to believe that they always would be.

However, the coming of the automobile changed all this. With its greater speed and its broader, softer tires, it threw up suffocating clouds of highway dust such as the oldest inhabitant had never dreamed of even in the driest of seasons. And not only that, but the vehicle that raised the dust was so rapid in its movements that it left its dust far behind, to be coped with by slower-moving traffic. Dirt roads frequented by the motor car deteriorated rapidly. The tiny particles sucked up by the fast-moving tires were blown away by the wind. Small towns which were built along the through roads were the worst sufferers; and Phelps, being practically a one-road village perched astride the old Buffalo-Albany stage road, began to be plagued by intolerable dust as soon as the motor car became hardy enough to venture from one town to another. But, strange as it may seem, the initial impetus of the movement for improved and dustless roads came not from the harassed populations of the small towns and rural districts, but from the automobile clubs and associations. These were soon joined by the hotel men's associations and tourist bureaus.

The New England Yankee was among the first to see the financial possibilities of the touring automobilist, and when the motor car was still chugging along on a single cylinder, with the driver spending half of his touring time making repairs, the state of Massachusetts was spending two million and a half on improving its roads in a single year, while the state of New York spent only fifty thousand dollars in two years. The impressive rows of ciphers that began to appear in the reports of the New England tourist business were not long in attracting the attention of the New York authorities, however, and New York did some serious thinking about improving its roads.

As motor cars increased in number and efficiency the spectacle of motorists from all over the country flocking into New England to spend their summers there on account of the excellence of the roads was more than the New Yorkers could stand—and the purse strings came open with a bang. What seemed at the time like a monumental highway program went into operation, and after stabbing around here and there for purely political purposes, the state highway authority began to take itself seriously and tried to formulate its construction into through routes.

One of these routes was coming up through the state, hoping eventually to fill in all the chinks between the Hudson River and the city of Buffalo. The private citizen knew little about what was going on, and when the people of our town saw the state engineers running one of their groping preliminary surveys up the old stage road they took it for granted that we were lucky enough to be on the map. It was a feeling of false security that was far from justified. Only the higher-ups knew what was going on, and they weren't saying anything about it.

Quite naturally Andy Brackett, with his whole financial stake tied up in horses, was not going to hail with any enthusiasm a main line motor road passing in front of his door. As a matter of fact, he did not want it anywhere in the township and would have kept it out of the entire county if he could. Not being able to effect a by-pass of the county, however, he was not above making a deal with the townships lying to the south. If you'll give me your support on (*buzz-buzz-buzz*) I'll get back of your proposal to designate the county route of the new highway up through your town.

Not being in the slightest degree interested in politics, I knew no more about what was going on than the rest of the rank and file, and it came as a good deal of a surprise to all of us when the Green Pack Peddler, who was born on Grand Street and had a natural taste for politics, brought the news to Tom that a deal was being arranged by Andy Brackett to scuttle our chances of being included in the new highway routing.

At first Tom wouldn't believe it; he didn't think that Andy Brackett would be guilty of such an underhanded trick.

The peddler shrugged his broad shoulders. "You know the reputation Andy's got for horse deal. He cheat a man out of his eyeballs."

"I know all about that," said Tom. "A horse deal is a horse deal—it's dog eat dog, and all the players know it. I tell you, Andy's all right. He's a nice fellow."

Sol shook his head dubiously. "And you talk like that of your competitor, and probably your best enemy!"

"Why do you say he's my enemy, Sol? He's never done anything to me. I don't think he likes me especially, but he's always pleasant."

"Of course pleasant. That iss part of his business. But you stand for what he hates—the bicycle, the motor car. These things, someday, who knows, may run him out of business. And, don't you doubt it—he will smesh you if he can."

"Nonsense."

"There iss no nonsense about it. It iss true. Already he has hurt you, and you don't even know it."

"What's he done to me?" Tom demanded.

The peddler swept his hand in the direction of the street. "Why has bridge been closed for three weeks already, keeping public away from your shop?"

"It's unsafe—that bridge has got a crack in the wall."

"But three weeks! Why iss it not mended?"

"It's a serious break and they're trying to find out what caused it, and they've got to let it settle a while—and anyhow, what's Andy Brackett got to do with it?"

"He iss the boss!"

"But Stoner is the Supervisor. He takes care of the roads and bridges."

The peddler smiled. "Stoner must do as he iss told, and Andy iss the man who tells him. If Andy can ruin your business he will. Already he must haf hurt it. Am I right?"

"I've lost a lot of business that would have come across the bridge, but I can't blame Andy for that."

"You are a stubborn fellow," said the peddler. "I see that you must have proof, and I will try to get it for you."

He shouldered his pack and went out, but he was back within an hour with a roll of white cotton cloth under his arm and a folded paper clutched in his hand. "You are going to move temporarily," he said with a delighted grin.

Tom blinked at him. "Move—? Me—? Where to?"

"To the old photograph gallery by the entrance to the Brackett Stables. The building iss small, but for bicycles it will do, and in the rear iss plenty room for automobiles —in plain sight of the barns."

"But—but, Sol, I've got this place. I can't possibly carry another."

Sol chuckled. "You can carry this one, and it iss only

temporary besides. I have option with a right to put up sign. That iss why I have brought the hollands. I will myself paint the sign for you." He tacked up the cloth and painted rapidly.

DURING REPAIRS TO THE BRIDGE THE UNDERSIGNED WILL OPEN A TEMPORARY GARAGE AND BICYCLE REPAIR SHOP ON THESE PREMISES WHERE CUSTOMERS OLD AND NEW WILL BE WELCOMED AND TREATED RIGHT.

Tom Hunter

Sol stood and surveyed the sign, which was ready to post on the front of the gallery. "Now hiss enemy will be tangled in hiss eyebrows almost! To stomach that he will not be able. If bridge iss not open within a week I take great pleasure in paying for this experiment. But another sign we must have yet. I will paint it now." He tacked up another piece of the hollands and produced a second sign as rapidly as he had done the first.

THIS SHOP CLOSED DURING HIGHWAY REPAIRS TO BRIDGE. TEMPORARY SHOP AT PHOTOGRAPH GALLERY NEAR BRACKETT'S STABLES.

Tom Hunter

"If not mistaken," said the peddler, "Andy Brackett will lose hiss composure when he sees on your sign hiss name."

To say what may have happened to Andy Brackett's composure would be pure guesswork, for Andy was not one to make a show of himself, and he had plenty of reason for wanting to make no issue of the highway bridge. His cordiality to Tom suffered no visible change, though

· 148 ·

Tom himself felt very uncomfortable and self-conscious whenever they met on the street or in the post office—always expecting Andy to show signs of irritation, and never quite understanding how any man could be so poised and self-controlled under the circumstances.

As it happened, not a word came from Andy directly or indirectly; but a day or two after the signs were posted, Stoner appeared at the damaged arch with a gang of workmen, and in a short time repairs were completed and the bridge again opened to public use. The Supervisor seemed very much pleased to report that what had been taken for a structural defect had on closer inspection proved to be only a superficial crack, caused, in all probability, by the unusually cold winter followed by the hottest summer on record.

Tom's temporary signs promptly came down, and business returned to normal. This was very nice, but there was still that disagreeable threat of losing the new highway. Tom came over and talked to me about it, and while I knew nothing of any definite political deal Andy Brackett may have made, I knew enough about his business ethics to assure Tom that Andy would not hesitate a moment to make any kind of deal that he thought would save his own financial bacon. I would have liked to discuss the situation with Father, but he and Mother had gone to Europe and there was no way of reaching him.

I sent Tom to see O'Brien, the Democratic county leader from whom Sol had learned of the deal. Tom came back with a long face and the news that the county board was evenly divided. Only one more vote was needed to put over Andy's deal. If Stoner were reelected the new road would be lost.

Stoner was a Republican, and to be nominated on the

Republican ticket was tantamount to election. Only about once in a decade would a Democrat slip into office as town Supervisor, usually to discipline a stupid incumbent or as a tribute to personal popularity, and invariably by the skin of his teeth. The Democratic party was still kept alive by a little band of hopefuls who made regular nominations year after year with little expectation of election. The nominations were passed around among the faithful, giving first one and then another the dubious honor of being defeated in order to keep the breath of life in the organization. It was common talk that the candidates were sometimes chosen by the toss of a coin.

This year, however, there was no tossing of a coin. Vacy Boynton, the Democratic leader, decided to nominate himself. Then a tight little organization formed by Tom and Vacy started what was known as a "bottonhole" campaign. It consisted in buttonholing people and pledging them to a personal vote for Vacy. If they could pledge a certain number of Republicans to vote for Vacy, the election was won, since the Democrats rarely went outside their own party and usually voted blindly under the star. Tom and Vacy realized that in an out-and-out fight over the new road, Andy could lick them with one hand tied behind him. But if they could lure Andy into believing that his candidate was going to meet with only routine opposition and could keep him in that state of mind until after they had the required number of his flock under pledge, they saw no reason why Vacy should not win. And with Vacy Boynton in place of Stoner on the county board, the new road would be safe.

But somewhere, only a day or two before the election, a leak occurred, and Andy's organization went into action. Immediately some of those who had been pledged to Vacy came around and begged off; and the contest very quickly resolved itself into the one thing the Democrats had wanted to avoid—a local brawl over the new road. Tom and Vacy worked valiantly to hold their pledges in line, but in spite of anything they could do they kept losing them. The prospects were looking very glum the night before election, when Tom suddenly came through with what looked like a bright idea: why not hire some machines to carry the voters to the polls?

Most of the voters, he was certain, had never been in a motor car, and if they could get people to ride to the polls they'd feel more or less obligated to vote for the highway. Vacy was a little skeptical, but Tom's enthusiasm carried the day; and the next morning when the polls opened, four large and impressive motor cars hired from Geneva were drawn up at the curb to carry the voters back and forth. These made the two hacks furnished by Andy's livery look somewhat insignificant.

It was the most magnificent fleet of automobiles the town had ever seen, and Andy Brackett may well have been uneasy when he watched the crowds gathered around them looking them over. And he may have been even more uneasy when he noted the clouds of dust the big machines raised from the roads which his administration had provided. The pro-highway party had also been uneasy when they saw the great cloud of dust arise upon their initial sortie; but when they caught the drift of the public reaction and found that the roads instead of the cars were being blamed, they governed themselves accordingly, and from that time on they kept the fleet in motion.

As Towner, the banker, was coming out of his bank to go over to the polls and cast his vote for Stoner, two cars went whizzing past in the street, one in either direction, raising a double portion of the minutely pulverized surface of the highway. And by the time the old gentleman had entered the Town Hall he was snorting and snuffing and wiping his eyes.

"What's the meaning of all this dust?" he demanded as Andy Brackett came up to speak to him.

Andy drew him aside. "It's all these blasted horseless carriages," he said. "Young Hunter and his gang are using them to bring in their votes."

"But why in the devil don't you order out the sprinkling wagon?" the banker growled, dusting off his clothes with his handkerchief.

"That's just the trouble, Morton, we can't. It's broken down."

"Some of their devilish tampering, I suppose."

"Well, that's what we'll intimate, but it isn't exactly so. The large hose connection has been rotting away, and several days ago it broke in two. A new one has been ordered, but that takes time; it hasn't come yet. You needn't worry, we'll see that they get the blame."

The banker laughed sourly. "Give 'em hell. How's the election going?"

"Not so well. All this dust is converting people wholesale. They come in here snorting and sneezing—and cast a vote for that young pup and his ten thousand dollar-a-mile road, taking his word for it that the new road will be dustless."

Towner's eyes flashed. "They can't get away with that!"

Andy Brackett lowered his voice to a whisper. "You needn't say I said so—but they might. This dust is raising hell with us. It's the kind of an argument that can't be answered."

"But who's going to pay for this folly?"

Andy Brackett shook his head. "I suppose you and I will. Most of the people voting here own no property to speak of; some of them are not even taxpayers."

Towner snorted angrily. "If I had my way I'd drive every one of those devil-wagons off the roads. They've got no place in a civilized community—terrorizing horses, maiming people. Did I tell you one nearly ran me down in Rochester? The damned contraption ought to be abolished, and here the state law allows them to go at twenty miles an hour on the open road. It's criminal, I tell you!"

"Well," said Andy, "we'll keep some of them away from this town if we can get our man in."

"The Assembly ought to be able to do something about it. What's the matter with Asa, anyway? Can't he get through a law that will give us a little protection?"

Andy smiled. "Give him time. This is only his first term, you know."

Towner went in and voted, and then remarked to Andy that he was going home.

"Better go on foot," advised Andy with a glance out of the window.

"I'll do nothing of the sort," snapped Towner. "I'll go home any way I see fit. No young monkey-wrench handler is going to keep me from driving my horse straight down the street as I've a legal right to do." He settled his hat a little more firmly on his head, gripped his gold-headed cane in his hand, and walked out of the place, slowly but with every indication of inflexible determination.

Tom Hunter heard loud voices on the street and went out to investigate. It sounded from a distance as if it might be a political argument, but as he came nearer he could see that it was nothing but Phineas Dodd, a voracious local usurer, berating Towner over one of their

· 153 ·

deals. The two were constantly trying to outdo each other, and quarrels between them were frequent. These were invariably provoked by Dodd and almost always occurred on the street, which led people to believe that Dodd must have been bested in the transaction and that Towner was really the better rascal of the two.

This argument, like most of the others, was almost entirely one-sided, Towner disdaining a public discussion of private matters. He was muttering some choice epithets under his breath as he untied his mare and clambered into his phaeton. But after he had picked up his reins he spoke only to the horse.

"Back up, Nellie—back up there!" He cramped the wheels, headed the mare for home, and drove off into the dust with Phineas Dodd hurling acrimonious imprecations after him.

A quarter of an hour afterwards, a pall of sadness fell over the town when the news went around that Morton Towner had been struck and instantly killed by one of the hired election cars as he was turning into his driveway in a cloud of dust.

It was Tom Hunter who brought the news to me.

"What are you going to do?" I asked.

"I've already done it."

"What did you do?"

"I called off the hired cars and sent them home."

14

The Smear

LIKE ANY COUNTRY BANKER MORTON
TOWNER had plenty of enemies, though none of them
had any comments to make so long as his body lay cold
and still in the darkened front parlor of the sepulchral
stone house beneath the towering elms of East Main
Street. Even Phineas Dodd kept out of sight until after
the funeral, and although he had previously spoken of the
pleasure it would give him to dance on Towner's grave,
he was never seen anywhere near the fenced-in spot where
the banker was buried. Neighbors, some of whom had
never been in the house before, flocked to the bier with
wreaths and flowers, and entire meals appeared at the
kitchen door so that the family would not have to be
bothered with cooking. The consensus of all, friend and
foe alike, was that Morton Towner was a distinguished-
looking corpse.

Hours before the funeral the streets of the neighborhood were crowded with vehicles from all parts of the
township, and Joe Spears, the storekeeper, dressed in his
Sunday black to act as one of the bearers, remarked to me
that he guessed every man who owed the bank a dollar
thought this was a good time to show himself.

A private service was first conducted at the house for
members of the family and invited guests, and invitations

were angled for, as in the case of a marriage in diplomatic circles. The Bracketts were invited, of course, Andy serving as one of the bearers along with Spears and some other prominent citizens. Not being addicted to attending funerals, though this was one of the popular diversions of the small town, I started for my office; but I did not get there until after the funeral was over, having been lured from my work by the mere presence of so many people on the streets. I met Tom Hunter, and together we joined the crowd awaiting the arrival of the cortege at the church. I don't know just why I went. It was probably because of a morbid curiosity, though I found myself rationalizing about paying my last respects. The truth was that I did not have very many respects for the late deceased, so it must have been something else.

The hearse had arrived and the casket had been carried into the church by the perspiring ushers, for Morton Towner was a large man and a not inconsiderable load. By this time the carriages had begun to unload, and I noticed Lucy Brackett and her aunt stepping down from the hack next to that occupied by members of the family. With her shining yellow hair contrasting vividly with the dull black she had on, Lucy was really something to look at, especially in the somber surroundings of a funeral. I saw Tom watching her, but he made no comment.

Not half the assembled throng could get into the church, and all through the long Episcopalian service men stood uncovered on the aged sod of the churchyard. Tom and I did not remain, however, and for want of something better to do we walked over to the cemetery, stopping at Tom's shop while he showed me the sketch for a non-kick automobile crank that he was planning to make.

"No more broken arms and bruised shoulders," he

· 156 ·

said, "if I can make this work. So long as the pressure comes from the handle, you can push as hard as you want to, you can give it all you've got. But the minute the engine kicks back it disconnects the pawl, and it can whirl around harmlessly as many times as it wants to."

I laughed. "What's a pawl?"

"The thing that makes your watch click when you wind it."

"How's Mr. Dorlon's arm getting along?" I asked. "Is he able to do any cranking with it yet?"

"Nope, and he won't for quite a while."

"Seems funny not to see his car stranded on the street somewhere. Doesn't Stew use it?"

Tom smiled. "He's mad at that car. Says he'll never drive it again."

"Why not?"

"Because the first time he went out to crank it after his father was hurt it backfired and knocked out one of his teeth. That was what really got me started on this non-kick crank of mine. Almost every day I see in the paper that somebody's been hurt cranking a car."

I nodded, for I had noticed the same thing, and though I never had encountered a serious back-kick I used every known precaution when I was cranking. "There's a real need for something of the sort," I said, "and you'd better not let the grass grow under your feet or somebody else will get to the Patent Office first."

Suddenly he raised a cautionary hand. "Listen! Horses' feet on the gravel—it's the funeral procession. If we're going to be there when it arrives we'll have to slip in the back way."

We hurried out the side door, across a vacant lot, and behind a hedgerow, which sheltered us from the street until we had reached the cemetery ahead of the funeral procession. And since we had come as sightseers we lingered after the services were over, watching the people clamber into their carriages and drive away. It was a long procession and this took some time. We were, however, just about ready to leave when we heard a voice behind us.

"Mighty purty funeral I call it." It was Vacy Boynton and he was speaking to us. "I reckon I oughta be mad at Towner," he went on. "He certainly knocked me out of bein' elected. But somehow I ain't got it in me to keep on bein' mad at a dead man. Our side sure was out in front when that accident happened. We had a good lead, and what's better we had Andy scairt out of his wits. I been checkin' over the books and I know what I'm talkin' about. I don't believe we got in half-a-dozen votes after that accident. It folded us up like a jackknife. Our side just stood around with their mouths open sayin', 'Ain't it awful—ain't it awful!' But lemme tell you some'pm—everything that comes to Andy Brackett's mill is turned into grist. 'There you are!' he says. 'That's the kind of thing that will be happenin' every day if this road goes through.' And that was the time when he sent his doorbell-ringers out. 'Come down to the polls and put a stop to this thing,' he says, and they did. That's God's truth—I got it straight."

"And twenty-three votes would have saved our road," said Tom.

"Yup, only we didn't know it at the time. You can't always predict what folks'll do after they get inside one of them little 'lection booths, no matter what they told you 'forehand. It's what you'd call fate, I guess. But anyhow the road's gone up the spout, and I guess it's gonna cost you a sight of business, Tom."

Tom nodded. "Guess so. But what really bothers me is that I hate to have the other towns get ahead of us."

"Funny thing it should be Morton who knocked out that highway just as we were putting over the winning run," said Vacy. "I don't reckon he would have give up his life to keep that road away, but he was pretty bitter about the taxes he was gonna have to pay. Oh, well, that's the way it goes. Hope we don't get blamed for his death."

Tom looked hard at me. "Could such a thing as that be possible?"

I was just about to say that I thought it was unlikely, when Vacy let out an emphatic snort.

"Hell, yes!" he said. "Folks have been sayin' things already."

We had been walking along as we talked and had paused at the cemetery gates when Tom said:

"So they're trying to blame the accident on us?"

"On you mostly, accordin' to what I heared," said Vacy, "but they might as well blame old Noah for the flood."

"They probably did," muttered Tom.

"No, I reckon not," said Vacy. "There was very little talkin' done after the rains started. But don't let this thing get you ruffled," he added soothingly. "It's just comin' from the other side, Brackett and Parker and the rest of that bunch. I don't know why you expect an'thing else from them. It's the way they always act."

"But they won the election," muttered Tom. "What more do they want?"

Vacy cackled with laughter. "Guess they must figger the best time to kick a man is when he's down."

He left us at the gate, and Tom and I walked down the hill together. It was easy to see that Tom was very much disturbed by what Vacy had told him. He kept referring to it as we went along and mumbling, mostly to himself, that it served him right for letting himself get mixed up in politics. From what he said I could see that he was mystified to learn that a man who could be as unfailingly pleasant to his face as Andy Brackett was, could be such a smalltime blackguard behind his back.

I tried to cheer him up by telling him that nobody took any stock in that kind of political chatter, which, I reminded him, was called by such names as hogwash and flapdoodle. He smiled and said he would try to forget it, but I could see when I left him at his place of business that it was still bothering him.

After that I did not see him for a day or two, and then I drove into his shop to have him straighten one of the fenders of the Rambler, which I had dented in backing out of the shed with a little too much speed and not enough caution. In the meantime I had been hearing nasty little insinuations that were going around and could see that the poison squad was still at work on him. How much of this he may have heard, I don't know. Vacy probably heard it all, and it is very likely that she carried most of it to Tom, for the young man was in a very explosive state that day, as you will see when I tell you what happened.

I had been there only a few minutes when old Ike Meeker came in shaking his head and sputtering.

"I don't know why you put up with it," he said. "It don't make rhyme nor reason."

Tom looked up. "What are you talking about?"

"I'm talking about that danged Asa Parker and the way he goes around slanging people."

"Oh, well, Meeker, don't believe all you hear," I said.

"I don't believe it," said Meeker, "but that's no reason

folks should go around tellin' low-down lies. I just happen to know Tom didn't have nuthin' to do with it. I was there with Tim Schermerhorn when the thing broke off. But I ain't takin' no chances on callin' Asa Parker a liar."

Tom stared at him. "What's this all about anyway?"

"Dust—and why they couldn't sprinkle the streets on election day."

"And why couldn't they?"

"Asa says it's because you crippled the sprinkling wagon by cuttin' off the big rubber hose."

"Asa's telling I did that?" shouted Tom, his face fiery red, his clenched fists looking as hard and compact as a sledge.

"I heared him say it not five minutes ago, right up there in Andy Brackett's stables. Ask Gid. He was there and heared it too."

Tom reached for his hat. "Just keep an eye on the shop till I get back, will you? I won't be gone long."

As he started for the door Meeker called after him, "If you're goin' up there to take it out of Asa's hide, watch your step, 'cause he knows plenty about the rough-and-tumble stuff!"

Tom made no answer but kept right on going. I think Meeker would have followed along if I had not discouraged it by saying that if Tom were left to himself he might change his mind, but that he surely wouldn't if anybody was with him. So Meeker sat around and waited with impatience for him to come back. I would have liked to run up that way myself, just to see what was happening. But I forebore, and a little later in the day Gid told me all about it.

Asa Parker was still at the barn when Tom suddenly appeared in the big open doorway. Asa was at the mo-

· 161 ·

ment being the good mixer, the man among men. He was in the middle of a smutty story when Tom stepped up in front of him, face flushed and eyes blazing.

"Did you say I crippled the sprinkling wagon by cutting the hose?" he demanded.

Asa's guard fell naturally into position. He was not going to be caught unready. "Well, what if I did?" he returned defiantly.

"You'll take it back—that's what! It's a lie!"

Asa's left hand flicked out quickly and knocked off Tom's hat. It was an old trick. When Tom tried to catch his hat or reached for it, Asa would wind up the affair with a single punch. Tom had heard of that trick, but he was not expecting it, and when his hat went off he started to bend over to pick it up. Then he remembered and came suddenly up, catching Asa unawares. A large fist, hard as a cobblestone, struck Asa's jaw with a terrific crash, and Asa toppled over backward, falling his full length. Tom was over him in one leap, seized the shoulders of his coat and hauled him to his feet.

"You'll take that back!" he thundered.

"All right—" Asa gasped, his eyelids floating.

When Tom released his hold Asa dropped back to the floor and Gid, who had come running from the other end of the barn intending to pick up what was left of Tom, derived no small pleasure from dashing a dipper of water in Asa's face instead. Tom was starting for the door when Gid called him back. "Don't be in a hurry," he said. "Asa may want another go at it."

Asa, still prostrate, raised a feeble hand to his jaw. "No, thanks," he said.

Old Meeker's eyes opened wide as Tom came walking into the shop. "What happened?" he asked eagerly.

"Not much of anything," said Tom. "I asked him to take it back, and he did."

Meeker blinked. "He did?"

Tom nodded. "That's right."

"Yeah—but—but—but what happened?" sputtered Meeker.

Tom smiled. "Well, I suggested to Asa that it might be a good thing for him to take back those words."

"Yeah—yeah—and then what?"

"Well—Asa thought it over. Took him a while to make up his mind."

"What then—?"

"Then," said Tom, "he agreed with me."

Meeker looked disappointed. "Is that all?" he asked.

"Isn't it enough? That's what I went up there for."

"But—but what's the straws doin' on your hat? They wasn't there when you went up."

"You know how that barn is—straw all over the place."

"But look at your knuckle," said Meeker. "The skin's broke open."

Tom looked at it. "That's right. I'm always whacking one of my knuckles with something around here."

"But that wasn't done when you left here," Meeker insisted.

"It wasn't? I don't see what I could have done to it between here and the livery barn."

Meeker rose from the bench where he was sitting. "If you had a fight with him you might just as well tell me about it, 'cause I'll find it out sooner or later."

"You have to have two sides to make a fight," said Tom, "and there was only one side to this, so I haven't got anything to tell you."

Meeker gave his hat a yank. "All right, I'll go and find out about it by myself." And he went out.

Tom had already begun hammering on my fender before Meeker was out of the door, but as soon as he was sure that the old fellow was gone he stopped his hammering and turned to me.

"I never had a fight before," he said. "It was a new experience to me. I didn't think I could ever bring myself to the point where I would hit anybody to hurt him. But when I saw the sneering face of Asa Parker there before me I hit to kill. And I didn't feel the slightest remorse when I saw him go down. I must admit that I was a little surprised to find that I wasn't sorry when I saw him lying there on the floor with the blood trickling from his mouth. No, sir, I wasn't sorry at all—I was glad that I was able to handle him—and I made up my mind that if he was alive I would make him take back what he had said. And when he did—you can't imagine what a contempt I had for him.

"No, sir, I never had a fight before. As a kid I was sickly and couldn't stand up to the other fellows, and I took a good deal of cuffing around before I discovered that I was fast on my feet. And after that I saved myself a lot of mauling by keeping out of their way. And I've been keeping out of the way of people ever since. But I don't believe I will any more." He walked over and picked up his hammer. "No, sir, I don't believe I ever will again."

15

Trial Spin

WHENEVER A NEW CAR CAME TO TOWN one of the first things Tom did was to have the owner take his friends and neighbors out for a little spin. There was still some difference of opinion over the motor car. Some thought it dangerous. Some disliked it on account of the dust or the smell. Others objected to it because it was something new. This resistance to newness has been underestimated by the philosophers and scientists, though the salesmen are convinced that it is one of the great primary instincts of humankind. A curious thing about this kind of resistance is that, once you break it down, you usually have an enthusiast on your hands.

Tom's idea was that most of the objections to the motor car came from lack of familiarity with it, and he felt that the sooner everybody had a taste of motoring, the faster the industry would make friends. Nobody thinks of the smell of the automobile today, though it is probably as strong as it ever was. Personally, I never found it unpleasant, but in the early days of motoring it was important because of the effect it had on horses. Some of them could smell a car when it was still a mile away, and they would begin to climb fences or tangle with trees or telephone poles before the car was even in sight. It had been the same way with the railroads when they had first come, but gradually horses had become accustomed to the trains, and now they would have to learn not to be afraid of the motor car.

I think it was the second day I had my car that Tom devoted half the afternoon to taking my friends for short rides. We thought it best for him to do the driving, so that there would be no nervousness on the part of the passengers because of my well-known inexperience. We went around the neighborhood from house to house picking up anybody we could get. Not one of our passengers that day had ever before ridden in an automobile, and almost without exception they would grip the seats as we were starting, though they invariably relaxed as we went along. Tom was very careful to give them no occasion for uneasiness. He started the car very slowly, he drove at a moderate pace, and when the ride was over he brought the car to a stop so gradually and so gently that the passengers hardly realized that they were no longer moving. There were no jack rabbit starts, no quick acceleration, no slamming on of brakes. Tom had no thought of showing them what the car would "do." If on this first ride he could convince the passengers that the motor car was at least as good as the horse, he would be satisfied.

The one thing that all our passengers seemed to be afraid of was collision. They did not see quite how we were going to get out of the way of approaching traffic without a horse to guide us. And another reaction that they shared in common was the illusion of flying as we went over the top of a hill and started to coast silently down. Even though we were not doing over ten miles an hour at the take-off of the grade, they would invariably gasp as they felt themselves going. There was, however, a definite reason for this: horses always descended the hills at a walk. Trotting a horse down a hill was bad for the horse—it was likely to make him knee-sprung—and it was also bad for the passengers since, without brakes, they had no way to stop the vehicle if the horse should stumble or step on a rolling stone and lose its footing.

For a week or so after I got the car I kept picking up people for these little spins and thought I had pretty well covered the ground, when one day I happened to meet Lucy Brackett on the street and she asked me why I had slighted her. I explained that I had stopped at her house twice without finding anybody at home. And that same afternoon I went again.

Lucy was in the yard when we drove up, and as Tom brought the car to a stop at the curb I leaned out and motioned to her. While she was coming across the grass of the terrace I stepped out and went around to open the rear door, which was fastened shut with a large brass safety hasp.

"You see I am a man of my word," I said.

She paused on the curb. "And you aren't going to give me a chance to get on goggles and a veil and all the rest of the things?"

"Not this time," I said. "This is just a sample ride. If you like it, I'll take you for an expedition another time, and then you can put on all the equipment and accoutrements."

"And you promise not to blow me all to pieces with the wind?"

"You have my word for that—though I don't know why you should be so cautious all of a sudden," I said as I took her by the hand, "the way you go tearing around on that demon horse of yours."

"Not any more." She stepped into the tonneau and

sank down on the seat. "Blue Grass stumbled and threw me over his head, and Uncle Andy wouldn't let me keep him any longer."

"Too bad," I said, remembering what she had previously told me about wanting a bicycle. "He was a very handsome animal, even if he was only one horsepower. By the way," I looked from one to the other, "you two have met, I suppose?"

As Tom was murmuring that he thought they had, Lucy was at the identical moment murmuring that she thought they hadn't. But I let the matter pass, busying myself with fastening the hasp, and then climbed in beside the driver. "The hatches are battened, sir," I said. "We can now cast off."

I remembered after we had started that I had left my office open, and I asked Tom to go around the block so that I could stop long enough to lock up. I turned in my seat and chatted with Lucy as we went along, but Tom tended strictly to his driving. The door of my office was open as we drew up in front. It nearly always stood open in the summertime from morning until night. I went inside and began to put books and papers in the safe, which stood near the street door. The distance from the curb to the front door was only a few feet, probably not more than six or eight, and I could hear quite plainly every word that was said in the car. I was somewhat surprised, after Tom's previous silence, to hear him say to Lucy as soon as I was out of sight:

"I hope you're not angry because I said we had met."

"Why should I be angry?" she said.

"You sounded that way."

"But we never have met in the conventional sense," she insisted.

"Then we were just—thrown together?"

Lucy chose to disregard the humorous implication. "I'm sorry I neglected to thank you for catching the horse."

I heard Tom laugh softly. "Oh, that's all right. I'm sorry I spoke to you quite so plainly that day. But it made me mad to have you worrying over that fool horse after he had almost killed you."

"Of course you realize why the horse acted that way?"

"I don't know much about horses," said Tom.

"I wasn't referring to the horse."

"All I know is, I heard you say he stumbled."

"And I don't suppose you have any idea what made him stumble?"

"You can't tell what makes a horse stumble. They're likely to stumble any time. I've had a horse stumble with me when he was walking right along in a field."

"Did somebody on the other side of the fence startle him, perhaps?"

"No, I've had them stumble when they weren't anywhere near a fence. I don't think a fence has got anything to do with it."

"Not even if—there is somebody with a bicycle on the other side?"

"That wouldn't have made a bit of difference—our horses weren't afraid of bicycles."

"Either you're very stupid or you're very smart—I don't know which," I heard Lucy say with an air of finality.

"But we have met," said Tom. "And that's something."

I waited for a moment to see if there was going to be anything more, but apparently there wasn't. So I slammed the door of the safe and went out, letting down the latch behind me. We took Lucy about five miles out of town, and on the way back the car began to miss on one cylinder. Only a person familiar with the two-cylinder car can appreciate what a calamity this was. It meant that fifty per cent of our power was gone, and that all we had left was in a single cylinder. This sent the car along in a series of vicious lurches.

"Like riding on horseback," said Tom.

"Not the way I ride," said Lucy.

"Hadn't we better stop?" I asked, having visions of tearing the car all to pieces with these monstrous lurches.

Tom shook his head. "Can't stop here," he muttered. "Road's too narrow, and the first team that came along would be sure to pile up."

"But," I protested, "is it good for the car to struggle along like that?"

"Probably won't help it any, but it may take some time to fix it and we don't want to stop where we'll block the road. Looks wider up there by the big tree."

"Very different from a horse," said Lucy. "A good horseman stops the moment his mount goes lame, no matter where he is."

"Guess we can make the tree all right," Tom insisted stubbornly.

And we did. He was able to pull out of the road here, and I loaned him the "trouble suit" that was part of the regular equipment of every car owner. The only difficulty was that the suit was far too small for Tom. The sleeves of the jacket came only a little below his elbows and the bottoms of the pants legs were about four inches above his ankles. As he went down under he looked more than a little like a man dressed for a masquerade. But he was in no carnival mood; I could see that very plainly. He was worried, for he had no idea how serious the trouble might be.

Lucy struggled as if trying to hold back her laughter until he was under the car, though I noticed that her trouble was over as soon as he could no longer see her. It seemed to me that she was baiting him, but I pretended not to notice. After a few moments he called for the pliers. I handed them to him and bent down to see what he was doing. He was tightening a little brass nut. When he had finished with it he wriggled out and reached for the crank which lay on the front floor boards. The engine started at the first turn.

"What was the matter?" asked Lucy as he stood peeling off the trouble suit.

"A wire came loose from a sparkplug."

I stuffed the trouble suit in a compartment under the seat, and we went rolling merrily on our way. Just as we were coming into town Lucy leaned over and asked if we would mind letting her off at Harper's house. She said she wanted to stop in and see Zelda, who was about her own age and her closest friend. Tom and I both had the same idea about this. We thought that Lucy was sparing her family the indignity of having her seen stepping out of a motor car at their door. Whatever the reason may have been, we asked no questions and let her out at Harper's horse block. She thanked me very prettily for the demonstration and promised, by way of recompense, to take me for a buggy ride someday.

As she turned to go she looked back at Tom with a smile. "Good-by, Mr. Huntley," she said.

Tom smiled and raised his hat. "Good-by."

I knew perfectly well that Lucy had intentionally miscalled his name. Tom knew it, too, and though neither of us mentioned the incident I kept wondering why she had done it. I went on up to Tom's shop with him, intending to look over the work he had done on his non-kick crank. We found Ike Meeker sitting on the bench before the door just as we had left him when we were starting out.

"Have I had any callers?" asked Tom.

"Nobody but Nellie McKim."

"What did she want?"

"She *said* she wanted to buy a bicycle. She's a homely woman, but mighty man, what a figger she'd cut on a bicycle—with her build."

"What'd you tell her?"

"I told her she'd have to wait till you come back. Yes, sir, she's a mighty well-built woman. What a wife she'd make for a blind man. And say, there was some'pm else she wanted to know—do you teach your lady customers to ride?"

Tom shook his head. "I sell machines and I repair them. That's all."

"Boy!" exclaimed Meeker, getting up and taking a little walk around. "I'd like to be your age and in the bicycle business. I'd teach Nellie to ride, and don't you forget it."

I followed Tom inside and found him sniffing the air. "She's been in here, all right," he said. "I couldn't mistake that perfume of hers."

There was an unmistakable perfume there. No doubt about that, though I would not have identified it if he had not told me whose it was.

Meeker came tagging along after us. "I don't know how much you young fellers know about Nellie, but she's got quite a story. With her looks, she was about the last girl in this town you'd pick for a big romance. Or mebbe it wasn't a romance. Anyhow it was some'pm pretty big in the life of Nellie and at least one man." He chuckled. "Might have been more than one—hard to tell about that.

I guess you boys never knew her father, Bart McKim. He's been dead some time, but he used to lead the choir over in the Baptis' church. Bart could have passed for a walrus anywhere if it hadn't been for his glasses. He even had tusks of a sort. In looks Nellie sorta takes after her pa. Same black hair, same moles, she even inherited her pa's mustache in a small way. But there was one place where she was entirely different from Bart—she never had nuthin' to say. Bart was a-rattlin' on all the time, you know. He was always soundin' off about one thing or another. The only time Bart was ever speechless in his whole life was when his wife come back from takin' Nellie to the doctor and told him that Nellie was in a family way.

"That gal had never had a feller in her life. Even in her school days no boy had ever give her a second look. She wasn't what you'd call smart. She got her school diplomer only by the skin of her teeth. That was another thing—her teeth wasn't good. Well, sir, after she got outa school she used to help in her father's hardware store, and his customers was mostly men. Jim Cotton, the builder, usta make the store his headquarters for talkin' over jobs with folks and payin' off his help. Then Grant Dixon, who laid concrete sidewalks, usta hang around there a good deal. He was a friend of Bart's, and anybody who wanted Grant to figger on a piece of concrete work could leave word for him there. And another feller who was in and out the store a good deal was Alonzo Babson. Alonzo had a coal shed at the Junction, and he was back and forth a good deal and not easy to find. So he kep' an order book at Bart's store, and if anybody wanted a ton of coal when Alonzo wasn't around, Nellie was in the habit of jottin' it down in the book.

"Well, sir, when Bart had recovered from his singular

attack of speechlessness he begun to take a parental interest in the situation and to press Nellie for the name of her betrayer. But Nellie wouldn't tell. She shut up like a clam, and that's all there was to that. Bart begged and pleaded, he even threatened to turn her out on the street or have her sent to a reform school, but Nellie just kep' shakin' her head and sayin' she promised not to tell.

"Then Bart tried prayer. He had the big rafters of that old Baptis' church a-ringin' night after night for the Lord to soften the heart of an unnamed person in distress and bring her to confession. But the Lord refused to have anything to do with such an unsavory situation, and Bart finally come to the conclusion he'd have to handle the matter for himself. Quite naturally his startin' point was with the three fellers who'd been hangin' around the store. He begin to watch them like a cat watches a mouse, and he wasn't the only one, neither, for the whole town was watchin' them, too. Bart was goin' on the old theory that there's a clue if you can only find it. But don't you get to thinkin' that them three suspects wasn't well aware of the exposed position they was in. They'd have been mighty glad to move outa there and make their headquarters elsewhere, but they didn't dare. They was all married men, two of 'em with children as old as Nellie. They didn't overlook the fact that by stayin' on they would attract a certain amount of attention, but they figgered they'd attract a dang sight more if they should pull out right then, so all three of 'em stood by. It was a pretty tight situation there, with Bart a-watchin' and his three friends knowin' they was under suspicion.

"The only one who wasn't under no nervous strain whatever was Nellie. She didn't seem to mind the stares of people as she went back and forth, and she treated them fellers there in the store same as she had always treated 'em. Nobody had ever seen anything wrong with Nellie. Never went buggy ridin', never walked out in the evenin' with a feller, never even sung in a choir. The only evidence against her was her condition.

"Folks had various theories about Nellie's opportunity for misconduct, but I contend mine's as good as anybody's. You recollect they got a place up on the second floor where they sell mattresses and horse blankets and suchlike. Well, them stairs comes right down by the back door; and what was to prevent Nellie from turnin' the key in the front door, one of the nights when her pa had gone to lodge or choir practice or some'pm, and then slippin' quietly up the back stairs to meet a friend? It's a good theory, but it ain't never been proved and it ain't never been disproved, because Nellie's never given so much as a hint. She went through her confinement without a squawk. Guess Bart thought she might give some'pm away under the anesthetic along at the end, but she never made a peep.

"It was a boy. Nellie named him Wellington, like as not because there wasn't no Wellingtons in the family, but she never called the kid anything but 'the Peanut.' The old folks hung onto the name of Wellington for a while, but the other name caught on, and pretty soon Nellie's baby was the Peanut to everybody in town. He was a bonny little feller, always full of smiles and laughter, for all the world like Grant Dixon, as folks usta whisper behind their hands. But as he grew up the boy turned out not to be dark and stumpy like the Dixons. He was tall and fair with a mop of light, curly hair—good deal more like Jim Cotton, back in the days before Jim had filled out quite so much and when he still had some hair on his head. Both these schools of thought has got plenty of supporters. And here just a few days ago I got another angle that's interestin'. Somebody was talkin' with one of the schoolteachers here a while back and it turns out that the Peanut is very smart in school—especially in arithmetic; and of course that started the wiseacres to goin' again, because Alonzo Babson was always very smart in school, especially in arithmetic. So now there's a lot of folks sayin' that Alonzo must be the guilty party. The one giveaway clue was a long time in comin', but it's arrived at last, they say. Well, mebbe I'm a skeptic, but I think the case is still to be proved.

"The funny part is that Nellie turned out to be a good mother. The Peanut was one of the best-behaved boys in this town. You see, he was brought up without any false idears about his origin. The McKims thought it was just as well to tell him themselves as to have one of his little playmates break the news."

"I used to see the little fellow around," I said. "What happened to him?"

"Oh, they sent him off out west some place, where folks wouldn't know so much about his history. Guess Gid's the only one who knows where he is."

"What's Gid got to do with it?" asked Tom.

"Not much of anything," said Meeker. "Just a friend of the family, I guess."

16

Get Out and Get Under

THE THIRD CAR IN TOWN WAS A REO. THIS also was a two-cylinder job, with the engine nicely buried under the front seat, where it was almost impossible to get at. Concealing the power plant in this inaccessible spot must have been a leftover from the days of the "buggy-aut," as Mr. Duryea called his invention. Henry Ford's first car, as well as a number of his later ones, also tucked away the motor under the seat. It was not until the coming of the four-cylinder car that the engine was placed out in front under a bonnet, where it was easy to get at. And it was the Columbia car, offspring of the famous Columbia bicycle, to whom the honor was to go for having the courage to fly in the face of so well-established an American tradition.

I still look back with distaste on the hours I spent lying on my back under that two-cylinder Rambler, with mud and oil dripping down into my eyes or anointing my hair. And I still recall the waves of heat that used to rise from the floor of that car after the engine had been running for an hour or so—a feat that, for all its temperamental behavior, it quite often performed.

When questioned on the subject, the makers, and even the salesmen, used to shake their heads and talk wisely about safety. The only safe place for the center of gravity of so powerful and so heavy a machine as a motor car was as near as possible to the center spot between the four wheels. The very thought of putting the motor, the heaviest part of the car, out there over the front axle, used to make them shudder. But there was room for only two cylinders down there in the darkness under the seat, and the center of gravity was all but forgotten when the public demand for more power brought the four-cylinder motor into vogue. Then their talk was all of accessibility.

During those two-cylinder, double-opposed years the motorist was a groundling who did not feel quite at home in handling a wrench or other tool unless he was lying flat on his back and working in some dark recess largely by the sense of touch. Once he was on the road—where in those days most of the repairs were made—the Reo owner had no advantage over me; but for repairs or adjustments to be made at home he had cut a trap door in the floor of his barn, which enabled him to do the work standing up instead of lying down. He admitted, however, when we were discussing the problem, that he would almost as soon do the work lying down, because of the cramps that came in his neck when he was working directly overhead through the trap door. I could not have a trap door, since the shed I used as a garage had no floor in it. But perhaps it was, all things considered, just as well.

The Reo, like my Rambler, was a pleasure car, but the fourth car to come to town had a touch of the utility vehicle. It was bought by Dr. Richards to use in visiting his patients. The Doctor had always kept good horses and had found them adequate, though there was nothing he hated like taking care of a couple of horses. His son was a good horseman, and as long as the boy had stayed around home the question of doing chores was negligible. Young

Doc attended to them or saw to it that some other boy did. But when he went away to school the problem very soon became acute. Reliable stableboys were hard to get, and the Doctor had the misfortune to get hold of two or three of the unreliable sort, one after another.

The first one went off on a spree and forgot the horses for two days. The second one neglected to put the halter on the grey, one night, and the greedy little animal got into the oatbin and so stuffed herself that she was in the hands of the veterinary for more than a week. The third boy fell asleep in the barn while smoking his pipe, setting fire to the edifice which came very near burning to the ground with all its contents. Then the Doctor came to Tom and commissioned him to purchase one of the Oldsmobile curved-dash runabouts—secondhand, of course.

I rode in this car before the Doctor did, and I must say that it was the best single-cylinder job I ever saw. It wasn't much bigger than a boy's express wagon; it steered with a tiller, on the handle of which was a tiny bulb-horn which made about as much noise as a jew's-harp. But I still insist that it was a nice little car. The engine was small and, for a single-shot motor, was remarkably quiet. It was advertised by the maker as "The Motor that Motes." I don't suppose that the top speed was much over ten or twelve miles an hour. But it made that speed without very much fuss and would make it right along. It was painted a bright vermillion and created a very favorable impression when Tom came rolling into town with it.

New, the car had been listed at $650, "including mud-guards," as stated in the advertisements. Secondhand it had cost the Doctor $300, and he couldn't have been more delighted with it if it had been imported from France at a cost of $3,000. The Doctor lived only two houses below us and I rode home with Tom when he was making the delivery. The Doctor rode around the block with Tom once or twice and then took over the tiller. He found the little machine so easy to handle that he insisted on taking his wife for a ride without any further instruction or experience. Tom tried to induce him to wait another day or two before taking anybody out with him, least of all his wife.

But the Doctor was bullheaded. He had been giving advice so long that he had reached the point where he couldn't take it, and he brushed away Tom's objections without even listening to them. He was at this time along in his sixties, tall, a little portly, and he had a shock of iron-grey hair as straight and almost as coarse as the hairs of a mucilage brush. Though on Sundays he was never seen without a frock coat, he compromised on weekdays with a sack coat cut rather long. But he never compromised on the black stovepipe hat which he regarded as the *indicia* of office. That was a seven-day habit, and he was never seen without it. I think it must have been the silk hat that made him look so funny as he went rolling up the street with his wife by his side.

She was a handsome woman, considerably younger than the Doctor, but she was very much his type and was not at all nervous to be going out with him on his initial trip. She was carrying a parasol when they started, probably because she happened to have it in her hands when he suggested her going along. As Tom and I stood and watched them go chugging up the street we could see her waving the parasol at her friends on the various verandas as she passed.

Tom wondered if they would ever get back all in one piece, and I admit that I was a little skeptical about it myself, especially as the Doctor drove straight up through the business section of the town.

"Now why did he do that?" exclaimed Tom. "Why couldn't he have done his experimental work on some of the back streets of the town, where there's no traffic to speak of?"

"He probably doesn't remember how to turn a corner," I said.

Tom exhaled nervously. "Whew! If that's true he'll run halfway to Buffalo—those little cars will make forty or fifty miles on a gallon."

We kept peering up the street, looking for signs of the returning travelers, but we saw nothing even remotely resembling a motor car.

"Guess we'd better get out the Rambler and follow their tracks," suggested Tom. "No telling what's happened to them."

At just that moment a tiny squawk behind us informed us that nothing of an untoward nature had happened and that they had simply gone around the block. They rolled past us in fine feather, both of them having a wonderful time, and, feeling a little sheepish, we retired from the curb and walked over to sit on the steps of the Bannisters' veranda, just across the street from the Doctor's house. How many times they went up and down that street as we sat there I would not want to say, but the Doctor was gaining in self-confidence all the time, and we suddenly saw him execute a U-turn at the crossing beyond the Presbyterian church.

"I'm afraid that's the beginning of the end," muttered Tom. "He'll try that in a place where the road is too narrow, and his wheels will go up on the curb and dump that little wagon upside down. Wouldn't take much to tip it, you know, it's so light."

Just as the Doctor was passing us on the return trip he suddenly began turning while the car was still in the middle of the road, and I thought that Tom's prediction was going to be immediately fulfilled. But once more the Doctor fooled us. Instead of trying to turn around he had very neatly swung into the driveway and was heading for the Bannister barn, which he had rented as a garage until he could dispose of his horses. We thought he was coming in with quite a little speed, but it was all of a piece with the rest of the things he had been doing and we were not particularly worried, until suddenly we heard him shouting in stentorian tones:

"Whoa! Whoa there! Whoa, I tell you—!"

We leaped to the corner of the house, from which we could see the car approaching the open door of the garage at unabated speed. Tom shouted to him loudly, telling him to cut the switch, but the Doctor was himself shouting at the car in such frenzied tones that he never even heard Tom's voice. And all the time, with its neat little chugging sound, the pretty vermillion car was rapidly approaching that open doorway.

The Bannister barn was built on the crest of a rather sharp little declivity, with the main floor on a level with the high ground and a basement on a level with the low. The Doctor's wife remembered this as the car was drawing nearer and nearer to the barn without any slackening of speed, and having no desire to go crashing through the opposite wall of the barn at a distance of some fifteen feet above the low ground, she showed what she afterwards insisted was great presence of mind by standing up and stepping out of the car, which had no doors to hinder her. In so doing she swung her parasol around and knocked the Doctor's stovepipe hat down over his face in such a way as to completely obscure his vision at the moment when the crash came.

Fortunately the barn was old and the clapboards rotten. The studding had been weakened by dry rot, and at a probable speed of twelve miles an hour at the moment of contact, the curved-dash runabout cut its way through the side of that barn as if it had been built of paper. The front half of the car was completely hidden from sight by the time we got there, and the Doctor was pinned to the seat like a large piece of overstuffed upholstery. His first move, when we dragged him out, was to extricate and put on the battered stovepipe hat which had probably saved his face and perhaps his life. What we couldn't understand was why the car had not gone the rest of the way and what was keeping it on an even keel. One look outside the barn was enough of an explanation. The front axle was firmly wedged in the crotch of an old apple tree growing close behind the barn.

The Doctor's wife, though shaken up, had received no serious injuries, and the two were able to leave the scene of the accident under their own power.

"What will you give me for the wreck just as it stands?" the Doctor asked Tom as we were all coming out of the driveway and the rest of the town was rushing in.

"I couldn't tell you without looking it over," said Tom.

The baker's boy, who happened to be passing, was more of a gambler. "Will you take twenty-five dollars?" he asked.

"It's a deal," said the Doctor.

And that is how the little vermillion roadster came to be called "the Doughnut" all the rest of its days. It was

the only car the Doctor ever had, though he lived to a ripe old age and saw the national registration of cars pass the three million mark. And, while he never was interested in owning or driving a motor car again, he never tired of boasting that he was the only man in town who had ever driven an automobile up an apple tree fifteen feet above the ground.

There was no waiting around for the tow car and the hoist to come and salvage the wreck. There was no such thing as a tow car at that time, and anybody's trouble was everybody's trouble. In the small towns especially, people still felt the responsibility of being neighborly, and without even being asked they at once went to work to rescue the roadster from the apple tree. Somebody remembered where he had seen a couple of heavy planks. These were brought, and ropes, and a ladder or two; and by the time Tom and I had returned with the Rambler and the tackle we thought would be necessary to haul the car back to solid ground, we found the men of the neighborhood had already taken care of the job.

Of course they did not know that the ownership of the car had changed while it was perched up in the tree, but I do not believe that the change of title from one of the town's most prominent citizens to one of its humblest would have made the slightest difference. People in the rural districts were at that time much more dependent upon each other than they are now. Since the coming of the machine the farmer, with a couple of gallons of gasoline, does work that used to require the services of a dozen of his neighbors. The so-called farm cooperatives of the present day are strictly business concerns; they have nothing to do with neighborliness.

With the exception of Andy Brackett and one or two others who had a heavy stake in the horse and stood a good chance of being wiped out financially by any very marked success on the part of the automobile, I never saw any serious hostility to the motorist. Occasionally a farmer with a scary horse would give way to a little violent language if you happened to meet him at a bad spot in the road, and there was the story about the fellow who had become so irritated over the dust raised by motorists that he buried a crosscut saw in the road, leaving the business edge projecting just high enough to ruin all four tires of every car that passed. The weapon is said to have worked so successfully that the farmer had some thirty-odd cars which had been engaged in a reliability run stranded almost in his dooryard. He thought their presence there boded him no good, so he took to the woods. As the story goes, he had to hide out for three days while new tires were being shipped in from some distant point.

There is little doubt that there were localities where the harried natives sought to discourage motoring by scattering tacks in the roadway. These retaliatory incidents were extremely rare and, in the main, the motorist received more kindness from the rural populations than was usually his due.

I remember that one Sunday morning, soon after the Dr. Richards apple-tree-climbing experience, I saw a dust-covered roadster stalled in the middle of the street in front of the post office as people were starting for church. Tom Hunter was just arriving as I came along, and the first thing he did was to ask the crowd to help him roll the car over to the side of the road, where it would not be quite so conspicuous and would be out of the way of passing vehicles, almost entirely horse-drawn. In spite of its Sunday raiment the crowd responded with enthusiasm—so much enthusiasm, in fact, that they drove it up against a hitching post with force enough to break one of the front fender supports.

The damage to the fender looked serious, and someone in the crowd immediately passed the hat for contributions to pay for repairs. Without any trouble at all he succeeded in raising $1.50, which was handed over to Tom with whimsical instructions to keep the change.

Tom felt a little embarrassed to be working on so noisy and dirty a job at such a conspicuous time and place, and after making a few of the customary tests without being able to start the motor he told the owner he thought they had better get the car off the street. Volunteers who had rigs nearby quickly responded, and without bargaining over the price Tom borrowed a length of rope from the firehouse and started the tow on its way.

The driver of the rig, obviously enjoying his part in the operation, drove along smiling and nodding to people, and when on reaching Tom's shop the owner offered to pay him for his services the fellow acted a little hurt.

"Think I'd take pay for that?" he demanded. "We ain't that kind of folks around here."

"I know, I know," the car owner insisted, "but it's Sunday, and I've caused you quite a lot of trouble—"

The native shook his head. "Sunday—or any other day—don't make no difference. I ain't one to give a man a lift and then let him pay for it."

"Well, you're mighty generous," said the car owner, "and I appreciate your kindness. Will you have a cigar?"

"Don't smoke. But if you'll hand me that rope I'll drop it at the firehouse as I go by."

Once Tom had the car in the shop, the trouble was soon found and remedied. But the fender was flopping, and before the car could go back on the road the support had to be removed for welding by a blacksmith. The owner was distressed. It was very important, he said, that he should get on his way immediately. He simply could not wait another day.

Tom looked dubious. "Every blacksmith shop in town is closed," he said.

"But if you could just get a blacksmith to open up and do the job today, I'd pay him almost any price."

"Joe Darrow is the nearest blacksmith. That's his shop there at the bottom of the hill. He's in church right now, but after church I'll see what I can do."

Joe was most obliging about it. He quite willingly opened up his forge and made the repair. He was insistent about only one thing—his charges, which amounted to fifteen cents.

I once had a similar job done at another blacksmith shop. The price was the same. It was the established price for welding a piece of solid metal the thickness of your finger. There were numerous braces of the kind on wagons and carriages. The breaking of these was not infrequent, and while the local blacksmiths had no fixed scale they all charged about the same for the same kind of work.

The point that I am making is that the early motorist was received with more consideration than hostility. He was treated fairly and charged justly. He paid no more for the gasoline he used in his car than the housewife next door paid for the gasoline she burned in her stove. If motorists were shot at—and there were authentic cases where they were—it was their own fault.

17

Rathole Speculation

TOWARDS THE END OF HIS FIRST YEAR IN business Tom Hunter saw breakers ahead. Times were hard. Money was scarce and Roscoe Towner, now in full charge of the bank where his father had spent his life, was busy saying No to borrowers, when he was not running to the bank door to call in a maker or an indorser of an overdue note.

Roscoe was making a supreme effort to fill his father's shoes, though he must have known that his father's distinguished appearance in the bank was forever beyond his reach. Nature had presented Roscoe with a queer-shaped head, the greater part of which was located far to the rear of his thick, puffy-looking ears. His face was small and gave the impression that it had been compressed from something larger. This lack of proportion was intensified by a great, bushy crop of straight, clay-colored hair which surmounted his head like a turban. Roscoe rather fancied his hair and added to its already conspicuous appearance by wearing it very long, with what the barbers called a "round" cut, which meant that the neck was shaved in a semi-circle extending from ear to ear.

Roscoe had inherited none of his father's tendency to avoirdupois. He was, in fact, slight. In height he was somewhat less than average; and whereas his father had been ponderous in his movements, Roscoe was quick and inclined to be jaunty. He wagged his head from side to side when he walked, and he used to cock it when in conversation, in a way which gave him the appearance of paying close attention when he was really not listening. Roscoe had an annoying habit of keeping up a continuous stream of sounds, "Hum—hum—I see—I see—," so long as the other person was speaking, and then at the end, of asking a question which showed that his attention had been wandering and that he did not see at all.

On his first appearance at the bank after the demise of his father, Roscoe had taken to carrying a cane. Not the gold-headed cane that his father had carried through the years, but a straight ebony stick topped by a knob of ivory. This walking stick, which must have belonged to a tall ancestor, was far too long for him and instead of enhancing his importance only added to his insignificance. The general consensus of opinion around the town was that it would take more than "that black billiard cue to fill the old man's boots." This proved to be a slight miscalculation, for when people went in to renew their notes or extend their mortgages they were almost certain to regret that they had not attended to the matter while the old gentleman was still alive.

Tom Hunter had an inkling of all this when he visited the bank to see if a loan could be arranged for a prospective customer who was willing to buy a car provided he could use it as security for part payment of the purchase price. Roscoe did not get in the usual number of "hums" and "I sees" while Tom was explaining his application. He did not need even the appearance of attentiveness to deal with this matter. A sour smile, a shake of the head, and a little two-letter word would be sufficient. When the moment came, however, he let himself go and uttered several words.

"No reputable bank would even consider a loan with a motor car—especially a secondhand motor car—as security."

"Why not?" Tom demanded. "You loan money on a horse or a piece of farm machinery."

"Both an essential part of our economy, whereas a motor car is distinctly nonessential. It's a plaything. No, no, Mr. Hunter" (since taking over the bank Roscoe had withdrawn himself from familiar contact with people, and every man not a servant was "Mister" to him), "we couldn't consider such a rathole speculation, as my father used to call such things."

Tom gave him a puzzled look. "Rathole?"

Something resembling a smile came over Roscoe's face. "Pouring money down a rathole—you know the saying?"

Tom conceded a feeble laugh. "Sometimes it's hard to tell whether a hole in the ground belongs to a rat or something else," he said. "I can't see why you think an old plug is such a gilt-edge security. Even a horse can die, you know."

"Yes, yes, I know all about that, but a horse isn't superseded every year by a new model."

"No, and if a motor car is standing in a stable you don't have to keep pouring oats into it so it won't starve."

Roscoe leaned out over the counter. "For your own good, Mr. Hunter, let me tell you something. Big banking interests, of which we are a member, have made an exhaustive study of the motor car industry, with the idea not only of advising our clients but of making a possible investment ourselves, and we have been forced to the conclusion that it's altogether too risky. These companies are constantly reorganizing, reincorporating, absorbing each other, or amalgamating. You start off with stock of one company and by the end of a year you've been through two or three reorganizations, and you end up with the stock of a totally different company, that wasn't even in existence when you bought your original share."

"I don't know anything about their financial doings," said Tom, "but I do know that all the time we're getting more cars and better cars. And I read in *Motor Age* that there's a bank out in Detroit that'll take a mortgage on a new car and let the buyer pay for it in installments."

"Perhaps in Detroit," said Roscoe, "but we don't do that kind of wildcat banking around here. We've got our depositors to think about. In times like these nobody will loan money on such questionable security. Money is tight. Do you realize what the farmer is getting for his potatoes? Twenty-five cents a bushel. Hardly enough to pay for the seed. Forty-five cents a bushel for wheat, and all the other crops at the same levels. This is an agricultural country. When the farmer has money, we all have money; and when the farmer is short, we all have to pull in our belts. By the way, if I may ask, how is your own business going?"

"Not any too good. This is the dull season, you know. My work is worth about twenty-five cents a bushel, too."

"Yes, I understand. My father warned you about that business before you ever went into it. I guess that sawmill proposition wouldn't look so bad to you right now, would it?"

"It looks just as bad as it ever did. What is there to saw around here?"

Roscoe shook his head. "Some people simply will not benefit by experience. Why don't you forget this fly-by-night thing and take up some substantial business?"

Tom grinned good-naturedly. "I guess you don't think any more of my business than I do of yours," he said, and he turned and went out.

If the loan had gone through Tom might have stayed at Mrs. Bannister's a little longer, but when it didn't he moved his effects into the room back of the shop. He had by this time built on a small addition, in which he had installed a homemade shower and some secondhand toilet equipment, with a roomy closet for his clothes and liberal storage space. Some of his meals he cooked for himself. For most of the others he went to Fred's Lunchroom, though, with his healthy young appetite to cheer him on, he used to be tempted into going to the Inn for a square meal more often than he could afford.

Tom had not seen Asa Parker to speak to since their encounter at the barn. Once or twice he had caught a glimpse of Asa on the street, but Asa had kept out of his way. Then one day, to Tom's utter astonishment, Asa had come walking into the garage.

"Don't get me wrong," said Asa with a sheepish grin, "I haven't come back for any more of the same. Just dropped in to apologize and to tell you that I'm sorry that somebody gave me some bum information. Maybe you won't believe this, but I'd have been here anyway when I found that my facts were twisted—even if you hadn't come up there to the barn to—call my attention to the fact. Boy, what a wallop you pack! Where'd you ever learn to hit like that?"

Tom was in a bad state of confusion. Asa's unexpected appearance had been enough to stagger him, and the apology had upset him completely. He had never received an apology before and did not know quite how to handle it. Then the compliment on a fighting prowess that he neither possessed nor desired had completed the job, though it eventually furnished a way out, for it was something he could answer. "Oh, I—I used to slug around with George some," he prevaricated, "just for the fun of it, but George never thought I could hit."

Asa nodded slowly. "Um-hum, George—just what I thought. He's the only other bucko who ever gave me such a poke as that. Must have been ten years ago, but I remember it as if it had happened yesterday. Where is old George?" Asa asked heartily. He picked up a jack hammer, brandished it like a dumbbell, and laid it on the workbench again.

"Out on the place, I guess. He's working it now, you know."

Asa picked up the non-kick crank from the bench. "What's this thing?"

The inquiry annoyed Tom. He wasn't going to have Asa or anybody else prying into that. "Oh, it's a new crank I'm—well, I'm trying it out for a fellow."

"What's the joint in it for?"

"Supposed to make it easier to use, I guess."

"It's made all wrong," said Asa with a laugh.

Tom bristled. "What's the matter with it?"

"The proper way to make a crank is to fit it with a bottle of liniment and a roll of gauze bandage that wraps itself automatically around the arm!"

He laughed loudly and Tom took advantage of the diversion to herd Asa into the back room.

"What do you think of this?" said Tom. "I've been making some improvements. Had to have a place to keep things. Seems to me I never have quite enough elbow-room."

"Pretty nice," said Asa. "Good little office—but you

ought to see the size of the offices we have in Albany. Big enough for a convention hall. But what's this? Looks like a drafting table. You know how to do that kind of work?"

"Not really," said Tom. "Just kind of—fussing around with it—trying to teach myself how to draw mechanical stuff—here's the new part, back here." He waved his caller toward the open door of the new addition.

Asa obligingly stepped over and looked. When he saw clothes hanging in the closest he said, with an air of surprise, "You don't mean to say you live here?"

Tom nodded. "Sure I do."

Asa glanced around. "But where do you sleep?"

"Right in here." Tom drew down the wall bunk, then snapped it back into place.

"That must come in handy," said Asa, with what was intended to be a roguish smile. "But I thought you lived down at the other end of the town."

"I did," said Tom, "but it was a little too far away. Come along and I'll show you the front part. Got quite a showroom in there."

Asa started to drag a little when he again got his eye on Tom's workbench, covered with strange, half-finished gadgets with which Tom was experimenting, but Tom brushed him right along. "Got a new bicycle saddle in here I want to show you," he said noisily. "Made by a fellow in Rochester." Asa tried to get in a word, but for once in his life Tom talked him down. "It's as soft as a pillow," he rattled on. "He claims you're riding on air." He couldn't think of anything more to say about the new saddle, so he swung over to another subject. "When do you go back to Albany?" he asked as he shoved Asa through the door and into the showroom.

Asa made a humorously wry face. "I don't know. Got to win an election first. If I make the grade I'll go back the first of the year."

"Well," said Tom, "I imagine you're safe enough. The Republicans couldn't lose the county if they tried."

"Oh, yes, they could," said Asa. "They used to lose it right along, when Frank Rice was in the saddle. I don't say we will lose it—that is, unless a lot of local opposition develops. Folks around here don't usually make much of party lines when a local boy is running for state office. They take the position that it's an honor to the town to have one of its citizens in the legislature or any other office of the great Empire State. Don't you feel the same way yourself?"

"To tell the truth, I never thought much about it." Tom stopped to consider. "I don't take much interest in politics."

Asa laughed. "Oh, you don't, eh? Well, it seems to me I remember a merry old battle over a state road, not so long ago, where you gave a perfect imitation of a foxy politician. But," he added ingratiatingly, "after all, politics is nothing but a game. Give 'em the best you've got and when it's over shake hands—win or lose. Isn't that the way you feel about it?"

"Well, I don't like hard feelings, if that's what you mean."

Asa shook his head approvingly. "That's the old spirit. Give 'em hell—win if you can, and if you can't—forget it."

"Sounds like good sense," said Tom.

"I'll add just one thing to it," Asa could not help saying. "When it comes to a state election, give the home boy the breaks. Now let's see that wonderful saddle."

· 196 ·

Ike Meeker prided himself on keeping his eyes open. He saw what was going on, Ike did. Ike was never seen wandering along the street in a daze or a daydream. He always knew right where he was and right where he was going, and he saw and identified everybody who passed him. He spoke to those he knew and sized up those he didn't know. Not even a dog or a horse could pass him on the street without receiving a definite scrutiny. "Guess you forgot your horsewhip today," he once called out to old man Stebbins, who was driving by in the street; and when old man Stebbins looked in his whip socket, he found it empty. By George, he *had* forgotten his whip.

Ike Meeker had discovered two fires in his day, just by keeping his eyes open, and being a good man in an emergency he had promptly reported them both. In the case of the Titus barn it didn't make much difference; they hadn't used the barn in years and it was empty. But in the case of the coal sheds his immediate alarm had saved what was practically the winter's supply of coal for the town. It was with this background and this enviable reputation to live up to that Ike Meeker went into action one morning at twenty minutes after ten, when with his darting eyes he had caught a glimpse of Asa Parker standing just inside the door of Tom Hunter's garage brandishing a large hammer in his hands.

With his quick sense of awareness Ike Meeker knew that this meant trouble, and very serious trouble. He had not been satisfied with Tom Hunter's explanation, the day the young feller went tearin' off up to Brackett's barn with blood in his eye to make Asa eat his words about the disabling of the water wagon and came back a little later with a tame story of Asa Parker's apology. Meeker didn't forget those straws on his hat, and he didn't miss the cut on Tom's knuckle. And while he couldn't look into the matter that day, what with gettin' home to dinner and so forth, he attended to it the next day and received from Gid a colorful blow-by-blow description of the bout, which by this time had grown into an encounter of almost epic proportions.

That Asa Parker had taken a pretty considerable beating was quite evident when Meeker chanced to meet him on the street the day after the fight. But Ike Meeker was enough of a student of human nature to know that Asa Parker would never let the matter rest there. He would, Meeker was confident, pick another fight at some future date; and when that time came, it would be a fight to a finish—or mighty dang near it. It was with this ominous conviction in his mind that Ike Meeker detected Asa Parker in Hunter's shop, swinging a hammer in what was most certainly a menacing attitude.

Meeker did not even wait to see or hear the commencement of hostilities. He went into the well-known Meeker action at once. He ran to the blacksmith shop to spread the alarm; but the blacksmith had gone to the hardware store for a box of carriage bolts, as Meeker afterward learned. But Meeker was not a man who was easily discouraged in spreading an alarm, and, having found that the blacksmith was out, he started on a run for the office of the nearest justice of the peace, which happened to be located part way up the bandstand hill. He felt sure of finding help here, in addition to the majesty of the law. Meeker, badly winded, came rushing into court as I was in the midst of a lawsuit. He was too much excited to stand on ceremony and, without even addressing his remarks to the court, he began to yell for help.

"Come with me—all of you!" He waved his hands

around. "There's a hell of a fight going on—somebody'll be killed!"

The constable leaped to his feet. "Where is it?" he shouted.

"In Tom Hunter's shop—Asa Parker's in there beatin' up young Tom—I knew he would!"

"But they just had one fight," the constable protested. "And from what I hear Asa took a good lacin'."

"Don't argue!" screamed Meeker. "That feller's a killer —he was swingin' a big hammer when I come by—and I'll bet you one of 'em's dead by now!"

The courtroom was empty before the justice could bring down his gavel to declare an adjournment.

We found Tom standing in the middle of the floor with nothing more lethal in his hands than a bicycle saddle, but the constable caught him from behind and pinned his arms.

"Where is he?" the officer thundered.

Tom was taken completely by surprise. "Who?" he asked.

"You know who—better take a look there in the back, somebody."

Somebody did—and found the place empty.

"Who are you looking for, anyway?" asked Tom.

"Asa Parker."

"Oh! I can tell you where he is. He's gone up to see Jim Van Valkenburgh."

Meeker leveled a shaking finger at him. "But I saw Asa in here! Do you deny it?"

"Of course I don't deny it. He dropped in and stayed a little while, and then he went on again."

"Yes, and what did he come in here for?" the constable demanded, still intent upon uncovering a crime.

"I think he came to ask me to support him for the Assembly."

"And what else? There was some'pm else, wasn't there?"

"Come to think of it—there was."

The constable glared at him. "What was it? Better come clean!"

"He came," said Tom, "to get a little air in his back tire."

18

Riding on Air

WITH ALL THOSE EARLY CARS, TIRE trouble was thrown in gratis. It was about the only piece of necessary equipment for which there was no extra charge at the time of purchase, though the motorist paid plenty for it as time went on. Tops, lights, horns, windshields—all were extras, in regard to which the buyer was given a limited amount of choice, at a good stiff price. Even the mudguards were treated as extras by some makers. And as for giving a man a spare tire, such a thing was not dreamed of. Indeed, it was a long time before even the space to carry an extra tire was provided. Tire trouble was a delicate subject which the makers did not wish to bring up, and they felt that by providing racks and holders for the spares they would only be reminding the buying public of a disagreeable subject that might much better be disregarded.

From the very beginning, car makers side-stepped the tire question. They put it entirely up to the rubber companies. Cars were guaranteed for thirty days against defects in workmanship and materials, but the manufacturers would not guarantee that your tires were good enough to get you home with the new car. I once had a blowout while driving home from Rochester with a brand-new car, and in addition to the nerve-shattering inconvenience of changing a tire in the hot sun on the dusty roadside, I had to pay upwards of $50 for a new one. Then, after a long and acrimonious correspondence with a tire company in Akron, Ohio, I was, as the end of the season approached, given an "adjustment" which would allow me a reduction of $2.67 on a new tire. Imagine my joy when, some twenty years later, that company went into the hands of a receiver.

The clincher rim had been patented by Mr. Thomas B. Jeffery back in 1891 for use on the bicycle, and by enlarging and strengthening it a bit, it was a natural for the tire of the motor car. Unless a tire was securely fastened on a rim, there was no telling what it might not do after it had blown out with a bang and ripped a hole in the side wall the length of your hand, or possibly of your foot. The clincher rim was built on the felly, and it was put there to stay. When you changed a clincher tire you had to pry it from the rim while the rim was still on the felly of the wheel. The demountable rim did not put in an appearance until 1907, and another five years had elapsed before its adoption by car makers had become anything like general. Meanwhile the motorist was down on his knees beside his car, struggling to pry the inflexible bead of an ossified tire from the rusty jaws of a clincher rim.

The truth was that, while the makers would spend millions putting some small improvement on their engines, they would not spend a five-cent piece to make the changing of tires any less arduous for the motorist. Even the set of tire irons included in the tool kit was niggardly. Eugene Sandow, the current strong man, who could tie horseshoes in knots with his bare fingers, would have had a hard time removing a clincher tire from the rim with the best of those tire irons, which were of about the size and strength of the average can opener.

In every man's kit these miniature tire irons were quickly superseded by a leaf from a broken spring, of which in those days there were plenty scattered around in the junk of every garage and repair shop. Also in the kit was a jack and a pump, for after every tire change the tire had to be pumped up by hand—and the average pressure in those old days of fabric tires ran from sixty to ninety pounds instead of the twenty to thirty pounds that we now enjoy.

One of the greatest difficulties in changing a clincher tire was getting the valve stem of the tube in the proper place. An eighth of an inch too far one way or the other would mean a pinch—with a resultant blowout within only a few miles. And to get one's fingers over the rim, under the bead, and around the stem was something that would have taxed the powers of Superman. Tom Hunter solved this by making what he called a "tire fork." This was a sturdy hook like a two-pronged rake, with a stout hickory handle about three feet long. This really did the business, and if I could have prevailed upon him to apply for a patent on it he might well have made himself a neat little nest egg, for no passing motorist ever saw that tool in use without wanting to buy one. Tom made and sold some fifty or more of them, at one time or another, but he simply did not take the tool seriously.

"Aw, shucks," he said when I was urging him to have it patented. "Anybody could make one. You might as well ask me to patent a toothpick." And that is as far as I was ever able to get with the commercial development of Tom's tire fork.

Those early tires were all built with a smooth tread. For several years after the motor car came on the market in considerable numbers it was regarded as a fair-weather vehicle which dodged for cover at the first raindrop and stayed there until the roads had pretty well dried out. It was no doubt for this reason that the nonskid possibilities were not explored before they were. But as cars improved both in speed and reliability and as they were given enough power to pull themselves through the mud, they were weatherproofed against rainfall from above and splashing from underneath. Motorists began to have less regard for the weather, and as more of them ventured out on the slippery roads they found themselves slipping into the ditches or stuck in mudholes.

That was when the "Bailey Treads" first came into the picture. These consisted of raised spots on the tread, about the size of a dime and the thickness of a dollar. The garage man offered them to you without much enthusiasm. "Well, they're supposed to give you better traction, and possibly a little better wear, but I might as well warn you that they raise a little more dust."

"They cost extra, I suppose?" Everything cost the motorist extra.

"Only a couple of dollars a tire."

I bought a pair for my rear tires, which, by the way, were larger than the front. I bought them entirely because I thought they had a smart, an expensive look about them. That they had any effect whatever on slipping or skidding I never could see. But those Bailey Treads caught on, so much so that they really started a trend, and soon all the tires were covered with little blisters of individual design. One maker made his oblong, another diamond-shaped. Some were staggered and some oblique. One maker used the letters of his name for a design. However, at first they were all more or less of a selling scheme—cost the maker no more to make, and the customer a couple of dollars more to buy. Nobody took them seriously, least of all the customer. He knew that they did not hold him on the road, but he thought they looked well on the car and made interesting tracks in his driveway, and so he willingly paid the extra cost.

One tire maker, however, large and successful, was so geared that he could not go in for the spots. His tires ran on a narrow, flat tread with nearly flat side walls that were supposed to defy rim cutting and the resultant blowouts. He therefore made it his business to expose the fallacy of this ornamental trend on the tire tread, and he must have spent millions in the advertising campaign he put on. He heaped ridicule on the pretty pictures his competitors were putting on their tires and suggested, with what he regarded as rich sarcasm, humorous designs for people who fell into particular classifications: a line of little elephants all the way round the tread for Republicans, mules for Democrats, and the like. I don't know that any of his designs were ever followed, but I know that his competitors kept making their bubbles higher and thicker and tougher and more effective, until the time arrived when a motorist who discovered that the nonskid protuberances on his tire had worn down to the tread would either recap the tire or prepare to junk it.

Meanwhile the maker with his smooth tread and his flat side walls has passed entirely out of the picture.

Dozens of ingenious methods were tried to obviate skidding, but one of the most amusing was a tread called the "Midgely." This Midgely Tread embedded in the wearing surface of the rubber a layer of spiral spring made of fine, though tough, wire, the coil of which was about the size it would have been if wound around a lead pencil. The idea was that as the tread rubber wore down, the exposed wire of the spring would wear through, leaving millions of little wire claws to grip the road and keep the car from skidding. I never owned a set of Midgely Treads, though I saw hundreds of them. The little claws came through as planned. They made a curious scratching sound as they ran over a piece of hard pavement, but they were completely useless in the mud and were soon abandoned.

Another curiosity in the tire field at about this time was a nonpuncture inner tube, in the walls of which a thin layer of feathers was embedded. The tube itself was filled with a fluid which would harden soon after being exposed to the air. And the function of the feathers was presumably to pass outward with the flow of the fluid, when a puncture occurred, and form a nucleus about which the fluid could harden and plug the hole. For years the self-healing inner tube defied the efforts of the inventor, but it seems now to have reached a solution. If the methods employed in stopping the bullet holes in the gasoline tanks of a warplane can be applied to the plugging of a puncture, roadside changing of tires will soon be a thing of the past.

Of all the troubles with which the early motorist was beset, tire trouble was undoubtedly the most frequent. It was ever-present, or if not actually ever-present it was ever-threatening. The truth of the matter is that the fabric tire never was adequate for the job it was called upon to perform. Real tire satisfaction was never achieved until the coming of the cord construction. Of course the motorist was always hopeful. He spent his money for one alleged improvement after another, though year after year went by with tires practically no better. By 1912, cars would really travel, but the motorist who got 2,000 miles out of a tire which had cost him sixty dollars or more felt that he was getting his money's worth; and the composure with which the early motorist would take the bang of a blowout or the pounding of a slower puncture seems almost unbelievable today.

I seldom went for a ride without a puncture or two. I expected them and was well equipped to handle them; and though I cannot truthfully say that I looked forward to tire trouble with any pleasurable anticipation, I must admit that I was not entirely unaware of the fact that I could cope with it with a certain amount of skill and dispatch. Nobody could get the jack under a wheel any more quickly than I could, and after a number of unfortunate experiences in having the jack tip and the car slip off, I learned to carry a stout section of oak plank with me, clipped under the running board where it was easily accessible. Of course I did not need the plank in the garage or on a pavement, but on a soft or muddy piece of dirt road, there was nothing like it.

With one of Tom's tire forks I could disrupt a rusted clincher from the rim in a matter of minutes, sometimes seconds. I could raise the bead, insert my hand, and draw out the tube. I could as quickly slip in another, or remove the casing if need be. I was equally swift about getting the tire back on the rim. Then came the real test of strength—pumping up the tire by hand. Sometimes this would take fifteen minutes of back-breaking labor, sometimes more. Pumps were temperamental. They did not always work equally well. The delicate leather washers wore or dried out. A pump that worked beautifully today would do badly tomorrow. You not only had to know your pump, you had to know how to repair it. Tom Hunter had taught me how to take care of my pump and had furnished me with a set of spare washers. So I felt that I was ready for any eventualities; and I needed to be, for one night on the way home from Rochester I had seven punctures in the thirty-three miles.

I was carrying only two spare inner tubes, and had to put on five patches by matchlight. Patching a tube took time, perhaps half an hour per puncture. When I got home that night, there were blisters on my hands from pumping. But there was relief in sight, for at just that time the "tire bottle" came on the market. This consisted of a brass tube that would hold enough compressed air to fill four tires the size of mine.

A little later the small compressor pump driven by your engine came into use. When you were ready to pump up the tire, you started your engine, threw a gear in mesh, and sat and smoked or held hands with your girl friend until the tire was inflated. A simpler form of engine pump was one that screwed into a sparkplug hole. But the result was the same: the engine did the work of pumping up the tire.

A puncture today would make a motorist scream with rage. Personally I have not had one in over ten years. I have driven a car to California and back without changing a tire. But in the early days of motoring a puncture, while not especially welcome, was at least something that the motorist could understand. It was not like having your motor begin to miss or perhaps die entirely for no apparent reason. There was nothing mysterious about a puncture. It came because the air had gone out of your tire. And all you had to do to make a repair was to get some air back inside and keep it there. But not only were we stoical about punctures, we were positively boastful about them. My seven-puncture trip home from Rochester kept me in material for conversation for days and days. In fact, it was one of the best stories in town, until somebody eclipsed it one night by having fourteen punctures in the eighteen miles between Geneva and Canandaigua. This story always seemed a little bogus to me, since all these punctures, except three or four, came from the same tiny piece of metal—probably the point of a tack—that was found embedded in the inner surface of the casing when it was taken to the repairman the next morning.

During all that time we were on the wrong track. Instead of making better tires, the manufacturers were simply making punctures less painful. Their tardy adoption of the demountable rim was just another step in the same direction. It made tires easier to change, but they had to be changed just as often as before.

Tom Hunter made half-a-dozen inventions to ease the changing of tires, but he was just as stubborn about them as he was about his tire fork. He made the first long-handled jack I ever saw and the first casing-spreader. He installed an automatic compressor long before they were on the market. But he insisted that these inventions were of no more permanent value than a new way of blowing your nose would have been.

"Some day a fellow will come along who'll cure the cold," he said. "And then where will my wonderful improvements be?"

It was Tom's idea that relief would come from a "disposable" tire. Some cheap substance would be found, he was sure, that would bring down the cost to only a dollar or two apiece. A new tire would be good for one or two thousand miles, and as soon as it began to show wear it would be thrown away and another one put on. It never occurred to him that tires could be built that would easily give 25,000 miles of service. He was a dreamer, but not as much of a dreamer as all that.

Patching a tube with rubber cement was never anything more than a temporary repair. It might get you to the nearest town where you could have a patch vulcanized. A cemented patch simply would not stand the heat, and many of the famous multiple puncture stories were nothing more than the repeated failures of a cemented patch to stay in place on a hot day inside the casing of a hot tire. I was a comparatively new motorist when Tom called my attention to a little portable vulcanizing set advertised in one of the automobile magazines. He read them all and there was little that escaped him. At this time the big shop vulcanizers were heated by steam, but this little portable used gasoline.

It was made of cast iron and was in the form of a cup with a clamp to press the part to be patched close against the smooth bottom of the cup. The patch, made of vulcanizing rubber, was put on in the usual way and the cup was attached and clamped in place while cold. About an ounce of gasoline was then poured into the cup and a match applied. By the time the gasoline had burned away, the job was finished, though the cup still had to stay in place until it was cool enough to remove with the fingers. From that time on I vulcanized all my own patches, and it was not unusual for passing motorists to see me at night by the side of the road hovering over a brightly blazing fire in my vulcanizing cup.

Often these passing motorists would stop and come running to my aid with a fire extinguisher. And for them to call out of the darkness and ask me if I needed any help was almost inevitable whenever I used the vulcanizer after dark. The feeling of fraternity among motorists was far stronger then than it is today, but of course there were not so many of us. A stranded car might stand by the side of the road for an hour or two before another motorist came along, but when one did, the casualty was pretty sure of help or even of a tow if needed.

I did not often ask the driver of a horse vehicle for help, though once I did. I was changing a tire on one of the more desolate stretches of the Cherry Valley Turnpike when a thunderstorm blew up. Thunderstorms in that part of the world can be very severe and I had no desire to be caught in this one, which looked black and ugly as it spread itself over the sky and began to rumble ominously. I did not have a tire fork at this time, and when I tried to remove the casing from the rim I found that I could not start it with any of the tools I had. The storm was coming closer all the time and I was in a desperate plight, when a farmer drove along in a one-horse lumber wagon. In my desperation I stopped him and asked if by any chance he had an iron bar or any other kind of heavy instrument in his wagon that I could borrow long enough to dislodge the tire. What I really had my eye on was the iron rod with which the tailboard of his wagon was fastened.

He shook his head. "Nope, ain't got nuthin' like that. Don't carry such things with me when I'm just goin' to town. What is it you're tryin' to do, anyhow?"

"I'm trying to pound the bead of that tire out of the rim," I explained, putting my hand on it and indicating what I meant.

"Well, if you'll hang onto my horse a minute I'll see if I can help you."

I took the horse by the bridle and he clambered down.

"Is this the part you mean?" he asked, tapping the tire with the toe of his boot.

"That's it," I said. "I've got to knock it loose from the rim."

"That shouldn't be so hard," he said, and he hauled back his foot and kicked it a mighty blow.

The tire began to give at the first impact, and by the time that he had sent his cowhide boots against it half-a-dozen times, the casing was hanging so limp that I could have taken it off with the handle of a spoon. The storm caught me before I had reached the nearest town. But at least I was on my wheels and rolling, and I managed to get into the shelter of a church shed before the worst of it broke. As I sat there in the shed waiting for the rain to stop I made up my mind to buy a pair of cowhide boots.

19

Washout

As the cool weather came on and people found their motors harder to start, fewer automobiles were seen on the road. Bicycles, too, were going into storage. People rode them if they wanted to go somewhere in a hurry, but it was getting too chilly to ride for pleasure. Tom must have been feeling the pinch, though he was not given to complaining about his personal problems. And when I tried to feel him out on the subject one day, all he would say about it was that he was getting a little more time to put in on some of his own inventions. He was at the moment quite excited over a little gadget he had just made for lighting the gas flame in automobile headlights without moving from the seat. The driver first turned on the gas by opening a little valve on the dashboard. Pressing a button located beside the valve produced an electric spark just above the gas jet in the headlight.

The one he installed in my car worked perfectly, but his installation in another car did not do quite so well. Either there was a spark lag from a weakened battery, or the driver was too long in applying the spark after turning on the gas, for the headlight exploded with enough force to blow the door of the headlight fifty feet away, shattering the glass and completely ruining a somewhat expensive reflector, which was hard to replace. Another disappoint-

· 214 ·

ing feature of this invention was that a Patent Office search showed that the idea had already been patented and was in use.

By this time, however, Tom was interested in something else—the fall weather had brought forcibly to his attention the great difficulty of starting a cold motor by hand cranking. His first idea on this important subject was the outgrowth of his gas lighter. He proposed to introduce a small amount of illuminating gas into each cylinder and ignite it with a spark from the dry cells.

"If a little of that gas has got enough kick in it to blow a headlight to pieces it certainly ought to have enough power to turn over an engine," he said.

This method of starting on the spark would work if the engine was warm and one of the pistons happened to be in just the right position. But that was not enough for Tom. He wanted something that would work every time, regardless of the position of the pistons—something that would whirl the engine over and continue to whirl it until it started. Then one day he came in and threw a rough sketch on my desk.

"There it is," he said, "a compressed air starter."

"Compressed air?" I repeated, not very much impressed.

"Sure—why not? If it's good enough to stop the cars for the railroads, why isn't it good enough to start motors for the rest of us?"

"But where will you get your compressed air?"

"Just where the railroads do—from running the engine." He picked up a pencil from the desk and explained the sketch. Enough compressed air would be kept in a storage tank to turn the engine over, say, fifty times. If that was not enough he'd make the tank bigger. As soon as the engine started, the compressor pump would be thrown on and the storage tank filled again.

"How do you know it will work?" I asked.

"It's got to—the principle is sound."

"The principle of your gas lighter was sound—and see what happened."

He grinned. "So you think I ought to build one before we go any farther?"

I nodded. "Isn't that good sense?"

"It is," he said. "I'll do it. Heaven knows I got plenty of time right now."

Another development of the cooler weather was that it made people think about indoor diversions, and some of the more ambitious youths set out to see if they could get enough signatures to warrant the giving of a subscription dance. Burgess Harper, Zelda's brother, was one of the moving spirits, and when he came for my signature he asked if I thought Tom Hunter would be interested.

"I don't know the boy myself," said Burgess, "but Zelda says he's all right. He sold her a bike, you know, and she's in there every little while to get a squirt of oil put into it, or some air in the tires, or some such thing. What do you think?"

"I agree with Zelda," I said. "He's absolutely all right, but I don't know whether he dances or not."

Burgess asked him, as he told me a day or two later; and while Tom seemed very much pleased to have been invited he said he would have to decline, since he did not know how to dance. However, on the night of the party I saw him standing in a crowd of onlookers outside the door of the hall. He had hung pretty well back in the crowd so as not to be too conspicuous to the people inside, but tall as he was, he was not making a very good job of it. I did not speak to him, as I thought from the way he had his hat drawn down over his face and his shoulders thrust upwards he was trying to keep himself as anonymous as possible.

It was a jolly affair, with an out-of-town orchestra and the hall decorated with autumn leaves. With fifty couples we used to feel that we could have only three pieces of music, but since there were six on the stage that night Burgess must have had around one hundred signatures on his list. Lucy was there with Asa Parker, who was now paying her a great deal of attention. I could see that Zelda was somewhat upset, as she had always regarded Asa as her own personal property. I was tempted to tease Zelda about it but thought better of it; and as it turned out, it is just as well that I did.

Tom came into the office the next day, ostensibly to tell me about his progress with the new starter, but after he had pretty well exhausted that subject he asked me if I knew where he could learn how to dance. I told him that there was a class in town for younger children, but he shook his head over that. He said he never could bring himself to the point of getting up on the floor with a lot of kids and showing how awkward he could be. I told him that there would be a regular grown-up dancing class a little later in the winter, but that did not seem to help much, as the class would not be starting for several weeks. Then I happened to remember that I had read something in the paper about a dancing class at Oak Forks, a little hamlet a few miles down the railroad.

This information caught Tom's interest at once. He said he would like it if he could go to a class where he didn't know anybody. He hated to get up and make a

· 217 ·

monkey of himself before people he knew. I promised to find out about it for him, and did. It was a class for adults, mostly young married people, and the teacher, an attractive young widow from Geneva, was delighted to have an unattached young man to offset some of the preponderance of females with which her class was afflicted. Fortunately the class was just starting when Tom joined, but he found to his dismay that he was the only beginner. The others went because they liked to dance, or possibly just because of the dearth of social life at the Forks.

Mrs. Sweet, the teacher, took her new pupil in hand at once. If her class was to get any benefit from this tall, angular boy with the friendly grin, she realized that she must get him out on the floor as soon as possible. She was a capable instructor as well as an attractive woman, and she had him doing a rudimentary version of the two-step in a single lesson. The perspiring youth nearly perished of embarrassment when she first got him up on his feet, though she was considerate enough to do it after she had started the rest of the class dancing and had been preoccupied with their own efforts.

"Keep your head up, Mr. Hunter," she had to keep telling him. "If you want to be a good dancer you must never look at your feet."

"But if I don't look, how can I tell where they are?" he protested good-humoredly.

"You must go by the feeling."

"But you forget how far it is from my head to my feet."

"Very well. Now just watch mine and you'll see how yours ought to go."

She showed him the step a few times and then came over and stood beside him, grasping his hand firmly. Back and forth they went in an out-of-the-way corner of the hall, while the rest of the class romped merrily around and around and around. After the dance she introduced him to a few people, and a little later came and took him to meet another group. This was repeated until he had met them all. Then she turned him over to her assistant, though she came back several times and put him through his paces until he began to feel quite at home on his feet.

Promptly at ten o'clock the class broke up. Two passenger trains were scheduled to pass there at ten-twenty. Mrs. Sweet and Peggy, her buxom piano player, were going east, and Tom going west. The others, all of them living reasonably near by, went home or about their own affairs. The railroad station was not open at this time of night, but arrangements had been made with the station agent to leave a key outside, with which they would let themselves in to keep warm around the potbellied stove which stood in the middle of the floor.

On the first night Mrs. Sweet showed Tom where to find the key and herself unlocked the door. Then she took him by the arm and guided him over to the lamp, which was in a high bracket. Ordinarily she lighted it, she said, by moving over a chair, but Tom was able to reach it from the floor. He liked Mrs. Sweet and did not feel at all bashful in her company. He liked the competent way she unlocked the door and guided him over to the lamp. No nonsense, no foolishness. She knew what she was about and evidently understood how to handle men. The three stood around the stove and talked until the westbound train whistled at the semaphore and came slowly in on the siding. This was the signal for them to turn out the light, lock the door, and go out on the platform to await the arrival of the eastbound train. It happened the same way each of the next three weeks. But the following week Tom's train came in first, and after dis-charging a single passenger, quite obviously under the in-fluence of liquor, prepared to pull out immediately.

"Aren't you waiting for the other train?" Tom asked the conductor.

"Not tonight," was the answer. "We're passing at Phelps. All abo-o-oa'd!"

Tom let his train go without him.

"Are you going on our train?" asked Mrs. Sweet as the last car passed and he made no move to swing aboard.

"No, ma'am," he said. "I'm going up on the freight that comes a little later."

"But, my dear boy, you needn't have waited here with us. We can take care of ourselves."

"Oh, I can catch a ride all right, and I didn't like the looks of that fellow who got off the train."

"Oh, I'm sure he would never bother us."

"You never can tell—he was pretty drunk, and there's no watchman or station agent or anything around here. The whole place is shut up tight."

Mrs. Sweet came over and took hold of him by both arms. She did it in a nice way. Friendly, but not too friendly, he thought.

"It was very kind of you, very considerate," she said. "Peggy and I both appreciate it—but please promise me that you'll never do it again."

"No, ma'am, I can't promise that," he said, grinning good-naturedly. "You wouldn't want me to make a promise and not keep it."

"Of course I can't force a promise from you," she ad-mitted, "but I can tell you what I very much prefer, and when you know that, I'm sure I won't need any promise."

They returned to the waiting room and stayed there until the eastbound train came in. Tom saw them aboard, and after the train had pulled out he locked the station and walked the five miles home through the darkness. He tried to make Mrs. Sweet believe that he had caught a ride on the freight, but she would never admit that she believed it.

There was no change in their relationship, which remained strictly that of teacher and pupil. It seemed to Tom that she tried hard to make a good dancer of him; and so far as Tom was concerned, he tried hard to learn. The last night he was there she gave him a lecture on his responsibility of being a strong leader when on the floor. "Make up your mind where you want to go, what you want to do—then do it."

"But what if my partner has a different idea?" he asked.

"She won't. But if she does, you must have your way regardless."

"Regardless of her wishes?"

"Absolutely regardless."

"I'll remember that," he said, "the first time you resist my leadership."

That was the night the buxom piano player was absent —down with a hard cold—and Mrs. Sweet had to rely on local talent for her music. With the girls taking turns, they managed somehow; but as the class was breaking up, a storm which had been brewing all the evening suddenly materialized and sent all the resident members scurrying for home. Mrs. Sweet hastily caught Tom by the arm and together they ran to the station. They found the key and went tumbling inside just as the deluge struck.

Tom lighted the lamp and then walked over to the door

and peered out. "I wonder if some of the others aren't coming in."

Mrs. Sweet had her back turned. She had dropped her hat on the bench and with both arms raised was trying to repair the damage done by the wind to what had been a very lovely arrangement of her dark and wavy hair. "Probably not," she said. "I imagine they are all trying to get home." Still patting at her hair, she was slowly turning to face him. "We seem to have the place all to ourselves."

He admired the slender grace of her pose. He liked the mulberry-colored gown, which followed the lines of her figure with very gratifying fidelity. She was, he was thinking, very young to be a widow; he wondered if she could possibly be thirty.

"One might almost say," she added, "that we are alone."

She came over and stood beside him and together they peered out at the great, jagged forks of lightning now rending the troubled skies and coming nearer and nearer with every detonation of the deafening thunder, while the tempest howled and whipped the limbs of the neighboring oaks as if they had been willow wands, wrenching off branches and hurling them to earth with a vicious crash and a blast of angry rain. Then suddenly the lightning seemed to be all around them and they were jarred and shaken by the terrifying afterclap of the almost unbearable thunder. In the eerie light they glimpsed the black outlines of a telegraph pole which had tottered and fallen with its crossarms elevated as if in supplication.

Mrs. Sweet instinctively clutched his arm. "Oh, I'm so frightened!" she cried.

"Don't be afraid," he said. "That won't do any good."

"But I can't help it. Lightning always terrifies me!"

"Then let's get away from the window." He led her to

one side. "Here, this is the most protected corner. We can sit down here."

And thus they sat while the storm went raging overhead and slowly passed off into the distance.

At last Mrs. Sweet sat up straight. "Listen!"

Tom listened. "What was it you heard?" he asked.

"Nothing! That's just it—the telegraph is dead."

"Come to think of it, I haven't heard a click out of it since that pole went down."

"Now we *are* alone. Even the railroad company has gone off and left us."

"We couldn't read their old ticker anyway," said Tom.

"No, but as long as we could hear it we knew that the company was still with us. Didn't that little sound give you the feeling that somebody else was near by—or at least on earth?"

"I'm afraid I didn't think much about it. But don't you worry, there'll be a train along here sooner or later," he said soothingly.

"Which do you think it will be?"

"Maybe sooner, maybe later. Might come any time. It takes a lot to put a railroad completely out of commission."

"But how can trains run with telegraph poles lying across the tracks?"

"This one outside may be the only pole down."

"And it may be one of hundreds," she said. "Tracks do wash away, and bridges may be down. We aren't able to do anything about it, but at least let's be realistic."

"Oh, it may not be as bad as you think," said Tom, still trying to reassure her.

"And it may be worse," she said, "for we're soon going to be in the dark."

"What makes you think so?"

"I can smell the wick burning—and that means the oil is gone."

Tom, who was telling me the story, slowly nodded his head. "She was right—and it was the only lamp in the place."

"What did you do?" I asked.

"What could we do? We sat in the dark until we were rescued by the wrecking train just before daylight."

20

Landslide

THE FIRST TUESDAY AFTER THE FIRST MONDAY
in November was a bright day, but cold. Republican
weather, I heard everybody saying. Took a nasty, wet,
rainy, gloomy day to bring out the Democrats. I kept hearing the wiseacres saying that all day. I was not personally
on hand to predict the weather at six o'clock in the morning, when the polls opened. Too dark to see much, though
Andy Brackett told me later that the light wind from
the north seemed reassuring to him as he walked rapidly
towards the polling place of his election district. Andy
never failed to be on hand when the polls opened, and
usually he voted the number one ballot. This was a little
courtesy reserved for the leader; it was supposed to bring
good luck. Andy, however, did not put any great amount
of faith in good luck. His presence there so early in the
morning was intended as a good example to the faithful
and to show that he practiced what he preached about
getting in your vote early.

Nobody ever said good morning on election day except
as an afterthought. The customary greeting was, "Voted
yet? You better get up there and make your little X-mark.
Now don't put it off, do it now. . . . How about you?
You voted yet? And you? Oh, you haven't? Why not? Better get up there right away." They seldom asked a man

how he was voting. People knew all about that—or thought they did—long before election.

In small towns there was very little fence-sitting. Either a voter was or he wasn't. If he was, little attention was paid to him, except to see that he did not forget to vote. If he was disgruntled or had been saying harsh things about the administration—he was likely to find that he had been singled out as chairman or secretary of some political meeting; or if he was important enough, he might even be named as a delegate to a county or district convention. Often the news of a voter's unrest reached the leader before the canvassers had even begun their work. Such things usually had a way of getting around. But this year, though people were uneasy, they were also uncommunicative. Andy sensed that something was in the wind, but until the ballots were counted he never dreamed how much there was to it.

The Democrats had as usual made their nominations, from governor all the way down to dogcatcher. Their state-wide campaign was more than ordinarily vigorous and noisy; although in a county so hopelessly Republican they spent little of their cash or energy, giving our town no more than a matinee performance of their "Cavalcade of Democracy"—a traveling troup of speakers and entertainers who went around in a special car, rallying the upstate spirit of party loyalty with orators and performers who, for the most part, had never before been north of the Harlem River or west of the Hudson. Vacy Boynton, whose name was still down as leader, was buying cabbage and potatoes that fall for a produce house in Wheeling, West Virginia, and had no time to give to politics. He couldn't even be found when O'Brien, the County Chairman, came to town to make arrangements for the visit of the Cavalcade, so the advance agent of Democracy turned in desperation to Tom Hunter. He did not know Tom, but he had not forgotten the showing the boy had made against Andy Brackett at that spring election when Towner was killed.

Tom said he was out of politics and refused to take any part for himself; but acting entirely for Vacy he made tentative arrangements for the rally—which Vacy left him to carry through all by himself. Fortunately there was not much for him to do. Even the printing was furnished by the State Committee; Tom had only to stamp the time and place on the posters and see that they were displayed. The Cavalcade played to a crowded house, very much to the relief of Vacy's assistant, who refused to sit on the stage but viewed the performance from the standing room in the rear.

The rally staged by the Republicans was quite different. They scorned a ready-made performance by a road company. Their big meeting must be indigenous to the soil. They brought out their candidates and showed the people the caliber of the men who were asking their support, and though I was not there I heard it said that Asa had made not only the best speech at the rally, but the best of his budding career.

Tom was completely disgusted when election day came and Vacy voted early and went off for the day to a shipping point where he was taking in potatoes. After all, a job was a job, Vacy said, and he'd be back when he was through.

Tom was feeling pretty low when he dropped in to see me along about noontime. Something, he said, was going on, though he did not know what it meant. Voters were coming in so fast that the checkers at the polls could hardly keep up with them, and Democrats who had not voted since the days of Grover Cleveland were driving in from the farthest corners of the township, bringing their hired men and neighbors with them.

"And people I always thought were Republicans," he complained, "keep sending word they'll come in to vote if we'll have a rig come to get them."

I laughed. "That doesn't sound very serious. Why not send a rig for them?"

Tom shook his head. "That's just the trouble—we haven't got the rigs to send. No money to hire them, and only two or three volunteers with rickety buggies and slow old nags that are asleep on their feet. I don't know why Vacy can't look after elections for himself and leave me out of it."

He went away downcast and discouraged, muttering that he supposed he'd have to do the best he could with his superannuated conveyances. But these calls kept piling up on him until midafternoon, when he became desperate and went out and borrowed the only Democratic automobile in town to bring the voters in.

Tom had taken the step with many misgivings, remembering all too well what had happened the other time, but there was a streak of stubbornness in him that made him go through with it. If people refused to come in the motor car he could begin to worry about making other arrangements. But nobody did refuse. This time, because of recent rain, there was no dust to reckon with, and everybody seemed to be delighted to have a chance to ride in an automobile, many of them for the first time.

When Andy Brackett heard what was going on he threw his grey derby hat into the air. "That settles it!" he cried. "Remember what happened the last time they tried that?"

Vacy, arriving just as the polls were closing, was of the same opinion. He drew a long and sour face and declared that Tom had made a bad mistake. Both Vacy and Andy Brackett changed their minds, however, when the ballots were counted and it was found that the Democrats had carried Andy Brackett's own election district for the first time in fourteen years. A little later Asa Parker was reeling under the impact of a similar calamity. Claims of a state-wide Democratic landslide began to leak off the through wire before ten o'clock, and by midnight the Republican State Chairman had admitted a sweeping victory for the Democrats, although in upstate New York this was not regarded as final until confirmed by the Rochester *Democrat and Chronicle.*

Only one dim spark of hope was left to the Republicans. The County Chairman had refused to concede the election of the Democratic candidate for Member of Assembly. The count was extremely close, the Chairman said, and the result would depend upon the returns of a few election districts in the sparsely settled Bristol Hills neighborhood between the lakes, which had been Republican ever since the Civil War.

Asa and Andy were both on the early train the next morning when it drew into the county seat, where the board of canvassers was to meet for the official entry of returns. But it so happened that Bristol Hills was a little too far off the beaten track to catch the drift of the times and Asa found that he was reelected to the Assembly by less than fifty votes. On the train going home Asa was very quiet and sat looking out of the window with hardly a word. For a while Andy watched him in silence, and then he concluded that the young man needed a little advice.

"Well, Asa," he said, "you were the only one of my horses to come under the wire. I'm proud of you."

"Proud? I feel pretty much humiliated."

"Humiliated? Why, you were the only man on the county ticket to come through! At least you've got the job for another term."

"Oh, I got the job all right—by an eyelash."

"What more do you want?"

"Think of the lost prestige. I lost one vote out of every three that I got at the last election."

Andy, as he told me afterward, refused to be impressed. "That doesn't mean a thing," he said. "These landslides are a freak. They're like a stampede among the herd. The animals are in a panic while the excitement is on, but afterward you'll find them all back in their stalls right where they belong. Patience is what you need in politics. These things have to be waited out. Here's the angle we're giving to the papers: in spite of an unprecedented landslide, the immense personal following of our popular young Assemblyman brought him through to a victory in which he was completely surrounded by the casualties of older and more experienced men. Great things are in store for a man who can weather the storm and turn in a victory on such a year as this."

Asa's eyes began to sparkle. "Have you got that written down?"

Andy drew out a clipping. "It's the lead editorial in today's *Repository-Messenger,*" he said.

Tom came stalking into my back office and slammed a telegram down on the table for me to read. He could not understand why in hell they had sent it to him. So far as the election went, he had no individual connection with it whatever. It was all in Vacy's name. He was just Vacy's agent or substitute or something. O'Brien understood all about it, and Tom simply couldn't see how such a stupid mistake could have been made. Those fellows in New York must have received their information from somebody there in the county—probably from O'Brien himself —and how they could make such a mistake as this he couldn't figure out. There was only one thing he could be sure of, and that was that Vacy would be good and mad when he heard of it.

"What makes you think he will hear of it?" I asked.

Tom waved his hands excitedly. "He'll be waiting for it! He'll be expecting it—after nosing out the unbeatable Andy Brackett on his own home grounds. And what about the local telegraph operator! I'll bet you he's spread the story already that Tom Hunter has had a personal message of congratulation from the big Democratic moguls in New York City."

We heard someone come into the outer office and Tom stepped over and peered through the crack of the door. Then suddenly he threw it wide open with a shout.

"Sol! The one person on earth I wanted to see! Put down that pack and come in here."

Sol came in, his round, moonlike face wreathed with smiles. "Some election, my friends?"

"A small election," said Tom, "and a great big dilemma for me."

"A dilemma iss bad. That's not what I came for. I came to celebrate with you a fine victory, young man. Since I leave you alone—you haf made magnificent job of yourself. When you beat Andy Brackett you beard the lion in his den!"

"That's what has made all the trouble." Tom put the telegram into his hands.

Sol's face was wreathed with smiles as he read it. "This iss magnificent—it iss monumental." He turned over the telegram and glanced at the other side. "But where iss the dilemma?"

"You won't find it on the back," said Tom. "It's right there on the front where everybody can see it—they sent it to the wrong man!"

"I see no wrong man. Why do you say it?"

"But I'm not the leader—Vacy's the real boss, and he'll think I'm trying to steal his thunder."

Sol smiled and slowly shook his head.

"Don't you catch on?" Tom demanded. "I can't show him that telegram. It never should have been sent to me, and I want to know if there isn't some way that I can have one sent to Vacy in his own name that will make him feel all right."

"Listen, my boy—I just come from Canandaigua. O'Brien iss no fool. He knows all about what hass been going on here. How much did your friend Vacy halp with the rally?"

Tom swallowed hastily. "Well—"

"Huh—that's what O'Brien told me. And how much halp from Vacy on election day? All day he load potatoes! You give Vacy credit for that? Bah!"

"All right," said Tom, "suppose he didn't do anything about it. He's still the leader just the same."

"Vacy iss your landlord, nothing more. For years he try to beat Andy Brackett; could he do it? Never. But with you it iss different. You try once and get Andy groggy; you try again and knock him out. So now who should get credit?"

Tom shook his head stubbornly. "But, Sol, I don't want any credit. If Vacy hadn't been so busy I wouldn't have lifted a finger to win the election. I'm no politician and don't want to be."

Sol threw up both hands in protest. "Sh-h-h-h!" he cautioned. "Don't let anybody hear you say that—not even your lawyer! It might cost you good political job."

Tom looked at him skeptically. "What job?"

Sol shrugged his thick shoulders. "I don't know—hass not been made yet. What job you should like?"

"I don't want any job."

"Then you are independent? For money you haf no need?"

Tom smiled ruefully. "I wish I didn't."

A satisfied smile broke over Sol's round face. "That iss different. You need job—so you should want job. I do not like to hear so hasty talk."

"But I never thought anything about a job."

"Naturally. That iss why you should give plenty time to think all about it. But you must make up your mind. Nothing iss so hard to get as job you don't know whether you want it or not."

"Listen, Sol, I don't know the first thing about jobs. I wouldn't even know how to hold one."

Sol shook with laughter. "But you don't have to know anything. All you need iss to be honest—a little honest— just so you don't get caught."

Tom laid his hand on the telegram. "But we've still got this to think about."

"Tack up on the wall of your shop for all to see. Then iss no mystery."

"But what about Vacy?"

"Vacy will understand. If not, O'Brien will tell him.

You haf done the impossible. If a little later the party see fit to reward you, iss it fault of yours?"

"But, Sol, I don't—"

"All right, all right! You don't know what you want. The grand house-cleaning comes January first. You haf plenty time to think it over." Sol moved towards the door. "I must go now, but I will come again. We will talk more when you haf had time to think."

"I wish you wouldn't go, Sol. I haven't said half I wanted to."

Sol waved his two hands in the air. "Ah, I haf much to do. I should not be here today. But when I hear of your magnificent victory—then I cannot stay away. I am afraid from your inexperience you make little mistake and lose what should be yours. In this town iss only one person who does not appreciate you."

Tom looked puzzled. "Who is that?"

"Yourself. See to it that yourself does not turn out to be bad friend to you."

As they stood talking Sol glanced out of the window and then hastily jammed on his hat. "Here comes old Meeker," he said. "I'd better be going or he'll talk me deaf, dumb, and blind."

But he need not have worried, for Meeker had not yet reached the door before he had resumed an uncompleted argument with Vacy, who had come up from the other direction.

"So you still don't believe it's Jim Cotton, hey?" demanded Vacy.

Meeker snorted disdainfully. "Pff! I certainly do not."

"Just the looks ought to be enough for you."

" 'Tain't enough."

"All right, I got evidence."

"That's what I need. Let's see your evidence."

"The evidence don't belong to me, and if it did I wouldn't carry it around in my pocket."

"You mean it's hearsay evidence?" demanded Meeker.

"I don't mean nuthin' of the kind," said Vacy. "It's real evidence, and I'll tell you what it is—I've just seen one of Jim Cotton's *baby pictures*."

"Uh-huh. How'd it look?"

"Identical!"

"That's what you say."

"It's what everybody says who sees the picture. You can go and see it for yourself."

"Where is it at?"

"Lizzie Pardee's got it."

"Where'd she get it?"

"Remember her brother Ed, who used to run the photograph gallery? The tall one that died? Well, he took it. Lizzie found it in with a lot of his old pictures and negatives and tintypes."

"Yes, but how does Lizzie know who it is?"

"It's wrote on the picture. 'Jimmie Cotton, five years old.' She says it's Ed's handwritin'."

"Uh-huh, I'd like to see for myself."

"All you got to do is go up and ask Lizzie. I reckon everybody in town'll be up there to see it."

"Likely. I'll be goin' up that way this afternoon. But let me remind you of some'pm. Do you remember the way the Peanut used to sing in school? He could sing like a bird."

"What kind of a bird?"

"A songbird. He was a boy soprano."

"He could sing all right, I guess. What of it?"

"Didn't anybody ever tell you that Alonzo Babson was a boy soprano?" said Meeker with a significant smile.

"Huh, I've heared him sing myself, but I still don't think Alonzo was the father. Don't think he had it in him. Alonzo never had any children by his own wife, you recollect."

"But boy sopranos don't grow on trees," Meeker insisted.

"You think photographs do? You know pictures are evidence in a court of law. You get your looks by inheritance, but almost anybody can have a voice. Caruso, Jenny Lind, all those folks just come right out of nowhere."

But Meeker was unwilling to give any ground. "How many boy sopranos have we had in this town? Just two —Alonzo and the Peanut. Very significant, I should call it."

Sol threw open the door into the front office. "My apologies, shentlemen, if I make interruption, but I must shoulder my pack and get on." After he had swung the heavy green pack to his shoulder he turned and called back to Tom: "While I am gone you will do some thinking, huh?"

As the door closed behind the peddler Vacy shouted jovially to Tom, "So you got a telegram!"

Tom stopped in the doorway, leaning against the jamb. "How did you know?"

Vacy laughed. "Everybody knows. That's what I stepped in to tell you about—if you take it right down to the paper you can get it in this week's issue."

"Nobody would be interested in a thing like that," said Tom slowly, shaking his head.

"I would," said Vacy promptly. "Ain't you even gonna let me see it?"

Tom fished it out of his pocket and handed it over.

"I don't know why they sent it to me—that telegram should have been sent to you."

"Nuthin' the sort. You done all the work, and you ought to get the credit. I been worryin' about it a mite because I hadn't sent in your name as chairman, and I was afraid they might send the telegram to me. Guess Bill O'Brien musta fixed it up, he knew what was goin' on all right." He folded up the telegram and handed it back. "It's a nice one. Nice as I ever see."

"Wouldn't you like to have it for a souvenir?" said Tom.

"No, no," said Vacy with cordial generosity. "I got a telegram. It's got my name on and everything, and I've put it away for posterity. You'll want that for your children. Didn't you never get a telegram before?"

"Never did."

"Kinda excitin' to get one—you never know what's gonna be in it, and you think somebody's dead."

"Where'd you hear about this telegram?" asked Tom.

"Oh, I don't know. It's all over town. Could come from the operator, you know. But there's one thing they're sayin' that musta come straight from Andy Brackett, and I want to warn you not to pay no attention to it."

"What is it?"

"Oh, they're circulatin' a story that you're gonna get a big job in Albany for beatin' Andy."

Tom turned to me. "Hear that?"

I nodded. "It wouldn't be a bad idea," I said.

21

Horsepower

THE BASIC TROUBLE WITH THE EARLY MOTOR cars—aside from the hundred-and-one minor defects and miscalculations that kept them from running—was insufficient horsepower. It was probably the term "horsepower" that threw everybody off the track. If the potential energy could have been measured by a unit with some other name, both the manufacturers and the buyers of motor cars would have been spared a great deal of misunderstanding and disappointment.

Everybody had a pretty fair idea of what a horse could do, and in the public mind that idea represented roughly one horsepower. A team could do twice as much as one horse—that was common knowledge—and by the same reasoning ten horses could do ten times as much. When a buyer was told that he had an eight-horsepower motor he immediately visualized eight chargers out there in front, champing at the bit and ready to do his bidding. This visual concept was just as misleading to the people who made the cars as to those who spent their money buying them. The manufacturer knew, if he stopped to think about it, that one horsepower was a unit numerically equal to a rate of 33,000 foot-pounds of work per minute. He also knew, if he stopped to think about it, that the horsepower generated on the crankshaft was a very different matter from the horsepower that reached the point of friction between the rear tires and the road.

It was the horses in the picture that made the trouble, and as long as they remained the trouble continued. In fact, the motor car did not get out of the woods until all the world began to understand that a horse has no more to do with horsepower than a cat does with catechism.

I freely confess that when the horsepower of my first car was mentioned I saw all those horses out in front, pulling and prancing and all ready to go. But I must also confess that they vanished, never to return, when we reached the first hill that amounted to anything. That the builders of motor cars had the same idea in the beginning is quite obvious from the form taken by the earliest cars, which were without exception patterned after the buggy. If any further proof is required it will be found in the name "horseless carriage."

Most of the early cars had only two speeds, low and high; and though the high was not so exceedingly high, the low was certainly disconcertingly low. To go up a hill on low was a slow and disagreeable business. The engine ran fast and noisily, the innumerable gears in the planetary transmission either hummed or howled, and the car crept along at a snail's pace. It was embarrassing to have people look askance at you with a manner that very plainly said, "Old Dobbin never made any such fuss as that in getting up this hill." The next time you came to that hill you charged at it with everything you had, determined to go up on high if it took the last ounce of power the engine could muster up—and it usually did. If you failed to make it, and there was any way to avoid that hill by going around on another road, you'd try the other road.

By the time I had been driving the Rambler a month I had taken the measure of every hill that was anywhere around. I knew the hills that I could get up on high and the ones that I couldn't. I had found ways to get around most of the low-gear climbs, and I had tried a few grades that I could not get up at all and on which I had no ambition to make a second attempt. Whenever you saw me going the long way around or taking people over a lovely, quiet back road that was very little known, you could understand that I was avoiding difficult hills that I did not care to cope with in the presence of guests. This familiarity with the country stood me in good stead as long as I stayed on the home range. It was not until I became ambitious and ventured off into strange territory that I ran into any real difficulties.

I was taking a particular interest at the time in a girl from a neighboring town and was naturally anxious to make a good impression on her parents. They had been invited to spend a week end at a cottage on Cayuga Lake, not far from Ithaca. I should have known better than to have ventured over into the lake country, which is notorious for its hills, but train service was most inconvenient for them, and I volunteered to take them in my car. They were not motor enthusiasts—far from it—but it seemed the lesser evil and they accepted. We went by way of Geneva and the high ridge of land lying between Seneca and Cayuga Lakes. This proved to be a fine, safe, level road, but as we approached our destination, which was on the shore, we found ourselves far above Cayuga's waters and faced with the necessity of descending a steep and tortuous grade.

I had never been either down or up such a prodigious-looking hill in a motor car, though Tom Hunter had drilled me in going down "on the engine" and I knew how to do it. But even before I had begun to go down I had started worrying about the difficulty of getting back up again. I worried about it all through the week end, and early Sunday morning before anyone else was up I sneaked off and walked part way up the grade to see if it was really as bad as it had looked on the way down. It was worse.

While returning to the cottage I stopped to talk with some people who were fishing from a small pier and learned that there had been a number of serious motor car accidents on that hill. "But isn't there some other way to get up from the lake?" I asked.

The male native just shook his head, but the female was a little more expansive. "Not on this side," she said.

I jumped at that. "You mean there's a road on the other side?"

"Oh, yes, there's a good road over there."

"But—where does it go?"

"Right along the ridge, all the way to Auburn."

"Is it hilly along the ridge?"

"Flat as your hand—once you get up there."

"How's the road going up—anything like this one?"

"No, sir! There ain't anything like this one, not around here there ain't."

"Would a car have any trouble going up it?" I asked.

"Well, that depends on the car, I suppose; but cars do go up it all the while. It's long but it ain't very steep, and there's a nice view from the top."

I had little trouble in getting my guests to agree to a change in the itinerary, and to my satisfaction as well as my complete astonishment we found a comparatively easy grade from Ithaca up to the ridge. We did not by any means make it on high, but neither did anybody have to get out and push. And as I now remember, we had only two punctures between Ithaca and Auburn, a matter of some forty-two miles, which was considered very good going.

It was after we had left Auburn and started towards Geneva that our troubles began. These came in the form of a series of short, sharp hills, through which we were detoured by construction work which had closed the main road to travel.

The first of these hills we went over on high. The next one or two we made partly on high, with some low-gear work near the top. It was a hot day, and with all this climbing the motor became very hot. I could hear the grease frying underneath the floor boards as we went along. And soon after I heard this frying sound the clutch began to slip. It happened when we had almost reached the top of a grade. The engine ran all right, but it did not deliver enough power to the wheels to keep the car in motion. As the car came to a stop the two women in the back seat leaned over and asked in concert:

"What's the matter with it?"

"The clutch is slipping," I said through my grinding teeth.

"Are we stuck?" asked the girl's mother.

"I'm afraid we'll have to stop and wait for the engine to cool off."

"In this hot sun!"

I asked her father to get out and block the wheels so we could release the two brakes. Then I invited the women to get out, and the father and I pushed the car over the top. We pulled over into the shade and I threw a handful of sand into the clutch-band to give it something to bite on, for it had been taken up as far as it would go. But even with the sand it began slipping again on the next hill, and all four of us had to get out and push it over the top. I had those two women out half-a-dozen times before we were through with the hilly stretch. They barked their shoes and they spoiled their white dresses, they burst the

seams of their gloves and tore holes in their veils. The experience put an end to what might have been an unfortunate romance and furnished me with a secret conviction that I must have a new car—a car with plenty of power.

I laid down a $250 deposit on the new car not long afterwards. It was the Model N, the first of the Ford cars to be offered at $500—the announcement of which had caused a great furor all over the country and had driven Tom Hunter into great transports of delight. He was waiting for me on the front steps of my office when I came in, dirty and disgusted and completely exhausted, after my greatly anticipated week end on Lake Cayuga.

He had a clipping in his hand cut from the Ford announcement.

I will build a motor car for the great multitude. It will be large enough for the family but small enough for the individual to run and care for. It will be constructed of the best materials, by the best men to be hired, after the simplest designs that modern engineering can devise. But it will be so low in price that no man making a good salary will be unable to own one—and enjoy with his family the blessing of hours of pleasure in God's great open spaces.

Tom had been so excited when he saw the full-page announcement, with an enormous picture of the car, that he had wired for the agency. Without waiting for a reply he sold six cars on the strength of that picture. He had also booked some thirty people for demonstrations. As the day passed without any response to his telegram he began to worry. Perhaps he shouldn't have taken any money from people until he had received an answer. He did not wish to become involved in any charges of fraud and misrepresentation.

I calmed his fears and put the checks he had taken as deposits into the office strongbox for safekeeping. He never did get a full agency but had to be content with a subagency under the Geneva branch.

All day long, after the announcement appeared in the morning paper, people hung around Tom's garage, waiting for further news. They welcomed the arrival of the poor man's car, but many of them were timid about buying a car made by Ford until the great patent litigation between Ford and George Selden had been settled. Mr. Selden had applied for a patent on a self-propelled vehicle back in 1879. In the application his vehicle was described as "a safe, simple, and cheap road locomotive, light in weight, easy to control, possessed of sufficient power to overcome an ordinary inclination."

Ford always contended that George Selden was aiming at a traction engine at the time his application was filed, since the automobile as such had not at that time been dreamed of. When the patent was granted in 1895, however, the situation was quite different. Motor cars were already running in Europe and Charles Duryea had not only completed his "buggyaut" but had won a race with it. And since the spring of 1893 Henry Ford's first car, a little contraption not much bigger than a wheel chair, with two cylinders made out of pieces of steampipe, had been running around the streets of Detroit, stopping often to make adjustments and repairs.

But Mr. Selden, a skilled patent attorney, had kept his priority well protected, and the Patent Office granted him a so-called "combination" patent, holding that by combining a carriage with its body machinery and steering wheel, with a propelling mechanism and an engine, the applicant had made something new and was entitled to a patent. With the patent in his safe Mr. Selden sat back and watched the growing industry develop. He had tried from time to time to interest manufacturers in his idea, but without success. However, with his patent secured he found himself in quite a different position, and soon Wall Street money was seeking him out. As the new century was just about to begin, William C. Whitney, with an eye to picking up a little easy money, entered into an agreement with Selden for the control of the patent, and hardly was the ink dry on their signatures before a vigorous campaign was started for infringement of the Selden patent.

To show the industry that they meant business, the Selden interests launched their first attack at one of the largest and most successful of the manufacturers, the Winton Motor Carriage Company of Cleveland. Winton put up a fight and was beaten hands down in the trial court. He entered an appeal, more for bargaining purposes than because he thought he could ever win the case. The terms of the patent were broad, its priority overwhelming, and most of the other big motor car manufacturers were trembling in their boots over the prospects of paying huge sums in back damages for the motor cars they had sold since their organization. If they allowed the Winton case to go to a final decision and lost, they would be at the mercy of the Selden interests. The time to compromise was while Winton was still on his feet. So nine of the big fellows—Packard, Pierce, Peerless and the rest—joined in the Winton compromise and made peace with the patent owners by forming the Association of Licensed Automobile Manufacturers with the right to operate under the Selden patent. They agreed to pay for the privilege one and one-quarter per cent royalty on the retail price of all cars sold by them.

Most of the big independents came flocking in, but Henry Ford refused to pay what he insisted was tribute, and the A.L.A.M. came down on him with an infringement suit which proved to be the most colossal piece of litigation the automobile industry has ever undergone. It was not a pretty fight. The stake was large and both sides were out to win, with no holds barred. Legal ethics and good sportsmanship had been thrown overboard before the starting bell, and both contestants entered the ring with no inhibitions against dirty work.

Whole volumes of testimony were taken and the case had dragged on for some years before Judge Hough was able to render a decision sustaining the patent. Of course this was only the end of Round One, but the A.L.A.M. seized upon the opportunity to inject a little frightfulness into the campaign by advertising a warning to prospective purchasers of Ford cars that they would be held personally liable for infringement of the patent and would be prosecuted to the limit of the law. Mr. Ford says in "My Life and Work" that the more enthusiastic of his opponents gave it out privately that there would be criminal as well as civil suits, and that a man buying a Ford car "might as well be buying a ticket to jail."

I heard this statement repeated over and over at the time. It was the favorite argument, not only of the opposition, but of all the Ford competitors, and when Ford announced his new "Universal" car at $500, the warnings of the Licensed Association became so threatening that Ford was eventually driven into running a series of full-page newspaper advertisements aimed at reassuring the little fellow, the common man, that he could buy a Ford without any danger of prosecution. It was a good piece of underdog propaganda containing this conclusion:

> If there are any prospective automobile buyers who are at all intimidated by the claims made by our adversaries we will give them, in addition to the protection of the Ford Motor Company with its some $6,000,000.00 of assets, an individual bond backed by a Company of more than $6,000,000.00 more of assets, so that each and every individual owner of a Ford car will be protected until at least $12,000,-000.00 of assets have been wiped out by those who

desire to control and monopolize this wonderful industry.

The bond is yours for the asking, so do not allow yourself to be sold inferior cars at extravagant prices because of any statement made by this "Divine" body.

N.B.—This fight is not being waged by the Ford Motor Company without the advice and counsel of the ablest patent attorneys of the East and West.

Some were reassured by the statement and some weren't. The total worth of the members of the Licensed Association ran into the hundreds of millions, while Ford was admitting in his advertising that his company was worth only six millions. I constantly heard these figures tossed around by people whose total assets could not possibly have been more than a thousand dollars, but who would have liked to be prospective customers for a Ford car. The less they had, the less they were worried by the thought of litigation; but there were cautious people in town, quite a few of them, people with a little nest-egg, who came and talked with me about it and in spite of my reassurance went off and bought some other make of car.

The case dragged along until 1911 before the final adjudication was made. This proved to be a double-barreled decision which sustained the validity of the patent but also ruled that there had been no infringement on the part of Henry Ford or any other manufacturer whose engine was based on the four-cycle motor. This included practically all of them, since production of the two-cycle motor had been entirely abandoned by the automobile trade.

The Otto four-cycle engine was already in existence before Selden's original application for a patent had been filed, but his claims were large and somewhat vague, and Ford had no way of proving that the principles of the

Otto engine were not included. It was Selden himself who unintentionally furnished the proof by introducing one of his old diaries in which he had mentioned the Otto engine. He had, however, mentioned it unfavorably, and the court interpreted the entry as evidence that Selden had no intention of incorporating the four-cycle principle in his patent application—thus demonstrating once more the futility of keeping a diary.

This great victory not only put an end to the payment of millions of dollars annually to the Selden interests, but it also removed the threat of the A.L.A.M. to prosecute individuals purchasing Ford cars. Ford had a wonderful chance for a libel suit against the A.L.A.M. but he let it go and concentrated on building cars.

The Ford car I ordered from Tom was never delivered. Production difficulties of one kind or another kept delaying the deliveries until I refused to wait any longer. So I lifted my deposit from the Ford and with Tom's assistance placed it on a Packard Model 24, one of the first really good motor cars ever built in this country. Tom lost other customers, some through impatience and quite a number through fear of reprisals of the A.L.A.M., which was quite generally credited with being the real cause of Ford's delay in production.

But perhaps the most important and most widespread result of the announcement of Mr. Ford's Universal car was the reawakening of interest in getting a good road through our town. By this time the other road had been built and was enjoying great popularity. All of us who had cars used to go over to ride on it, though we had to drive across ten miles of neglected country roads to get there. People kept coming to me to ask if something couldn't be done, but I told them that they had once had their chance and muffed it. They kept pestering Tom about it, especially after election. They felt that now was their chance, while Andy Brackett's power was temporarily in eclipse. I explained to Tom one day in the presence of the Green Pack Peddler that Andy had deliberately forfeited any further participation of our county in the state highway program for the next two years.

The peddler howled with laughter. "Go tell that to new administration," he cried. "I hear they are hunting for excuse already to throw highway law out of window—and they like nothing better, I guess, than humiliate mighty Andy Brackett, now that he iss down on hiss back-end. Go see Bill O'Brien, tell him what iss going on here. This may be big chance to bury Andy Brackett as political figure, dust to dust, and eshes to eshes."

"But, Sol, you forget there is a law."

"But any law can be repealed—and new law passed. The new administration iss already hungry for big highway contracts."

"But where will the money come from? The funds are appropriated."

Sol laughed loudly. "New appropriations can always be passed."

Long after the peddler had gone Tom sat looking thoughtfully out of the window. "What do you think about it?" he asked. "Do you think there is anything to what he said?"

"There might be," I answered.

22

Putting on the Brakes

AS TIME WENT ON I KEPT TRYING TO GET
Tom to make a suitable set of drawings for his compressed
air starter, a set that could be used on the application for
a patent. And I needed the facts and specifications from
which I could formulate the inventor's claims. These
claims, I had come to understand, were of the utmost importance since no inventor's patent could go beyond his
clear and definite claims. But by this time Tom had turned
his attention to something else—brakes.

Not one of the early cars had really good brakes. The
manufacturers were as consistent about under-braking as
they were about overrating the power. The brakes of the
old Ramblers and Reos, the Maxwells and Fords, the
Buicks and Olds, would be considered suicidal today, and
they would have been suicidal then if the cars had been
capable of a little more speed. The brake drums of that
Universal car of Mr. Ford's were not much larger around
than a teacup. And though the brakes of the Packard 24
were a big improvement, they fell far short of sufficiency.
On a level they would do very well, but no car was to
be trusted on a hill.

This was not so dangerous when you were going down,
for you could always use the engine as a brake. It was
when you were going up and stalled the motor that the

inability of the brakes to hold the car became something to be reckoned with. Even if you could get the gears into reverse, as few drivers ever could or did, you still had to go down the rest of the hill backwards, which was always unpleasant and frequently fatal.

As cars became more numerous drivers became more venturesome, and there was hardly anybody who did not at one time or another stall on a hill. This was a situation that was especially likely to happen to an inexperienced driver who bungled his gears while attempting a quick change in a tight spot. Even if your brakes held under such circumstances, the situation was bad enough; but if they failed you and the car began to get away—the best of drivers was in a tough spot. I was caught in just that way near the top of a long, winding hill on the west shore of Canandaigua Lake. I managed to stop the machine by turning it crosswise of the road, with the hind wheels in the ditch. I had to pay two dollars to be pulled out by a farmer, but paid it willingly since I was greatly relieved to find my affairs not yet in the hands of my executor.

The manufacturers eventually got around to brakes, just as they got around to increasing the horsepower, but there were still thousands of old cars that would not hold on a hill. Tom Hunter's answer to this was sprags—stout metal bars jammed against the ground to prevent back slippage. He spent days and weeks experimenting with them, and even tried them on my car. His first pair operated by foot pressure, though he eventually turned out a design that would go into action automatically if the car started to roll backwards while on an inclined plane.

As I found him losing interest in sprags, I renewed my pressure for some Patent Office material for the compressed air starter. He actually went to work on it, but he still had brakes on his mind, and before he had finished anything that I could use he came rushing into my office with a new idea—he would extend the scheme of the starter to include air brakes. Best brakes in the world—the railroads wouldn't think of using anything else. They'd be simple, would do away with most of the rattling connections, and the only change in the starter system would be to make the tank a little larger.

It struck me as a really fine idea. I was almost as enthusiastic as he was, and while I hated to think of the delay, which he estimated at six or eight weeks, I advised him to go ahead with it. Of course he had his living to earn and was busy with his regular work most of the day, but I used to see the lights on in his shop at all hours of the night. However, for all his industry the weeks went by and the working model was not finished.

The new state administration went into office the first of the year, and then suddenly there was a great deal of undercover activity concerning the highway law. Hungry construction companies, which had heretofore confined their efforts to the building of subways, aqueducts, bridges, and other municipally inspired structures in and around New York City, began to howl for fat highway contracts. It was, of course, impossible to abandon the existing highway program, but it was not impossible to amend and supplement it; and since alternate routes were springing up here and there wherever the political pressure was strongest, people kept coming to Tom to ask why he was not making an effort to resurrect the road through our town. "If the party's so darn thankful to you," they said, "what's the reason they don't do some'pm about our highway that Andy sidetracked?"

This attitude seemed a little personal to Tom, but he

finally took the matter up with Bill O'Brien. Bill also thought it was personal and tried to settle by offering Tom his backing for a good state job. But Tom did not want a good state job. What he wanted was a good state road, and, following the peddler's hint, he insisted that if they could get that highway through they would have delivered the most telling blow that Andy Brackett's pride and prestige had ever received. O'Brien was afraid the state leaders would think the price too high to pay for Andy's scalp, but he promised his support; and eventually the link that Andy had so cunningly knocked out of the highway chain was slipped back in as an alternate route. Among the highway appropriations for the year, that little strip of road amounted to hardly a drop in the bucket; but to Tom, as well as to Andy, it assumed the proportions of the most important thoroughfare in the world.

Andy was feeding more horses than usual that winter. For some reason the fall sales had been very light. Andy would not admit that the motor car had anything to do with the situation, but Gid was a little more open-minded. And once more he went back to the canopy-top surrey to prove his case.

"Folks get these nutty ideas," he said to me one day. "Right now they all think they want one of these damn Ford runarounds. Why, I know lots of folks that has sold a perfectly good hoss to get one. Yes, sir—I can tell you their names if you don't believe me."

"Careful, Gid," I shook my finger at him, "you're talking to a motorist."

"I know—I know—you never did like a hoss. Never owned one in your life. Not much like your old man. Now there's a feller who knows a hoss when he sees one."

"Do you think the horse will ever come back?"

"Come back? Where's he gone?"

"To the bone-man, I think."

"Don't you never believe it. Just wait till next spring when the frost begins to come out of the ground and they get these hossless buggies out and try to take a little run in the country. They'll run into mud that's knee-deep, and it'll take old Dobbin to get 'em out. I tell you, boy, it's just like the canopy-top. It's a fad. Everybody that's got the price will get one, and prob'ly they'll have a little fun with 'em. Then after a while they'll all get sick of 'em. They'll get so't they can't stand the sight of the damn things. And then, you mark my word, they won't be worth a dime a dozen. That's the way it was with the canopy-top, and it's the way it'll be with the hossless buggy."

"How does Andy feel about it?" I asked.

Gid shook his head. "He's takin' it pretty hard. When he heard about that new state road comin' through he pretty damn near had a stroke. I was in his office when Rozzy Towner come in and told him. Rozzy got it from some kind of a bankin' service that he belongs to. I don't know how they do it, but they always tell him about things long before they happen."

"Yes, I know about that service," I said. "I've heard of it before."

"I don't know how they do it." Gid waved his hands hopelessly. "But they mostly get it right. Well, anyhow, when Andy heared about that road he let out a roar like a bull. 'That can't be so,' he yells. 'I got that fixed for the next two years!' The old boy took on so that he kinda had Rozzy scared. Rozzy backed towards the door and he says, 'Well, I've always found this service reliable,' he says, 'and I thought you'd like to know. In case you want to buy any options,' he says, 'it's comin' right up through on the old stage route.' Rozzy ducked out of the door as if he thought Andy was gonna begin throwin' things. And he didn't wag his head, neither, on his way back to the bank." Gid gave an imitation of the head-wagging. "He was walkin' more like a feller who expects to get kicked in the pants."

"Did Andy say anything after Rozzy went out?" I asked.

"Did he! He like to went right up through the ceilin'. 'That's your friend Hunter,' he says, and he called young Tom every name he could lay his tongue to. And, boy, is he bitter! If them two don't tangle on the street some day, I'll miss my guess."

"I hope it won't come to that," I said.

"So do I. I tole him the kid didn't have nuthin' to do with it. But that just made him all the madder. 'He's a weasel-brain!' he yelled. 'I knew it the first time I ever laid eyes on him. Dumb looks and a weasel-brain—that's what I'm up against.'"

I met Andy on the street a day or two later and walked along with him. I was careful to say nothing about the road, but he had himself in hand by this time and it was he who brought the subject up.

"How does your father feel about the new road?" he asked.

"He's still in Jamaica, and I don't suppose he's heard about it yet. But he's in favor of good roads."

"Yes, I know. It's always puzzled me. I can understand about you. You're young, still in the experimental stage, and you never did care for horses. But I can't understand how a horse-lover like your father could ever be in favor of hard roads. I know you won't agree with me, but I think this road is a great mistake. Half the charm and beauty of these little towns comes from their seclusion. And you know as well as I do that there can't be any seclusion on a road that's got a stream of devil-wagons tearing over it night and day."

I began to laugh. "It seems funny, Andy, to hear you talking like an old fogy, but that's what you're beginning to sound like."

Andy smiled. "Well, I'm in a peculiar position," he said. "If I say anything against the road, people think I'm just trying to save my own bacon. But had it ever occurred to you that we could have the new road by-pass the village? In that way young fellows like you, with your machines, will still get the benefit of the road, and we'll save the principal street of the town from becoming a race track."

I shook my head. "I'm afraid you'll find that most of the people around here won't agree with you on that."

Andy stood rubbing his chin and looking thoughtful. "I've always said that the American small town is the best place on earth to live. I've always thought that the small towns were the real backbone of our country. I've been saying it for years, and now I'm beginning to wonder if I'm going to have to eat my words."

I had never heard Andy talk like this before. Always he had been the confirmed, almost the unbearable, hundred per cent optimist. I did not know quite what to make of it. But the mood was gone almost as suddenly as it had come.

"Have you seen Lucy's new rig?" he asked, turning on me unexpectedly.

"You don't mean that you've bought her a bicycle?"

"A bicycle! Heavens no!" He burst out laughing. "I've bought her a new rubber-tired runabout. Beats your stinking old gasoline machines all to pieces. I'll have Lucy take you for a run around the block—the way you used to take people out in your car when it was new."

"You do that," I said, as we parted, Andy heading for his stables and I for my office.

I saw Lucy in her rubber-tired runabout the next day. It was a cute little vehicle with red wheels and a spindled box behind. It had red upholstery and was finished off without a top.

"Where is the top?" I asked as she drew up to the curb and waited for me to come out to her.

"There isn't any top," she said. "If there were, it wouldn't be a runabout. It would be a buggy."

"Oh, I see." We both laughed.

"Wouldn't you like to take a little ride around the block —just to see how it goes?"

I clambered in. "Delighted," I said, "only you mustn't go too fast. I don't want you to blow me all to pieces."

She put her nag through all its paces, showing it off with the utmost perfection of style and distinction.

"You've given a beautiful exhibition of horsemanship," I said as we came around the corner and swung into Church Street. "And now if you'll just drop me at my office, I see Tom Hunter is waiting in front."

I could see Lucy begin to bristle. "Well, he's certainly not waiting for me."

"Don't you feel that you owe him a ride?"

"I don't feel that I owe him anything—positively not anything."

I could see Tom also bristle as we drew up in front of him, almost exactly as Lucy had done.

"Well!" said Lucy, as if in surprise. "When did you get back?"

Tom gave her a puzzled look. "Where from?"

"Albany—I understood you had an important political job there?"

"I didn't know anybody believed those stories," said Tom with just a suspicion of scornfulness. "I thought they were told for purely political purposes." He motioned with his head at the red-wheeled runabout. "Isn't this something new?"

"Quite."

"Very elegant," said Tom, "and quite becoming, but you must have changed your plans in a hurry."

"How so?" asked Lucy, her chin slightly in the air.

"Weren't you planning to get a bicycle?"

"Wouldn't take one as a gift." She darted a look at me and I shook my head. "Where did you get that idea?" she asked.

Tom smiled unpleasantly. "From what your lawyer friend would call the 'speech of people,' I suppose. The story's all over town."

Lucy was annoyed. "It isn't! It couldn't be."

"That's what I heard." Tom spoke as if he did not relish being doubted.

"Who told you?"

He shrugged. "Oh, I don't remember. I heard it several times."

"And you can't tell me even one person who told you?"

He shook his head. "No, I don't remember who it was. But I do remember that it didn't cause any surprise. Everybody seemed to know about it."

"And you can't remember a single person?" Lucy was really becoming irritated.

"No, not any one definite person. It didn't come to me like an item of news, you know; it came more as an item of common knowledge—something that everybody seemed to know. And it was taken for granted that I knew, too."

"Just where was this—if you don't mind telling me?"

"I think the first time I heard of it was down at my shop."

"Who was there?" Lucy was being snippy, and Tom intentionally vague.

"A lot of the young people from around town. I don't remember any definite one. They come in there in little groups to get their tires filled, or some little adjustment."

"And you don't remember *one* who was there?" She might as well have called him a liar.

"You don't realize how often it happens that two or three of those youngsters will drop in together. You know how they go riding around in those little groups, and then when one stops in they all stop."

"But it definitely was from the younger ones that you heard it?"

"I heard it from them and from other sources too."

"What other sources?"

Tom pondered. "I heard it in the post office one day."

"What was said on this historic occasion?" asked Lucy, icily skeptical but still curious.

"Oh, I just heard one woman telling another that Lucy Brackett had finally broken down her uncle's resistance and was going to have a bicycle."

This was really getting under Lucy's skin. "Who said that?" she demanded rather sharply.

"One woman said it to another. I didn't know either of them."

"And you had no idea who they were, I suppose?"

"I didn't even look at them. I was waiting for my mail, and they were somewhere behind me in the line."

Lucy was pulling nervously on the reins and otherwise communicating her annoyance to the horse, which was now becoming decidedly restive. "You mean she said that loud enough for everybody in the post office to hear?"

"Well, I heard it."

"Can I take you anywhere?" she asked suddenly, a strange gleam in her eye.

But Tom was taking no chances. "Oh, no, thank you," he said quickly. "I have some business with the Counselor and couldn't possibly go anywhere just now."

Lucy tightened her hold on the reins. "Then I'd better be getting along before the horse takes matters into his own hands." She chirped to the horse and drove away, but she was not yet out of the block when Tom suddenly snapped his fingers.

"Now it comes to me who told me," he said.

"Who was it?" I asked.

He pointed his finger at me. "You!"

"Oh, did I?" I said. "I'd forgotten."

I was annoyed with both of them. I didn't see why they had to be so openly disagreeable every time they met. But I was a little curious about it, too.

23

M-P-H

SPEED WAS NOT, IN THE BEGINNING, ONE OF the most important considerations in the development of the motor car. The horse could go plenty fast enough to satisfy the ordinary citizen. But the trouble with the horse was that he couldn't keep it up. He had to stop and walk every so often. If you hurried him up the hills, he'd soon become exhausted, and there was also the danger that he would become "wind-broken." And ordinary prudence, if nothing more, required that the horse must also go down the hills at reduced speed and with maximum caution. All of these slowdowns kept gnawing away at the elapsed time required for you to get from one place to another. Your horse might be able to keep up an average gait of ten miles an hour on the level, but it was not easy to find ten miles that were on the level.

In the first automobile race ever held in this country, which took place in Chicago in 1895, the winner, a Duryea car, made the fifty-four-mile course in ten hours and twenty-three minutes. This was at a rate of less than six miles an hour, though it must be remembered that there was snow on the ground and the roads were bad. Under all the circumstances this was considered good time. A horse could probably not have done any better, if as well.

According to a brief dispatch in the New York *Herald*

under an inconspicuous caption "MOTO-CYCLES COMPETE" we learn that there were six starters.

Duryea, in a car of his own make, the winner.
H. Mueller, second, 1 hr. and 35 min. behind Duryea.
La Vergne, which gave up at 16th Street.
Morris & Salom, who dropped out at 15 miles.
Sturges Electric, which lasted for 12 miles.
Macy, entered by R. H. Macy, the New York merchant, which broke its running gear when about half through the course extending from Jackson Park to Evanston and return.

The *Herald* did not hesitate to coin a new name for the horseless carriage, calling it a "moto-cycle," but saw nothing prophetic in this contest and tucked its little three-inch, single-column story into an inside page, where it was almost completely hidden by advertising matter. The account in the *Tribune* was even more brief, though it was on the front page. None of the other New York papers touched the story. All were much more interested in a meeting of the Christian Endeavor, the Epworth League, and other pious folk who had gathered at Cleveland, Ohio, the day of the race and had staged a great public prayer for the conversion of Colonel Robert G. Ingersoll. This was regarded as hot news and was given a big play.

P. T. Barnum seems to have been the only person of consequence to sense the importance of that Chicago race, for he immediately added the horseless carriage to his Congress of Freaks. He even introduced the little curved-dash runabout in his circus parade, where it attracted almost as much attention as the dog-faced boy or the blood-sweating behemoth.

The top speed of the Duryea car could not have been

over ten miles an hour, even over good roads, but with no horse out in front this must have been breath-taking. Henry Ford never claimed as much as ten miles an hour for his first car. The first Haynes car, according to reports, had both a maximum and a minimum speed of ten miles an hour. In other words, it had no way to throttle down. Indeed, there were few cars on the market prior to 1905 with a road speed in excess of fifteen miles an hour. Some of the very highest price cars might have been pushed up to twenty-five miles an hour on the track, but for a long time such a terrific speed as that was deemed to be unsafe for the average driver on the public roads. When you stop to consider what those roads were, you are inclined to agree.

However, the desire for speed seems to be inherent in the human being; and once the inhibition imposed by limitations of the horse had been removed, man wanted to go faster and faster. The motor car manufacturers were quick to sense this tendency and they were just as quick to capitalize on it. When they found that the public were no longer satisfied with a car merely because it would go, and were demanding that it must go fast, faster than the other fellow's—they immediately went in for speed.

The bicycle had derived much of its popularity from racing, which was, when the automobile came on the scene, almost entirely in the hands of professionals. Velodromes had been built in or near every city of any size and enthusiastic crowds turned out to watch the pedaling of Bobby Walthour, Major Taylor, Frank Kramer, and a host of others. The manufacturers of motor cars, many of them graduates of the bicycle industry, were well aware of the promotion value of racing, and as soon as they had begun to build cars that would show any speed at all they pushed them out on the track and started an enthusiastic program of racing with competitors. Following the lead of the bicycle industry, the greater part of this competition was placed in the hands of professionals.

There were, however, a few of the automobile builders shrewd enough to see that in professional racing it was the rider and not the mount that was getting most of the publicity. Alexander Winton took advantage of this situation by racing his own cars and getting columns and columns of publicity for Winton. The keen eyes of Henry Ford had not overlooked this promising field for free advertising, and as soon as his company was well set up and ready to go he built a racing car and challenged Alexander Winton to a match race. He beat Winton, but the contest did not end there. Winton built a faster car and challenged Ford to a return match.

For some time the two masterminds continued a spirited competition, until finally Ford built a big eighty-horse-power monster he called "999," after the famous engine of the Empire State Express. However, on a tryout at the track Ford lost his nerve. He did not dare drive the big car in a race and hired a professional bicycle rider named Barney Oldfield to take his place. Barney wasn't afraid, but he did not know how to drive a car. So Ford taught him in a week, and Barney went in and won the race. He won it in an eighty-horsepower car steered by a tiller!

Ford's own track days were now over. He had established the reputation of his cars for speed, and from now on it was the professionals who would take the wheel. On Decoration Day in 1903, at Empire City Track, Barney Oldfield, driving a seventy-horsepower Ford, covered a mile in 1:01.6. Almost sixty miles an hour! Such speed was not only spectacular, it was colossal, stupendous. More than two hundred cars were parked at the track— of course this was within easy distance of New York City —but two hundred cars in one place at the same time! The industry was getting into its stride. A glance at some of the other entries may not be amiss.

Orient Buckboard	4 horsepower
Autocar	5 "
Darracq	12 "
Clement	10 "
Mercedes	18 "

Only three years before this, it was being seriously suggested in New York City that the best means of identification for car and driver was to have every car named, as boats are named; and it was this same year that three bicycle cops succeeded in arresting a motorist who was "speeding up Broadway at eight miles an hour." Officer Stover pursued the speedster to 72nd Street, where officer VanKeuren took up the chase. VanKeuren gave out at 92nd, but officer Vanderpoel leaped into the saddle and overtook the lawbreaker.

I wanted to get speed out of a car from the very beginning of my career as a motorist. Nothing less than fifteen miles an hour over the open road would ever satisfy me. And little by little the desire for more and more speed grew on me. When I first acquired the Packard, twenty miles an hour over a reasonably good road was all I seemed to need, but whenever I found a good piece of state road I could not resist hitting it up to twenty-five. This car was fast. I am sure I could have pushed it up to forty miles an hour if I had only had the nerve, which I never did.

One thing that I especially liked about the Packard was the speedometer, which had figures all the way up to sixty miles an hour. Whenever people asked me how fast it would go, all I had to do was point to the speedometer. But I remember very distinctly the shaking of heads in our town when in 1907, I think it was, the Thomas Forty, little brother of the famous Thomas Flyer, came out with full-page announcements guaranteeing for every car a speed of forty-five miles an hour over an ordinary country road.

The general impression around town seemed to be that this speed mania had gone far enough and that something ought to be done about it. Something had been done about it—the speed limit had been set at twenty miles an hour outside the cities and incorporated communities, with a penalty that could not be more than $100 for the first offence and not less than $50 for the second. This was a little improvement on the previous law, which had allowed a maximum speed of fifteen miles an hour on the open road.

With the improvement of the roads, however, as well as with the improvement of the motor cars the higher speeds became more practical; but the motorist always managed to keep a few miles ahead of the lawmaker. When the limit was raised to twenty-five the average speed of the motorist had gone up to thirty; and when at length the speed limit had inched its way up to thirty the general stream of traffic was moving at about forty, with one of the driver's eyes constantly on the mirror to be sure that a motor cop was not trailing along behind. No motorist dared to hope that the day would ever come when there would be no definite speed limit outside the towns and thickly settled communities, when the only limitation would be that the speed should be "reasonable" at all times.

As the cars on the roads went faster and faster the interest in automobile racing fell rapidly away, until only one or two of the "speed classics" remain. The track racing, while it drew immense crowds, was never as popular with the ordinary run of motorist as the road racing. This was something that came nearer to his own experience. The Vanderbilt Cup Race on Long Island attracted motorists from every state in the union. The event was run on a roughly triangular course laid out over the country roads of Nassau County. The length of the course was something over twenty-three miles, with a number of breathtaking turns, and a straightaway finish on a section of the newly completed Motor Parkway. The roads of the course, as well as the roads inside the course, were closed to the public at dawn on the day of the race and remained closed until noon, or the earlier completion of the event. This made it necessary for the public to get there at some time during the night.

It was in the fall of 1910, when this particular classic was at the height of its popularity, that it began to draw me like a magnet. I secured tickets through the Geneva Automobile Club, of which I was now a member, and drove to New York City by easy stages. My recollection is that we made the three hundred and fifty miles in three days. We put up at the Algonquin Hotel, and the night before the race, which occurred during the last week in October, wrapped in heavy overcoats and furnished with plenty of blankets and other equipment for keeping out the cold, we started for the course at about ten o'clock.

We drove to Times Square and turned left into Broadway, which we followed all the way to City Hall. As far as

14th Street we were packed in a solid line of horse-drawn traffic, which, however, thinned out considerably as we went further downtown. But it thickened again as we neared the approach to Brooklyn Bridge, across which we crawled in a parade of horse-drawn trucks, which were forbidden to move faster than a walk.

Figuring from the time we left the hotel, we could not have been more than two hours in reaching the Brooklyn end of the bridge, and from there on the traffic conditions were greatly improved. In fact, they were so much improved that we had a hard time finding our way, since the entire town had shut up shop and gone to bed, and there was nobody from whom we could inquire. With the aid of a rather sketchy route map that had been furnished with the tickets, we found our way to Metropolitan Avenue, where we joined a line of motor cars headed in the general direction of Jamaica and the Jericho Turnpike. At every street corner motorists kept turning in, and the single line soon became double. By the time we reached Jamaica it was treble, and after leaving Jamaica it spread out and filled the entire road. Any vehicle desiring to travel the other way was simply out of luck.

With all the head lamps pointing in the same direction, that highway was almost as light as day. By this time we were moving at a snail's pace, and stops were frequent, though nobody seemed to care. We were all bound for the same destination, all bent on having a good time. Baskets of fruit and sandwiches were passed back and forth between neighboring cars, and presents of cold bottles of beer were not infrequent. One big-hearted motorist who had been alongside us for some time finally uncorked a bottle of twenty-year-old brandy, which he offered with the remark that it would keep out the cold night air. Only

· 269 ·

one pull at it was necessary to convince us that it was as good as a central heating plant. The same good-fellowship existed all up and down the line. In forty years of motoring I have never seen anything like it.

Five miles from the grandstand we had to show our tickets, though in that solidly packed turnpike I don't know what they could have done if a car had failed to be provided with tickets. As we neared the grandstand our tickets were again examined so that the sheep might be separated from the goats, as special tickets were required for parking within the grandstand enclosure. Within the enclosure the fun and good-fellowship continued, with refreshment in the form of hot food and cold drinks sent out from the restaurant. Many of the visitors had come prepared to do some snoozing before dawn, but I doubt if anyone had caught so much as a wink of sleep when the bugle summoned us into the stand to take our seats.

I remember very little about the race itself. The drivers were sent off in small groups; but by the time they had completed one round of the course they were strung out over a distance of twenty miles. Never during the race did any two cars pass the grandstand near enough together to look as if they were competing, though one of our party, who had done a little too much visiting around while we were in the enclosure, insisted that each car that went roaring past was neck and neck with another just like it. The length of the race varied from year to year. On this particular occasion it was about three hundred miles, and the race was called as the tenth contestant crossed the finish line, around eleven o'clock. Then we had the fun of getting back to the city.

There was none of that good-fellowship on the way home. It was every man for himself, with a terrific cloud of dust to swallow up the hindermost. On the way out to the course nobody had been in a hurry. We had moved slowly, and since the roads had been sprinkled with a light rain the afternoon before, there had been little dust to reckon with. The return trip was a very different matter, for the heavy traffic had pulverized the surface of the dirt road, and the haste of the motorists to get back to their firesides or their neglected business now raised a cloud of dust as thick as a pea-soup fog. You had to keep the car ahead in sight; if you lost it for even a moment you were likely to ram into it. And if you slackened your pace, you were almost certain to be rammed into by the car behind. There were no traffic lights, no traffic officers, no traffic regulations on those dusty roads.

You buttoned up your duster to the throat. You adjusted your goggles. You pulled on your gauntlets. You put your trust in God—and then you stepped on her.

We were all as white as a miller's eyebrow when, late in the afternoon, we drew up before our hotel. Our taillight had been shattered by the car behind. The glass in one of the headlights had been broken and a fender knocked askew. Hollow-eyed and unshaved, by this time we were hungry again. But we had done a Vanderbilt Cup Race—we had done it up brown. We had had a good time, a swell time, an elegant time, and we had absorbed enough motoring lore to keep us in conversation for weeks to come.

I got hold of some afternoon papers and found out who had won the race. I made a special point of remembering the exact time, and I memorized the names of the cars and drivers of the contestants finishing among the first ten. The next day I combed all the papers for bits of color and good stories that could be incorporated in my eye-witness account. By the time I had reached home, it had become quite a work of art. I am sorry that I cannot now recall the details.

But racing was not the only form of contest with which the motor car industry was concerned during the first decade of the century. Racing was useful; it brought out the inherent weaknesses in cars much faster than ordinary touring over the roads, and it had proved itself as a business-getter and a power in promoting the popularity of motoring. But by 1905 many of the racing plants had passed out of the hands of the industry and were being run by big sports promoters on a strictly commercial basis. It was at about this time that the National Association of Automobile Manufacturers undertook to popularize the endurance contest by inviting entries for a run from Weehawken to Pittsburgh. The event was a failure, probably because it was backed by the manufacturers themselves. The contest for the Glidden Trophy, offered by Charles J. Glidden of Boston, was quite another matter.

The Glidden reliability trophy was open to members of the American Automobile Association, a body composed of automobile owners instead of manufacturers. It was to be an annual competition in a tour of not less than one thousand miles, run under rigid rules, with specified night controls and predetermined rates of speed. The object was to prove the reliability of the various makes of cars in the hands of the owners. Usually these tours ran through the finest summer resort country, with the night stops at the most luxurious and expensive hotels to be found. They were really done in the grand manner and gave to motoring a touch of elegance and social distinction it had never enjoyed before.

Society, with its Social Register under its arm, was at many of the night controls, and in some of the big resort hotels the only time the diamond pendants were dusted off all summer was when the Glidden Tour pulled in for an overnight control. Mr. Glidden's idea was to prove rather than improve reliability, but he so managed his contest as to attract only a very limited cross section of the industry. The electrics were, of course, disqualified by their very short range, and the magnificence of the tour had little of practical value for the builder of lower-priced cars. People lined the course to watch the magnificoes go by in their big, high, tulip-bodied touring cars, with banners flying and veils fluttering in the breeze, and then they cranked up their own old rattletraps and went jingling off home, rivaling the big fellows only in the amount of dust they could raise.

One year the tour was jinxed with fatalities, several of the high-bodied touring cars turning turtle on slippery roads. Another year, fires robbed the participants of much of their gaiety, two of the big White Steamers catching fire and burning to the ground. I happened to see one of these fires, which occurred not far from the State Experiment Station in Geneva, and though I was only an innocent bystander I was depressed for days over the destruction of that beautiful car.

The Glidden Tour was finally killed by the very thing it started out to develop—reliability. At the end of six years the cars had all become so reliable that there was no longer any contest and the cup had to be withdrawn.

By this time the motor mechanics had gone over the land like the grasshoppers. Parts and service were to be had in every little hamlet, and more important still, gasoline was now available at almost every country store.

Garaging away from home was still a problem, though the automobile salesman everywhere was making a special effort to talk the country livery stable keeper into making a little space for the night storage of motor cars. These old fellows were for the most part tough nuts to crack. The accommodations they provided were pretty dreary in the beginning. Usually they were no more than on old shed, often without a door, and not infrequently used by chickens as a roosting place. On one occasion when I went to get my car from such a storage shed I found an old sow with a litter of little pigs lying directly under it.

The little pigs went squealing in all directions when I started the motor, but the sow got herself wedged under the rear axle and we had to jack up the car to get her out.

First and last, the early motorist had a good many experiences with animals. Dogs were forever running under the wheels, and once a staked cow that had strolled across the road leaped in fright as my car came past and tightened the tether rope beneath the car and between the front and rear wheels. Fortunately, I was not traveling very fast and was able to stop before the situation had reached what might be regarded as spilled milk.

Another time I was driving up a long grade at top speed with everything wide open, trying to get into Albany ahead of a storm, when a farmer with a large flock of white chickens on one side of the road started to throw out feed for them on the other side. I was in too much of a hurry to count the casualties, but a cloud of white feathers came up around the machine like the driven snow. Later as I arrived at a garage in Albany an attendant called my attention to a dead chicken wedged beneath one of my mudguards!

24

Over the Top on High

PEOPLE USED TO TALK A LOT ABOUT STRIPPING their gears. I knew that stripping your gears was one of the big hazards of motoring, before I was ever inside a car. I didn't know what it meant, but I knew it was a bad thing to do. The day I bought my first car I heard a mechanic warning a driver never to try to pull out of a mudhole under his own power.

"If you do," he said, "you'll strip your gears dead sure—then where'll you be?"

This sounded a little frightening to me and I listened closely to find out where he would be. But he didn't say. They both seemed to understand and they nodded knowingly to each other. I concluded right away that they were just keeping it from me for my own good. But that conversation hung over me like a curse.

I used to wake up in the night and think about it. I tried to figure out what it could mean and whether it would merely damage the car or damage the driver as well. I was somewhat in the position of a child who wants to know about the facts of life and can't get anybody to tell him. More than once I mentioned it tactfully to Tom, but he always veered off, as a mother does in the case of a five-year-old who asks where babies come from.

After a little I became wary of the subject and did not

bring it up any more, but all the time I was keeping my eyes and ears open. One day I noticed a big, round, bulging metal object almost as big as a bushel basket that was tucked away under the floor boards. I had never noticed it before, and I pointed to it and asked Tom what it was.

"That's the gear housing," he said—and then he immediately passed on to some other subject.

So at last I knew where my gears were—they were almost directly under my feet—and if they went up, there was little doubt in my mind that I would go right along with them. Then one day when I was in Tom's garage he showed me a stripped gear. To my utter astonishment this turned out to be nothing more than a little flat cogwheel with some of the teeth knocked off. My mind was thus relieved of all thought of danger to my person, but I was still afraid of stripping my gears.

There was a tendency at one time to separate the gear-changing transmission from too close a proximity with the engine. Packard and one or two others tried placing it on the rear axle, without any conspicuous success. Competitors pointed to it scornfully as "unsprung" weight, which it undoubtedly was. I had one of these rear-axle gearboxes on my Packard 24, and while I never could see that the unsprung weight caused the slightest inconvenience or discomfort, I did object to the way the gears would slip out of position and unmesh whenever I was going over a particularly rough bit of driving.

The first time this happened to me was when I was making a detour around the construction work which had closed some five miles of the old stage road east of the town while the new highway was being put in. At this time there was no very strict requirement about the provision of detours around construction jobs, and the usual course was to let the traffic bump along in the ditches and across the fields, splashing through mudholes in wet weather and stirring up impenetrable clouds of dust during dry times.

This little incident happened just as I was going through a mudhole. I had shifted into second and put on some extra power to make sure that I would not get stuck —and as I stepped on the throttle the engine roared, but the car stopped moving. I knew what that meant—I had stripped my gears. No use running the engine, so I shut it off and waited for somebody to come along. The first wayfarer happened to be a farmer I knew. And he not only pulled my car out of the mudhole but took a message to Tom to come to my assistance prepared to tow me home.

Not so very long afterwards Tom came tearing up with a borrowed car and a length of rope. "What happened to you?" he asked.

"Stripped my gears."

"What makes you think so?"

When I had described exactly what had happened he shook his head dubiously.

"Certainly sounds like it," he said. "Has all the symptoms—but let me look around a little bit." He took hold of the shifting lever and worked it back and forth. Then he crawled under the car and asked me to slip it into low and intermediate and high and neutral. "Leave it in neutral," he called up to me. "I've got an idea."

When he had come out from under the car he switched on the ignition and set the spark and throttle levers for cranking. Then he stepped around in front. The engine started at the first turn. He came around and took the wheel. "I want to feel out those gears and see what they're like," he said.

He engaged the low gear—and the car began to move. He shifted to intermediate—and found that all right. Very cautiously he felt his way into high. The gears jangled a bit, but they engaged—and as he let cautiously up on the clutch the car settled down to business and pulled as it always did. The gears had not stripped, they had simply been thrown out of engagement by the straining of that long connection between the rear-axle transmission and the lower end of the shifting lever. The same thing happened to me a number of times, and always on rough ground; but never again was I scared into the illusion that I had stripped my gears.

That mudhole, by the way, was destined to become locally famous. So many cars were bogged down there that Andy Brackett used to keep a team of horses close at hand most of the time to tow out the unfortunates. For a large car he charged three dollars. A medium-sized car he would pull out for two. He made a special price of one dollar for a Ford, though this concession was largely academic, since Fords rarely were stuck there.

Up to this time nobody in town had ever charged for giving a car a tow, and Andy found himself the target of no trifling aspersions. Motorists called him a bloodsucker to his face and accused him of profiteering on the misfortunes of others. But Andy was not the only one. The profiteering motive had come quite definitely into the automobile picture by this time. In the beginning the motorist had been regarded only as a little queer—an eccentric fellow who wanted his carriage to go without any horses in front of it. People laughed at him and poked a little fun at him, but they never thought of taking advantage of him. The fifteen-cent repair at the blacksmith shop is an illustration of what I mean. That is what they charged me, it was what they charged everybody for a little welding job.

But three or four years after the first welding job I had another. It was almost exactly the same, except I think it came from the rear fender instead of the front, and it came from a Packard car instead of a Rambler; and the

identical blacksmith, instead of charging me fifteen cents, charged me $1.50.

"But, Joe," I protested, "don't you remember what you charged me the last time you mended one of these?"

Joe nodded, a little uncomfortably, I thought. "But I've had to raise my price," he said. "Conditions are very different from what they used to be. You fellows have taken a lot of my horse trade away. And there's another thing—

what did that car of yours cost when it came from the factory?"

"Four thousand dollars, but of course I didn't pay anywhere near that much for it."

He gave me a contemptuous smile. "Four thousand dollars, and you squawk over a little job because it costs you a dollar and a half."

Of course Andy Brackett and the blacksmith had both been subjected to a personal loss by the coming of the motor car; but they were not alone in their profiteering attitude. Gradually this extortionate frame of mind settled on the town like an epidemic. It was in a mild way akin to the slogan, "Soak the rich." Not that every person was rich who had a motor car, but the car itself represented an expenditure of a considerable amount of money for an unnecessary purchase, and the self-justification for the cupidity phrased itself in about this form: "If he can spend all that money for an automobile he certainly can't object to paying me a few cents extra."

At Brad Cowan's harness shop a carriage robe cost a dollar and a half. Anybody could buy one for that price. But if you went there and asked for an automobile robe, it would cost you three dollars—for the identical robe. Of course Brad's business had also felt the waning interest in the horse, and as time went on the selling and making and repairing of harness as a means of livelihood would steadily decline. If you wanted a rubber lap robe for your car you would pay about twice or three times the horse-and-buggy prices. A new strap to put over the top of my bonnet cost me two and a quarter, but Father bought one for his carriage for a dollar.

The change in most cases was so gradual that people hardly knew it was taking place. Indeed, the very people who had criticized Andy Brackett the most sharply were doing the same thing themselves within a year or two. I talked with Tom Hunter about it, from time to time, but he did not seem to think there was anything strange about it or anything portentous.

"People have got more money than they used to have," he said, "and somehow the coming of the automobile has shaken some of it loose."

"But that isn't quite the point," I said. "The automobile is doing queer things to people, and I can't help wondering whether it's more of an influence for good or for bad. I know of several cases where people have mortgaged their homes to buy cars."

Tom thought this was a good idea. He said that static wealth was of very little good to anybody. And he asked me if I had heard what they were telling about Andy Brackett. The story was that Andy was sending one of the boys from the stable down to the mudhole every night to dump a couple of barrels of water into it. If Andy was doing that kind of business Tom wanted to know about it. He thought it might be very useful information to have in his possession. So I went with him three times, during spells that were especially dry, and watched the place from dusk until nearly midnight. Nobody put any water in it, and as we found out later nobody needed to, for it was located directly over an old spring.

I was satisfied to let the matter go at that, but Tom's curiosity was aroused. He thought it very funny that with a whole twenty-acre field to choose from that detour should just happen to pass over an old spring, and he began to ask questions. One day he came into my office grinning.

"Well, I've found out something about our detour," he said. "At least, I know who laid it out."

"Who?"

"My old friend Gid Wilson. Andy was furnishing teams to the construction company and Gid got well acquainted with the foreman. When they were ready to close the road and lay out the detour Gid showed him where to go. Well, you know how those fellows lay out a detour—they drive their teams over it a few times, so the traveling public can see where to go—and old Gid led them right straight over that spring."

"But how did he know about it?"

"Worked on that Stebbins farm for years and knew every foot of it."

"You certainly have interesting friends," I said with a laugh.

"You mean Gid?"

"Gid and Meeker both. If it isn't one who's getting you into hot water, it's the other."

Tom laughed softly. "You don't know the half," he said. "Meeker got me into a tough situation only yesterday. I don't know whether I ought to tell you or not."

"Not another fight with Asa Parker?"

"Oh, no, nothing like that. There wasn't much to it, really. Just embarrassing, that's all. You know how old Meeker is always sitting around telling how cold his wife is—a good daytime wife, but the moment she gets into bed at night she draws into her shell like a turtle?"

I nodded. I'd heard it all a hundred times myself.

"Well," he went on, "I'd never seen her until yesterday. Didn't even know who she was when I saw her in Spears' store. Spears noticed that I didn't speak to her and so he introduced me. As you probably know, she's a very good-looking woman—pale skin, lovely dark eyes, nice figure, stands up very straight—but when he said she was Mrs. Meeker my eyes nearly popped out of my head, for it suddenly occurred to me that I knew this woman more intimately than any other woman on earth, though I had never laid eyes on her until that moment. All the little intimacies that Ike had described to me came flocking up into my memory, and I felt abashed and ashamed and embarrassed.

" 'Oh, so you're Mr. Hunter?' Her voice was soft and low. 'I've heard my husband speak of you.'

"I hardly knew what to say, and I stuttered around and finally managed to get out that I'd heard him speak of her, too. That seemed harmless enough to say, but she jumped on it at once. 'You have!' she exclaimed. 'Do tell me what he said.'

"I could see old Spears hiding behind his sugar scoop to cover his laughter. Of course old Ike had talked to him —and everybody else in town—just as he had to me, and he could see just the kind of a fix I had got myself into. I didn't know what else to say, so I pretended I hadn't heard her and I began to talk about the weather.

"To tell you the truth, I was really feeling ashamed of myself because I knew so much about that woman's private life. I could see that she was a darn nice person, as well as a mighty pretty female, and I realized that I shouldn't have listened to Ike."

I laughed. "I'd like to know how you'd stop him. He talks to everybody like that—everybody who'll listen."

"Well," said Tom, "I guess I could have shut him up if I'd tried. Anyway, I was feeling pretty ashamed when all of a sudden she turned on me. 'But, Mr. Hunter,' she said,

'I've been wondering what my husband could have found to say to you about me.'

"This drove Spears completely under the counter, and the best I could do was to say, 'Oh, he's spoken of you several times.'

"She looked very much pleased. 'He has really?'

"I nodded. 'Oh, yes, several times. Quite a number.'

" 'What could he possibly say? Do tell me.'

" 'Oh, little things—just sort of this and that.'

" 'But Ike isn't a great talker. I didn't know he ever talked about me. Do try to remember what he said.'

"I was pretty groggy by this time. 'There really isn't anything very definite that I recall—he just spoke of, well—your likes and dislikes, something like that.'

"She jumped on that with enthusiasm. 'Ike spoke of *my* dislikes?'

"Old Spears peeked up over the counter, but when he heard my answer to that he dropped out of sight in a hurry. 'Only in a casual way—nothing of any importance. Just an offhand remark that there was something you didn't take any interest in.'

"She gave me an astonished look. 'What did he mean by that?'

"She had me practically floored, and then suddenly I thought of a way out. 'It wasn't that you didn't take an interest,' I said. 'It was that you *did*.'

"I could hear a noise behind the counter that I think was old Spears rolling on the floor when she followed me right up and asked, 'In what?'

" 'In the new Ford. Isn't that right?'

"She said it was, and I promised to give her a demonstration as soon as I could get my hands on a car, and then I got out of there in a hurry."

25

Joy Ride

IT WAS AT ABOUT THIS TIME THAT A NEW phrase was added to the language. People began to talk about "joy riding." I don't know where the expression originated. I first saw it in a New York newspaper and heard it in current shows on Broadway. But even without the aid of the movies and the radio, it spread rapidly over the country, going wherever the automobile went. Joy riding had little in common with the necking parties of the succeeding generation. When we went joy riding we did not park in the first unfrequented lane we came to and put out the lights. Joy riders really went out for the ride and, within the possibilities of their cars and their tires, they kept going.

The first adventure of that kind in which I participated was on the night of a subscription dance for which I was one of the sponsors. I remember the occasion very vividly, for more reasons than one. The event was memorable not only because it was the first real joy ride ever taken in town under the title, but it was taken late at night after Tom Hunter's first ballroom appearance and after my discovery of certain things about him of which I had previously had no suspicion. My friend, Burgess Harper, was associate sponsor with me on this occasion. But he was too busy with arrangements to squire his own sister, and Tom, after much urging on my part, reluctantly consented to act as Zelda's escort.

He refused at first, because of his lack of ballroom experience, but I finally argued him out of that. I warned him that it would probably be the last dance of the season and asked him where he thought his ballroom experience was coming from if he stubbornly insisted upon staying away from dances. Eventually the real reason came out: he had no suitable clothes for an evening party. I told him that, as sponsors and floor managers, Burgess and I would be expected to appear in tails and white ties, but that plenty of the other fellows would be there in sack suits (as the business suit was then called).

What he needed more than anything else was a little reassurance to bolster up his nerve, for where women were concerned he was still the bashful boy from the farm. After he had finally agreed to go he lost all his shyness and began to look forward to the event with keen anticipation. He had his dark suit cleaned and pressed, and I think he bought a new necktie, for he wore a very dark and inconspicuous cravat that I had never seen before. Asa Parker happened to be out of town, participating in the deliberations of an Assembly committee which he did not dare to leave entirely in the hands of the opposition members, so I took advantage of the opportunity to act as Lucy's escort.

Tom seemed a little glum when I told him that, but he had given his word and he went through with it. He and Zelda always got along well, and after the party was once under way I am sure he had the time of his life. He had done remarkably well with his dancing lessons and, while he was no Vernon Castle, he came very far from being the poorest dancer on the floor. Indeed, he followed the instructions of his teacher so meticulously, especially in the matter of leading, that whenever he had a collision, which was not often, I began to look around for broken bones.

And it was at this time that Zelda confided to me a suspicion that had been a long time forming in her mind. She made me swear on a stack of Bibles not to mention it to a soul, and then came out with the assertion that she was almost certain that Tom and Lucy were in love.

I had a good laugh when she told me. "I guess you haven't seen them together," I said.

"Not until tonight," she admitted, "but they're dancing together right now."

They really were a magnificent-looking pair—both tall, both broad across the shoulders, both splendidly coordinated, Lucy so fair, and Tom swarthy with sunburn.

"They bristle at the sight of each other like ill-tempered bulldogs," I told her.

"They aren't bristling right now."

As a matter of fact, they weren't. The bristling seemed to have been suspended for the duration of that particular dance, but as soon as the music had stopped they began showing signs of hostility again.

I touched Zelda's arm. "Look at them now."

"That's one of the very things that makes me suspicious," she said.

"But, Zelda, Lucy's in love with Asa."

Zelda looked up at me and smiled. Her own unswerving love for Asa was a secret that we had long shared and many times discussed. "Lucy has never cared enough about Asa to quarrel with him."

"Great Scott, is quarreling a sign of true love?"

"One of the most infallible—you don't quarrel with people you don't like."

"Well, I certainly don't quarrel with the people I do like."

"You would if anything important came up. Lucy will quarrel with her aunt, she'll even quarrel with her horse —but she won't take the trouble to quarrel with Asa. He doesn't mean enough to her."

I smiled. "Oh, you're just saying that to cover up. You don't want me to know that Asa's slipping through your fingers."

"Asa's not really in love with Lucy. He just thinks he's in love. It's that blonde placidity of hers that attracts him. He'll get over it—especially if he ever sees her with Tom Hunter."

"I don't see any blonde placidity about her right now."

"They look like a pair of Titans fighting over a cloud. What do you suppose they're rowing over?"

"Do a pair of bulldogs need anything to fight over?"

She slipped her arm through mine. "Let's walk over that way and see if we can find out."

We started across the room, but before we could reach them the music for the next dance struck up, and a new partner waiting in the offing whisked Lucy away. With Zelda Tom was the soul of amiability. He was jolly, even witty. And with any partner other than Lucy he was most agreeable and full of fun. But the moment he returned to Lucy hostilities were resumed. Zelda and I enjoyed watching them, though we were totally at variance on the meaning of what we saw. Her thesis was amusing, but I could not believe that it had any validity. Lucy had a deep sense of family loyalty and I could hardly imagine her permitting herself any real heartthrobs over her uncle's bitterest enemy.

Lucy's Aunt Harriett had been suffering with a head-

· 288 ·

ache that night and had entrusted the chaperoning of the girls to Mrs. Harper. But Mrs. Harper, who was not particularly exacting in such matters, had left the chaperoning to someone else as midnight approached and, having cautioned the girls to come right home as soon as the party was over, she left the hall in the company of some people who lived down her way. That was how we four happened to go joy riding.

We walked out of the hall together and looked up at the sky. It was a magnificent night, with the stars, in the metaphor of Mr. Blake, throwing down their spears all over the firmament. An almost full moon was coasting slowly down the western sky.

"What a night for a walk!" I heard somebody say.

"What a night for a sail!" said another.

I waited until we were out of hearing of all but our own party, and then I drew my three companions into a huddle. "What a night for a *joy ride!*" I said in a low and highly conspiratory tone.

"I'm game," said Zelda promptly. "How about you, Lucy?"

Lucy was not so prompt, but she was no kill-joy. "Why, yes," she said slowly, "I'll go if the rest of you do."

"How do you feel about it, Tom?"

"I don't know what a joy ride is exactly—but where's the car?"

"Over in the shed," I answered.

"Shall we walk over there and get in?" he asked.

Everybody seemed agreeable, so we did it that way. Tom backed the car out and, without asking any questions, I helped Lucy into the front seat and clambered into the tonneau with Zelda. As we started away Zelda gave my arm a significant squeeze, indicating that now we should see what we should see. She evidently felt very sure that she was going to prove something to me, and I felt equally sure that I was going to prove something to her. But, as it happened, we did not prove much of anything either way, for those two on the front seat did not exchange a single word of conversation during the two hours that we were cruising around in the bewitching moonlight.

The car ran magnificently, as it nearly always did in the night air. Two or three times Tom turned in his seat to call my attention to the fact, which we had often discussed before. He had a theory that if some way could be found to introduce the right amount of moisture into the fuel mixture entering the cylinders, perfect carburetion could always be assured. Lucy did not contribute even that much. She slid down into the seat and, resting her head on the back, looked silently up at the stars. If we spoke to her she answered—in a monosyllable if possible; but she started no discourse of her own.

For a wonder, we had no trouble at all with the car. The air stayed in all four of the tires, and even the lights behaved. We had not intended to stay out more than an hour, but the time passed rapidly, and it was nearly three o'clock when Tom brought the car to a stop in front of the hall where the party had been held. Stopping there was the bright idea of Zelda, so that the girls could say, if questioned on the subject, that they had come straight home from the hall. This proved to be an unnecessary precaution. That particular question was never asked; for by breakfast time the next morning the entire town knew all about that joy ride.

We never knew who saw us, or where or when; but the moment I caught a glimpse of my mother's face the next morning I knew the cat was out of the bag. She took my word for it that it was just a lark done on the spur of a rash moment. She never doubted that it was all good, clean fun—it was the looks of the thing that bothered her. She thought it very unfair to the girls to tempt them into such a terrible indiscretion. She did not use the word "compromise," though nearly everybody else in town did. The reverberations of that innocent little jaunt in the moonlight were almost world-shaking. I saw men winking at each other and nudging as I passed. Women talking over the line fence stopped their conversation the moment they saw me and began picking at the shrubbery, as if to give the impression that they were pruning it. Several times I came near enough to hear some of what they were saying before they saw me—and what I heard nearly every time was the words "joy ride."

Something new had come into their life. Now they knew what those words really meant.

I happened to be alone in the office when Andy Brackett descended upon me. If Andy had had so much as a suspicion that anything "out of the way" had happened he would have come in and blown my head off with a shotgun. He said so in plain words—well, hardly plain, for the words in which he said it were decidedly ornamental. But they were emphatic and I think they were the truth. It was not, however, the fact that Lucy had done something unconventional that was burning Andy up; it was the manner in which she had done it. If we had gone for a ride in a horse-drawn vehicle I do not believe the little indiscretion would have caused more than a ripple. What made it a big scandal was that we had gone in an automobile. I don't know what might not have happened that day if Tom and Andy had met on the street, but by good fortune they missed each other.

Father came in only a short time after Andy had left. When I told him the story he smiled and made a suggestion. "Go down and get Zelda," he said, "and stroll over together and make a call on Lucy. Sit around there on Brackett's front steps for a while, where everybody can see you. And then come back here and forget the whole business."

It seemed like a simple thing to do and I did it. Mrs. Harper was too worldly a woman to be very strait-laced, and though she scolded me a little for not having a restraining influence over a couple of girls so much younger than myself, she thought the idea sound and called Mrs. Brackett on the telephone and told her we were coming. I had no more than reached the office after this strategic call when Tom Hunter came bursting in with a roll of drawing paper under his arm.

"Don't tell me you've finished the plans for the starter," I said.

He grinned. "Well, I haven't exactly finished them, but I had a wonderful idea last night when we were out in the car. I was thinking about punctures—of course, you know how they are always on your mind—and it suddenly came to me that we could use the compressed air from our starter tank to inflate the tires. Funny we never thought of that before. It can be done very simply. I figured out the method last night as we went along—size, shape, location, type of valve, size of every connection. And after I got home I went right to my table and finished up the drawing—and here it is." He unrolled the big sheet of paper and spread it on the desk before me.

"So that's what you were thinking about last night? I noticed that you were pretty quiet."

"Did I seem that way?"

"I can't remember that you spoke a word all the time we were gone."

"I hope nobody else noticed it," he said. "But what do you think of the idea?"

"I think it's fine, Tom. However, we should get the application filed for a patent or somebody will beat us to it. There must be hundreds of people working on ideas to beat this cranking nuisance, and sooner or later some ingenious lad is going to get around to compressed air."

He promised to go ahead with the work just as fast as he could. "Anything new on the Selden patent case?" he asked as he was rolling up the drawing.

I said I hadn't seen anything recently, and he shook his head over the delay. "There's a lot of business being lost," he said. "Thousands of orders must be going to other companies that would naturally be coming to Ford. People hate the thought of buying a lawsuit."

"I haven't changed my mind on the subject," I told him. "I still think the licensed people are putting that out simply as a smear campaign."

It suddenly struck me that Tom was totally unaware of the tremendous sensation we had caused with our harmless little joy ride. I was tempted to tell him about it, and then I decided that nothing was to be gained by worrying him and I made up my mind to let it go and see how long it would be before he found out for himself. Meeker told him about it the next day, but by that time the tempest had simmered down to practically nothing.

I stopped in on my way home to twit Zelda on the complete collapse of the big imaginary romance she had been building up between Tom and Lucy, but even after I had told her what Tom was thinking about during all that time when we were sitting in the tonneau waiting for something to happen, she refused to back down.

"Romance doesn't develop like a night-blooming cereus," she declared. "The afflicted parties are much more likely to sit there like a pair of mesmerized dummies, just as they did last night."

"But you forget that Tom sat there making an invention."

Zelda shook her head hopelessly. "You men are so stupid," she said. "He was thinking about that invention simply because he is mechanical and his mind works that way. But I am absolutely certain that they were both having a perfectly wonderful time."

And that is all the satisfaction that I got out of her.

Tom was back in the office within a day or two with the details of two recent patents aimed at the "alleviation of the danger and difficulty of cranking the engine of a motor car." One was based on the principle of the coiled spring, which was wound up like a clock and, when released, was supposed to turn over the engine half-a-dozen times. If the engine failed to start, the spring had to be rewound for each succeeding try. The other was an ingenious arrangement mounted underneath a sawhorse, where the cranking was done by stepping on the end of a long wooden arm like the treadle of a loom and letting your weight do the work.

Tom chuckled with delight over these two inventions, accounts of which he had found in one of his scientific magazines. They seemed to prove to him that nobody was following the direction taken by his idea, and he threw himself into the work of completing his model as rapidly as possible, though he did take a little time off to invent a new type of muffler cutout and a tire valve that would begin to whistle when the pressure fell below a certain point.

It was Tom's idea that the motor car should be simplified in every way possible, as he was convinced that most of the difficulty, both in driving and in taking care of an automobile, came from lack of familiarity on the part of the general public with the most rudimentary sort of machinery. He thought that the mechanical understanding of the average woman ended somewhere between a pair of scissors and a can opener. He placed the average man in a somewhat higher mechanical category. A man of ordinary intelligence, he thought, might grasp in a rudimentary way the principles of a coffee grinder; the extremely bright ones might even understand what made a lawn mower cut the grass when the wheels went around; but he had found that most of the people who aspired to drive and care for a motor car would have been put to it to explain the principles of a wheelbarrow.

He was not at all discouraged about it, for he felt quite sure that with a little instruction most of them could learn, and he went out of his way to explain to all his clients the real cause of every mechanical failure that was brought to him for repair. He warned them away from attempting carburetor adjustments but showed them how to clean out their fuel lines. The importance of proper lubrication was something that he preached about as the ordinary evangel harangues about salvation. And long before lubrication charts were dreamed of he was making them for customers on the back of an envelope and ringing with red pencil the points that were imperative. This in the days when the average car had fifty or sixty grease cups and often twice that number of oil holes to be given a few drops from a squirt-can.

Failures in driving he ascribed almost entirely to habits that had been formed by the continual use of a horse and buggy. There was nothing, he said, more conducive to mind-wandering than jogging along the road in a vehicle drawn by the horse. It is the horse, not the driver, that keeps the vehicle in the road. When traffic is met, it is the horse that does the turning out. On familiar roads the horse attends to the duty of turning the corners and avoiding pitchholes. And in driving after dark the burden of proof in finding the way is placed almost entirely on the horse.

Inattention to business was the rule and not the exception among drivers who had been accustomed to the horse. Tom claimed that in following an automobile he could tell, in nine cases out of ten, whether the driver was a former horse user. This was not at the time very difficult, since nine out of every ten drivers encountered on the road had, by the sheer weight of statistics, been brought up to travel by horse. The only good word Tom would say for the ex-horse user was that he rarely exceeded the speed limit.

26

The Weakest Link

I T SEEMS LIKE THE EASIEST THING IN THE
world to transmit power from one revolving shaft to another. In factories they do it with a belt, and Duryea,
Ford, Haynes and the rest of the pioneer builders almost
without exception tried the belt—but with very poor success. Of course, it was the simplest method of transmission;
and it was also the cheapest. All the experimenter needed
was a pair of flat pulleys and a strip of leather with a
shoestring for a lacing. The slipping of the belt on those
old experimental cars had a large part in convincing the
public that the motor car was a very precarious means of
transportation.

Though the pioneer builders may have used belts on
their first cars, not one of them did on his second. By the
time they started to build the second car, they understood
that the transmission of power to the driving wheels must
be positive, and what, they argued, is any more positive
than a chain? So a chain it was.

For the first five years of the new century the chains
had it; they had it almost unanimously. Indeed, the chain
was so popular (among the makers) that some of them introduced a second one and called it a double-chain drive.
This was supposed to be a very exclusive feature and very
expensive to build. It first appeared in this country on the

high-priced foreign cars: the Mercedes, the Daimler, the Fiat, the Mors, the Darracq; and soon we found it on our own Simplex, Stearns, Locomobile, and one or two other of the so-called quality makers.

But that extra chain ran into money. I can't recall a single car with the double-chain drive that sold for less than $5000, but I can recall plenty of them that cost a great deal more. Among the quantity makers, the companies turning out most of the cars, the single-chain drive was enough; and with the public the single chain was more than enough.

The chain drive was noisy, it was dirty, it was unsightly, and it required almost constant attention. The single chain flopped up and down as you rode along, making disagreeable sounds whenever you went over a bump, sounds that might be approximated by turning over a wash boiler half full of bolts and nuts. Being uncovered and unprotected, though smeared with grease and oil, it gathered the dust and the mud whenever there was any dust and mud to be gathered. It used to stretch with wear and get a little too large for the sprockets, and the first indication you had that anything was wrong was when it came off and dragged along on the ground, flopping like a boa constrictor. The chain of my Rambler came off one night when I was going up a steep hill far from home— they had a way of coming off on a hill—and this time the chain broke and wrapped itself around the rear-axle housing, so that I could neither go ahead nor back.

Ordinarily I was able to extricate myself somehow, but this time I gave up in disgust, lighted the oil lamps on the car, and walked the four or five miles home. Tom went out the next day and got it. The makers must have had thousands of such cases reported to them, especially in the cars with the single-chain drive. Eventually the buyers of the quantity cars turned their thumbs down on chains, and there was a stampede to the shaft drive.

The public is a hard thing to beat when it gets up its dander. It refused to accept the air-cooled car, and though that type of motor construction had much to recommend it and the builders spent millions to back it, air cooling for automobiles had to be abandoned, and the makers who refused to drop it went into bankruptcy. In much the same way, the public turned thumbs down on the steam car at a time when it could more than hold its own in any kind of contest with the gasoline-driven car. Stories have been current for years that the various steam cars were sabotaged and ruined by the combined forces of the Standard Oil Company and the makers of gasoline cars. I heard such a story about the Stanley Steamer, I heard the same one about the White, and when much later I heard it about the Doble Steamer, a mechanical marvel which was wrecked by frenzied financing before it ever reached the market, all the old familiar landmarks were there: sabotage, bribery, corruption, and chicanery—only this time the role of villain was being played by General Motors.

Many reasons have been assigned for the failure of the steam car to win popular favor. From my own observation, I should say that it was fear—fear of both fire and explosion. Then, too, there was the little matter of getting up steam, as well as the difficulty of securing a steam engineer's license. The American driver wanted something that was ready to go and something that was not quite so likely to blow him to kingdom come. With his mind made up on these two points, it has never seemed reasonable to me that he would need any help from either Standard Oil or General Motors. I hate to spoil so beautiful a mystery story, but I am afraid the answer lies in nothing more than good old American dander.

When in 1900 the first real automobile show was held in New York two-thirds of the space was occupied by steam cars. The balance was divided between electrics and gasoline cars, with the electrics predominating by a wide margin. There were, as a matter of fact, only three gasoline cars shown. Both the steamers and electrics were very condescending to the funny-looking cuckoo which had hatched out in their nest. But the cuckoo grew into a bird big enough to shove them both overboard even before it had its growth.

When Tom brought in my car after the episode of the broken chain, his first move was to invent a chain tool by means of which a motorist could repair a broken chain without even soiling his finger tips. The appliance consisted of a pair of hooks which could be drawn together by a small crank attached to a metal bar. He was very much excited about it until he had finished one and had shown me how well it would work. Then he tossed it aside and I heard no more about it.

Weeks later I saw it lying on his workbench and asked him what he was doing about it. He smiled. "Nothing."

"But what's the matter with it?" I asked. "It seemed to me it worked to perfection."

"Oh, it works all right. It's a good tool. But a man doesn't need one very often—probably not more than once or twice a season. I haven't had a chance to use it since I made it."

"Then you don't think it's worth trying to get a patent on it?"

He slowly shook his head. "I just made it for my own use, anyway."

"But, Tom," I protested. "You seemed very much excited about it when you first had the idea."

"Did I?"

"Of course you did."

"That's funny." He picked up the tool and took it over and hung it on a nail in the wall. I could see that he was doing it automatically, for he was thinking about something else; but I knew that his interest in the chain tool had come to its final resting place.

When these ideas came into Tom's head they tortured him like cockleburs until he had let them out and done something about them. If the solution proved to be easy he lost interest at once; but if it proved to be hard he would puzzle delightedly over the question for weeks and months.

The only one that had seemed really important to me was his self-starter. The need for this contrivance was as crying as ever, and his invention, if successful, might easily net him a fortune. I was determined not to let him lose interest, and the persistence with which he had stuck to it seemed to augur eventual success. However, Andy Brackett's hostility to the highway had again broken out, and Tom could not keep his mind on anything else until he knew the highway was out of danger.

After a very thorough feeling-out campaign Andy had reached the point where he thought his by-passing project had a chance to win, and he was putting everything he had into a plan to swing the road around the village and thus "preserve the natural charm of the place." He had done his groundwork by defeating, one after another, the various proposals that had been offered by the Village Fathers for a suitable type of pavement to connect the two ends of the new state road, which would terminate abruptly at the point where the old stage road touched the village limits on the east and the west. Indeed the signs "STATE MAINTENANCE ENDS HERE" had already been erected before Andy went into action with his by-passing scheme.

But Andy had misjudged the tenor of the electorate completely. For he found that while the voters would argue and squabble and wrangle with the greatest enthusiasm over the particular kind of pavement to be selected, they were practically unanimous about having the new highway go through Main Street. The net result of Andy's by-passing campaign was to bring an almost immediate agreement as to the character of the pavement to be laid and to hasten the arrival of the paving gangs, who soon had the street torn up for its entire length.

Naturally Tom, like every businessman in town, wanted the pavement to pass the door of his establishment and did not hesitate to say so. But Andy's umbrage was directed almost entirely against Tom. I reminded Andy several times that Tom did not invent the automobile and that he played, in fact, a very small part in a very large business that had grown up around the idea of automotive transportation. I told him repeatedly that if Tom had not opened a repair shop here somebody else would—and I suggested that almost anybody else might have turned out to be much more aggressive and pushing than Tom could ever be.

Andy was ready to admit the truth of this and would calm down for the time being. Then almost invariably he would go back to the highway—there was one thing that he could put his finger on. There was something that had originated with young Hunter. "Half-crazy crackpot,"

Andy would mutter. "What does he care about the town? All he wanted was to get one of these big through highways past his door. Stuck way up there the other side of the creek, he couldn't expect to get any business unless he could get a crack at some through traffic."

"But, Andy," I expostulated over and over again, "you can't expect to gum up the wheels of progress forever. Sooner or later that highway would have come through here, and whenever it came it would have hit you just as hard."

"I'm not thinking entirely of myself," he would say. "Please get that idea out of your mind. Naturally I don't want to suffer any more of a personal setback than I can help; but what's really on my mind is the good of the town."

More and more Andy seemed to be talking about the highway. The sight of the paving gangs kept it constantly before his mind, and Tom made a visible target towards whom he could direct his verbal barrage. Arguing against the tendency of the times or the march of progress, he could not have been anywhere near so effective.

But people will listen to the same thing just about so long, and then they will begin to be bored by it. I was talking with Joe Spears on the street one day when he suddenly interrupted himself in the middle of a sentence. "Excuse me, my boy," he said guardedly, "but I'll have to be on my way. I'll be darned if I'm goin' to stand here and have an ear talked off'm me by Andy Brackett. That feller's gettin' to be a damn nuisance, the way he goes on about the town bein' turned into a merry-go-round just so's Tom Hunter can sell a little gasoline to passin' motorists."

I kept hearing that sort of comment oftener and oftener as time went on.

Cars were getting better every year, and with the help of Mr. Ford they were becoming cheaper. In spite of his protracted litigation with the Selden interests he was turning out more and better cars. And as the case dragged along year after year quite a number of the people who had feared reprisals from the A.L.A.M. took their courage in their hands and bought Ford cars. As a matter of fact, Mr. Ford could sell all the cars he could make, and he could certainly make a great many. The wiseacres were talking about the "saturation point" in motor car production even before Henry Ford put out his famous Model T.

The tie rails and hitching posts had been pretty well driven away from Main Street even before the pavement had been put in. A few telephone and electric light poles had managed to survive, however, but with the coming of a hard, smooth surface from curb to curb, these were whisked off behind the buildings. The old arc lights came down, and a string of ornamental lampposts that looked like bronze outlined the walks on either side. With all this elegance, it was inevitable that something should be done to improve the appearance of the Town Hall, a gaunt, greystone building on the south side of the street, which marked the eastern terminus of buildings devoted to business. It had been erected back in the forties with no thought except that of utility, and it could have passed muster anywhere in the world as a gristmill or a storehouse.

The initial appropriation for the Town Hall, including the land on which it was to stand, amounted to $1500. This was, of course, insufficient, but it will give an idea of what the building must have been like. Whether the piazza, topped by a balustrade, was included in the original appropriation or added as an afterthought is immaterial, for it served only to make a bad matter worse. Architecture, however, butters no parsnips. The town had a hall over its head, and so long as it retained its somewhat secluded individuality as an agricultural trading center, asking no odds of the outside world, nobody ever stopped to give a second thought to the appearance of the structure.

Being designated by a spot on the red line of an automobile map and having a through route pass the full length of Main Street put a different light on the situation. The wealth of the nation would be flowing past the door. Wringing a living from the unwilling soil was no longer the only method of obtaining sustenance. Easy money was in sight. All that was necessary was to catch the tourist, make him stop, apply a little salesmanship—and there you were.

So it was the profit motive rather than a hunger for beauty that started the local renaissance. The grim face of the old stone building was lifted by a Corinthian pediment supported by fluted pilasters, at a cost that was considerably more than the original appropriation for both the land and the structure. The old bandstand was swept away at one end of the business district, and a handsomely landscaped parkway was introduced at the other. Postcards were stocked at almost every store in town. Gift counters began to put in an appearance. And the smell of the hot-dog, which had formerly been associated only with circus day and the firemen's carnival, became one of the hardy perennials.

Woodpecker Inn, across the street from the Town Hall,

also came in for a refurbishing and re-doing. But, alas, Old Tick was not there to add his high-pitched profanity to the turmoil of rehabilitation. He had sounded his last cymbal and had passed on to that blessed place to which good landlords go. In his shirt sleeves and carpet slippers he had stood on the porch of the Inn and watched the stage-coaches come rolling up to the big wooden stepping-block. He had seen the stagecoaches go and the horse-drawn busses from the railroad station come limping dustily in. He had watched with disfavor and disrespect as the village authorities had demolished and drawn away the wooden stepping-block to make room for the motor car.

"Jees Cri!" he had exclaimed when I asked him what he thought of the proceeding. "The way them fellers is actin', there ain't gonna be no room for a goddam horse to switch his goddam tail!"

Although the old innkeeper did not live to see the face of the Town Hall lifted or the surface of the street paved like a ballroom floor, he survived until the motor car was well established and was threatening in no uncertain way to chase old Dobbin completely off the roads. The coming of the new transportation, however, lessened rather than increased the prosperity of his caravansary. Motorists came and motorists went in ever-increasing numbers, but few of them ever stopped to sample one of his very excellent fifty-cent meals, though he had posted signs at the village limits inviting their patronage. Old Tick's explanation was simple.

"Must be a lot of goddam fools," he said, "or they wouldn't be ridin' around in them goddam unhossless buggies."

Monsieur Coquenard, Old Tick's successor, had quite a different idea, and one day soon after he had taken possession I saw him standing out in front directing the workmen as they put up a large new sign advertising a dollar dinner.

"What's the matter with your fifty-cent dinner?" I asked him.

"It is not the dinner, my friend, it is the tourist—he will not buy it," replied the Frenchman.

"And why not—it's a good dinner."

His expressive hands went into action at once. "Ah, it is a ver' fine dinner, but the tourists do not know that. It is as they go by they slow up and look—but they do not stop."

"Why not? You had a good sign there, didn't you?"

"*Oui*, I had a ver' good sign."

"It said meals were fifty cents—been there for years. It was Old Tick's sign."

"It was good sign—ver' good sign—but it was not the right sign."

"What was wrong about it?"

"The feefty cents! That was wrong. Let me tell you how I find that out. It is a few days ago a beeg machine—I theenk you call the Weenton—she stop just around the corner on the side street. The window is open and, as I am inside, I make to listen. 'Dees place, she look nice.' The man say that. 'It is clean, it is good order. Shall we go in?'

"Then I hear the lady say, 'But the price! For feefty cents, how can it be good!' "

"And they didn't come in?"

"Most assuredly not. It was an argument he could not answer. So now, my friend the lawyer, the price are one dollar."

I laughed. "But, Coquenard, isn't it the same dinner?"

Coquenard shrugged elaborately. "Assuredly not!"

"But what's the difference?" I insisted.

"That I shall explicate to you. The one dollar dinner is serve' on superb blue plate, my friend. Such china you do not see every day."

"But is that all the difference—just the china? Fifty cents extra just to see your food on blue china?"

"*Mais non!* It is I shall explicate further. Some part of the meal are the same, but the dollar dinner I make *magnifique* with most beautiful celery and olives."

"And that's all—you add nothing but celery and olives?"

"Ah, no, my friend. That is beeg mistake. For the motorist the dinner is special. You should see the chicken—there is nothing like it. It is something I have create' especially for the motorist. I have call it '*Poulet Weenton*' in honor of my two unknown frien' to whom I owe beeg indebtedness."

"But, Coquenard, isn't it the same chicken you serve to us natives with the fifty-cent dinner?"

He smiled. "In feefty-cent dinner you get good piece chicken on your plate. Ah, but in '*Poulet Weenton*' it is not on your plate—it is on separate platter garnish' with parsley and many other fine herbs in season."

Coquenard was right. When the news of his dollar dinner began to get around, the yard of the Inn was thronged with motor cars, and Tom and I had to wait half an hour one day before we could even get into the dining room. Never again would the landlord at the Inn exchange with a farmer, as Old Tick had habitually done, a jug of whiskey for a small porker or a good dinner for a basket of eggs.

The new order had indeed begun.

27

Tops

Tops came to automobiles as an afterthought. Nobody thought of including one with the equipment of the very early cars. The only reason a top was seen on Duryea's first experimental car was because he used a buggy body that already had a top. Many of the early models were not ironed with the necessary fixtures to put on a top, even as an extra.

As originally conceived in this country, the motor car is more closely related to the bicycle than to the horse-drawn vehicle. Some of them had only three wheels, many steered with a handlebar or tiller, and not one was designed to cope with the ordinary exigencies of the weather. If they wouldn't run in the rain anyway, why put on a top?

Largely on account of the weight of the motive power, it was found that the bicycle structure was too frail, and as the running gear was lengthened and strengthened the motor car very quickly came into competition with the horse-drawn vehicle. The carriage, however, was to a certain extent weatherproof. It did not short-circuit if caught in the rain, nor did a horse skid or bog down if the roads became a little muddy.

In 1900 not a car in the country came with a top, and an advertisement of the Oldsmobile appearing in the

Ladies' Home Journal that year quotes "Price Including Mudguards $650." A Buick advertisement in 1904 quotes top and lights at $125 extra. On some of the more expensive cars the top and lights came to $150 extra, and even $175. By 1905 competition must have come into the picture, for we find more and more of the cars coming equipped with tops, though in the Glidden Tour, which was inaugurated that year, several of the entries appeared without tops. Rubber coats, rubber hats, rubber robes were used to repel the rain, and one dealer offered a large poncho with holes for the heads of four passengers, two in the front seat and two in the rear. At just this time the canopy top came into high favor. It could not be raised and lowered, as in the case of the folding top, but it gave a free view of the country on all four sides and the top provided a carrying space for baggage.

There was something joyous and free about riding in a car without a top, and though the Rambler had come equipped with a three-hundred-pound canopy I removed it at the end of the first fortnight and never put it on again. Since I had no intention of being caught in the rain in that machine, I could see no reason for being encumbered with all that extra weight. However, as the cars became weatherproof, tops were added as regular equipment. Practically all of these were of the folding variety, and though they differed slightly in details they had many things in common. Some were listed as "collapsible" tops, some as "extension" tops; and on the very high-priced cars, they were likely to be called "Cape cart" tops. This sounded very exclusive, but was, in fact, only an adaptation of the covering used by a South African two-wheeled vehicle with two or three seats.

The long "extension" tops would keep the rain off your

head, especially if you pulled up by the side of the road when the storm began. The glass windshield had not yet come into use.

And then there was the little matter of putting the top either up or down. According to the advertising, the motorist could ride along in God's free sunshine, breathing in the pure and healthful air provided by a bountiful Nature; and if the weather turned threatening or the sun unpleasantly hot or glaring he could stop and "whisk up the top in a jiffy," or if conditions were reversed he could "whisk it down again."

I found on my first experience with an extension top that "whisking" was hardly the word. The weather had looked threatening when we started out, but it had not looked immediately threatening, and I thought I might as well wait a while before whisking up the top. My recollection is that I did not begin to whisk until after a raindrop had struck me in the face—and by the time I had succeeded in getting up the top, the storm was over and the sun seemed about to come out. The truth of the matter was that two able-bodied men, working in close collaboration and giving all their time to the task, could probably have raised and secured that top and attached the boot and side curtains in not less than twenty minutes, though the time would probably have been nearer thirty. With a practiced associate I once did it in eighteen minutes, though this record would never have been accepted as official, since we were greatly aided by a following wind.

The "one-man" top was a misnomer. You might as well talk about a one-man wrestling match. I have seen two strong men struggle with a one-man top for a full half hour, and I once had a rib broken by a one-man top that dealt me a terrific blow in one of our clinches. Year by year, however, the tops were improved. They were made lighter and smaller, though stronger. Better leverage for the operator was obtained by a rearrangement of the bows, though they never were easy to put up and down until power was applied to the job, and that was long after the closed car had been brought within the price range of the man of ordinary means.

Closed cars had been built as soon as a motor had been designed with power enough to pull so heavy a body. These, however, were all custom jobs and ran into big money, the body costing more than the average man's entire car; but they were so unwieldy and cumbersome that they seldom ventured off the city pavements. They were largely the product of carriage builders, who would take the measure of your chassis and make you a special body designed to meet your particular tastes or needs.

It seems strange that the car builders did not grasp the possibilities of the closed car long before they did. It must have been obvious to any man of foresight that the motor car would remain a vehicle for summer use until it was built in such a manner that the occupants could be warm and comfortable during the winter months. Just why the carriage builders themselves did not unite on this idea is an unanswerable enigma. It seems like a ready-made solution to the problem that must have been facing them with the waning popularity of the horse. Hundreds of carriage factories closed. Others went over to the manufacturing of wheels and open bodies for the makers of motor cars. Still the first decade of the century passed with the motor car still running on half time. Practically all the Army cars used during World War I were open touring models, and the closed car did not come into general use until after the end of the war. It was then that motorists began to use their cars the year around.

During the first decade of the century the changes came about slowly. Even essential changes, like the introduction of the magneto in place of the battery, were not accomplished in a single season. During this period half-a-dozen types of clutches were on the market, all of them slipping or grabbing, many of them so designed as to make lubrication extremely difficult. Cone, disc, internal-expansion, external-contraction, three-plate, five-plate—and one car risked its future with a twenty-seven plate clutch, with the plates made of discs of saw steel. Some of these clutches had to be lubricated every one hundred miles, and not one of them, it is safe to say, could go as much as five hundred miles without attention.

I once had a clutch go out of commission in the middle of the night while I was on my way home from a party. I had Asa Parker with me, and we were both dressed in evening clothes. The clutch had been slipping somewhat as we were driving to the party, which was about ten miles away from home, but there was no place near by where I could have it fixed, so I let it go and hoped for the best. Most of the hills were against us on the way home, and by the time we had crawled up two or three of them I knew we were in for trouble. On the level we were all right, but as soon as we started to climb the engine would run faster and faster but the car would slow down until we were making hardly any progress at all. We were part way up a winding grade known as the Alloway hill when the clutch gave up entirely and the car ceased to move.

I reached over and cut out the engine and there we sat. "No use burning out the lining," I said. "That clutch simply will not pull the car."

Asa lighted a cigarette, as he always did in an emergency. "Well—what next?" he asked.

"We're stuck. We can't back down and go around some other way, because there isn't any other road without a hill just as bad as this."

"What's the answer? Do we camp here overnight?"

"Either that—or else we'll have to tighten up the clutch."

"How much of a job is it?" he asked hopefully, knowing nothing whatever about a motor car.

I had a good laugh. "It's a whale of a job. In the first place it's down there under the floor in the dirtiest place you can imagine. And then it's a cone clutch, which is adjusted by tightening up ten small coil springs."

Asa puffed for a few moments in silence and then asked, "Did you ever do it?"

"No," I admitted, "but I've seen it done. And while it's not difficult, it will take both of us."

"I don't know a thing about machinery," he said.

"You don't have to. All you need to do is hold down the spring with a screwdriver while I take out the cotter and tighten up the locknut."

"Good heavens!" he exclaimed. "We can't do that in evening clothes. This is the first dress suit I ever had, and Heaven knows when I'll get another."

I lighted a match and looked at my watch. It was a little after two o'clock. "I don't imagine anybody will be coming along here before daylight."

"Certainly not a team—and nothing short of a team could ever pull us up. I think we'd better bed down here in the car and go to sleep."

"I've got quite a different idea," I said.

· 314 ·

"You want me to walk home and send Tom Hunter out to get you?"

"That's not a bad idea, but I think mine is better. We can strip down to our underwear and tighten that clutch. Then we can wash off our hands in the creek at the bottom of the hill, put our clothes back on, and drive home. . . . What do you think of it?"

He thought it over for a while. "I wear long underwear, you know."

"Well, what of it?"

"Oh, nothing—just that it's not much to look at."

"Neither is mine, but I'm not counting on having anybody look at it."

"How long will the job take?"

"Not more than an hour."

He thought it over. "Isn't it taking a kind of a long chance?"

"I don't think it's any very terrific chance. We've already been here half an hour and nobody's come along."

"Are you really willing to do it?" he asked uneasily.

"Of course."

"But a rig might come by with a lady in it!"

"What if it did? It's dark when I shut off the headlights. We'd step around on the other side of the car, and I'm sure we'd be able to spare her blushes—"

"That may be all right for you, but I'm in public life and I have to be careful what I do," said the budding young Assemblyman.

"Forget your public life," I muttered. "We're stuck and we've got to get ourselves out of here any way we can."

"But a man could ruin his career by making himself ridiculous in a public place."

I snorted. "What's public about this place—at two

o'clock in the morning?" Just to prove my point I went around and shut off the headlights, and instantly the place was as dark as a pocket.

The darkness convinced Asa in a hurry. "How can you work on machinery in the dark?" he asked.

"I've got a flashlight," I said. "You can hold it at the same time you're holding the screwdriver, and if anybody comes along all you've got to do is shut it off."

When Asa spoke again I knew he was won over. "You think it won't take more than an hour?"

"Tom did the job in half an hour," I assured him.

"All right," he said in a tone of surrender, "let's get undressed for the part."

We took off our coats and vests, and our shirts and collars and neckties, piling them on the back seat. Then Asa hesitated. "You're sure—we'll need to take off our pants?"

"I will," I replied. "In fact I've already got one leg off —and here comes the other." I tossed them on the seat. "I'm not going to take any chances of smearing a lot of grease on them. Dress pants are too hard to get."

"Guess it's got to be done," he said reluctantly. "I'll be with you in a minute."

I was very much tempted to flash the light on him, but I controlled myself and flashed it on the floor boards instead. The reflected light gave me a wonderful view of my companion, and in that long underwear he was just as ridiculous as he thought he was going to be. It bagged at the elbows and knees, and sagged at other points like a wet rag that had been thrown on the bushes to dry. I had to struggle to keep a straight face as we pried up the floor boards and set them on the ground by the side of the road. Then I gave him the screwdriver while I took the wrench and pliers, and we went to work. It was not a very complicated job, but it was even dirtier than I had expected. Semiliquid grease from the thrust bearing was smeared over everything.

In no time at all I was lubricated to the elbows, and it was not long before I could see Asa's comical underwear handsomely decorated with dabs of grease and finger marks. At first Asa was careful about keeping out of the grease, but after his hands had slipped a few times and were pretty well smeared he seemed to glory in it and would have wallowed if I hadn't been in the way. He became very much interested as we went on with the job, feeling no doubt that he was performing a necessary part, as indeed he was.

Mosquitoes were plentiful around there and in shooing them away Asa had managed to rub his hands against his face until he looked like a half-made-up minstrel. All in all he was a sight, but I have never seen him so interested as he was in that clutch-tightening job, and when on the last spring I let the locknut slip out of my fingers and drop into the dust of the road, he was flat on his belly and under the car after it before I could stop him. He found it without too much trouble, but he was completely coated with dust from head to foot when he came out.

We had finished getting on the locknut and were spreading the ends of the cotter key by tapping it with the pliers, making just enough noise to prevent our hearing certain other sounds of the night, stealing gently upon us from beyond the brow of the hill. Bending low behind the dashboard we did not see the glare of approaching headlights until the car, coasting noiselessly down the hill, was almost upon us. It was, in fact, a cheery hail from the driver that brought us both to our feet. He had stopped his car directly above us and, focusing his head lamps upon us like a spotlight, was inquiring if we needed any help.

He recognized me immediately when I straightened up and looked his way. "Why, it's Bellamy," I heard him say.

As he let off his brakes to come rolling down beside us I scambled out of the spotlight and stepped around behind the car. I knew by this time that he had women with him, for I could hear them laughing. On the spur of the moment I leaned out and motioned to him to keep going. I had no idea who he was, but I had a very definite idea that I did not want him to stop.

"Wait for us at the bottom of the hill!" I called to him. "We're going to back down and make a new start."

The squeaking of his brakes told me, however, that he was not going to follow my suggestion. So I cowered behind the car, moving up as he came down, and trying to keep my car between us. I could not see Asa anywhere, but I was not worrying about him at just that moment. Then directly opposite my car and only four or five feet away the good Samaritan stopped.

"Been to a strip-poker party?" he asked, getting a wonderful laugh from the audience in his tonneau.

By this time I had recognized him as Judge VanTyle of Sodus, boss of Wayne County and one of Asa's political gods. It was at this point that I became worried about Asa and began to look around for him—but he simply was not there.

The Judge tried for another laugh. "Maybe you've been to a masquerade, or were you just getting ready to go in swimming?"

"You're getting warmer," I answered. "It was a holdup."

"A holdup?" The Judge's attitude changed at once. "Oh, I'm sorry I joked about it. Did you lose much?"

"Lost my clothes—isn't that enough?"

I could see that he was trying to keep from laughing when he said, "I'll let you have my duster—I can't spare much else."

"Thanks just the same," I said, "but I don't believe I'll need it."

"Need anything else?"

"No, I think we can make a go of it all right."

"Be glad to help you any way I can. How did it happen?"

"We were having a little trouble with the car. The clutch was slipping and we had stopped to tighten it—when this fellow came along and poked a pistol in our faces and told us to put up our hands."

"How long ago did this happen?" asked the Judge.

"Must have been about half an hour."

"Is that so—which way did this fellow go?"

"The same way you're going now."

Sudden exclamations of horror came from the back seat of the Judge's car. "Gracious—! Good heavens—! We don't want to go on this way—we'd better turn around."

The Judge was no coward. "We'll keep going," he said promptly. "I'm more or less of a holdup man myself. If I should get your pants I'll bring them back. Sorry I haven't got some clothes I could lend you. You're sure you can get along all right?"

"Oh, yes, the car's all fixed now."

"Well, good luck to you. Remember me to your father." And the Judge's party rolled on down the hill and disappeared into the night.

As I heard the car rumbling across the bridge and knew that they were gone I began to look around for Asa. "Where are you, Asa?" I asked.

"Here I am." His voice came from under the car. "I knew something like this would happen," he grumbled as he came crawling out. "Why did you want to tell him such a whopper as that?"

"I thought it would make good publicity for you."

"For me—!" he cried. "Do you think he knew me?"

That gave me a good laugh. "With the grease on your face your own mother wouldn't know you."

Asa worried about it all the way home. In fact he worried about it for a long time, fearful that the Judge might tell it around so that it would get into the papers. But so far as I know the Judge never gave any intimation that he had recognized my companion of that memorable night.

It took no more than that one experience to shake my faith in the cone clutch, in which I had previously had a good deal of confidence. The effect on Asa was quite the other way. It aroused in him an interest in the motor car which he had never had before, and feeling that he was now more or less of an expert he began to want one for himself.

I felt pretty sure this would bring repercussions. And it did.

28

Motorist's Treat

THE IMPACTS OF THE MOTOR CAR ON THE horse-and-buggy world were so numerous and so diverse that it is not always easy to recognize them. One of the most curious that comes to mind is the creation of the fiction that it should always be the motorist's "treat." That horse-and-buggy world was a thrifty world. People did not throw their money around. Indeed, they did not let it escape their grasp without some very adequate reason. It was hard to come by, and once you got hold of it you tried to put it in a safe place. I have mentioned one phase of this subject before, in discussing the reasoning by which non-motoring people were able to justify overcharging the motorist simply because he had paid so much money for his motor car. From that position it was only a short step to the attitude that since he had money to throw away on such things he should be allowed to foot all the bills for the entertainment of the guests he took out in his car.

Of course they expected him to pay for the gasoline and oil. If there was tire trouble he paid for that. Should anything break or go wrong with the car, it was always the owner who had to go down in his pocket. These were all expenses that had developed along with the motor car, things that had never been thought of in connection with horse-drawn traffic. And seeing the motorist paying for this, paying for that, and paying for the other thing led very naturally to the point of allowing him to pay for everything.

If anybody suggested a drink, it was the motorist who paid for it. If you came to a good place to eat and by common consent stopped for dinner—there was never any fumbling for the check. The waiter brought it straight to the man who had come in carrying the duster and gauntlets. I once broke down with a carful of people far from home and had to spend a night at a hotel. Do you suppose one of my guests ever offered to pay his or her hotel bill? Not one. And when eventually, after also paying an expensive repair bill and footing the telephone calls they had made to their families, I brought them in safety to their own doors on the afternoon of the following day, they all acted as if they had all been rescued from a disaster after floating around for an unbelievable period on a life raft.

While the coming of the low-priced car and the bringing of motorized transport to the masses did much to extinguish the idea that it was *invariably* the motorist's treat, there is still a little trace of the idea left among old-fashioned people, especially those who were old enough to be taken around in the early days of motoring when the century was still young. And if you want to see how hard it is to kill a beautiful idea—and you live in a state where pleasure driving is still allowed—just suggest to a group of people that it might be fun to drive down and take in a movie and that you think they can all crowd into your car. Then watch carefully and see who pays for the tickets.

I was once allowed the privilege of buying a new hat for a man who was careless enough to let his get away while we were crossing a bridge. And I think that if I had insisted I would have been permitted to buy a new overcoat for a man who lost one out of my car—or said he did.

These things must be regarded as among the imponderables of motoring that were never thought of by Duryea, Ford, Haynes, Winton, Olds and the rest of that gallant company of tinkers who made possible the motor car as we know it today. Another of the imponderables was the effect on the railroads, to be brought about by the descendants of the chugging old one-lungers.

The motor car was just getting into its big rise in popularity when Andy Brackett came walking into the office one day. "Well, have you heard the news?" he asked.

"About what?"

"The New York Central Railroad."

"They're not double-tracking this branch?"

He gave me a sour smile. "Hardly. They're dropping a couple of trains."

"What's that for?" I asked, as if I didn't know what he was driving at.

"What's it for!" he thundered. "It's because your damned motor-buggies are taking away all their business. And let me tell you another thing—this is only the beginning. They'll be dropping them right along, just as fast as this gasoline craze takes away their passengers. If a train doesn't pay—they drop it."

"You ought to be pleased," I said. "You're a seclusionist."

He took off his grey derby and ran his finger around the inside of the band. "I am pleased because of just one thing—what is happening is exactly what I have been saying would happen. As for being a seclusionist, I certainly am that. But do you realize how much seclusion we're going to have when the road is all finished and the traffic begins to roar through the main street of the town—if we don't do something about it?"

"But after all, Andy," I said, "it's a public highway, and what can we do about it if people want to drive through our town?"

"We can see to it that they travel at a reasonable rate of speed. Do you see anything objectionable about that?"

"Not at all," I said. "I think that makes very good sense."

"May I quote you on that?" he asked.

I laughed. "You can if you want to, but I don't know why anyone would want to quote me."

"Oh, simply because you're a motorist," he said.

He went out soon afterwards and I thought no more about it until a day or two later, when Tom came in and told me that the Village Fathers had posted notices of a six-mile speed limit through the incorporated village.

"Six miles an hour!" I cried. "My car won't go that slow."

"Careful now," said Tom with a grin. "I understood you were back of this ordinance."

"Back of it? I never heard of it before."

"But Andy Brackett, who put it through, quoted you as being in favor of it."

I stood up and put on my hat. "I'll go over and tell Andy what I think of that kind of business."

Tom shook his head. "Don't do it," he said. "I've got another plan, and if it works you won't have to say another word to Andy. Just give me a chance to work it, for I'm sure it'll do the business."

"Aren't you going to tell me what it is?"

"I think it's just as well for you not to know. If I have any luck I'll come back and tell you."

He was back within an hour beaming all over his face. "It worked!" he cried. "It worked to perfection!"

It was just as well that he did not tell me what he was going to do, for I am sure I would have tried to discourage him. The Village Fathers, he explained, were not entirely satisfied with the speed limit. Some of them thought it too low, but Andy had insisted; so without letting Andy know what they were doing they decided to give it a test by setting off a measured stretch and arresting every vehicle that went through it in less than a minute and a quarter between the hours of four and five that afternoon. Tom had watched for Lucy Brackett, caught her on the street and stopped her. After he had succeeded in getting her to take him for a ride he goaded her into letting out the horse just before they came to the speed trap—and at the end of the measured stretch a constable had stepped into the road and arrested her for exceeding the speed limit.

"How did Lucy take it?" I asked.

Tom chuckled. "She was screaming mad."

"At you?"

"No—at the constable. That's the funny part."

"Don't worry," I said. "She'll get around to you in time. You played a dirty trick on her."

"But you will admit that it was a pretty good way to get back at Andy."

This baffled me. I kept thinking about it after Tom had gone. It was so unlike him to take a punch at Andy over Lucy's shoulder. He had always been a straight shooter, a fellow who preferred to meet an issue face to face and who hated the devious. I understood fully as well as Tom did that the restrictive ordinance had been aimed largely at hurting him. There had been no excessive speeding through Main Street, but Andy was building up a hostility to visiting motorists even before the new road had been opened to through traffic. There was little doubt in my mind that Andy would feel the sting of having his ordinance thrown in his face by the arrest of Lucy—and still I thought it was small business on Tom's part and did not like it. I was even more baffled by Lucy's attitude. She pretended to be angry about it, but I could quite plainly see that she thought it rather cute.

There were no fines or prosecutions under the ordinance, which was promptly repealed, much to Andy's chagrin; and the speed limit reverted to the state regulation of ten miles an hour in the closely built-up section and fifteen in other parts of the incorporated village. Andy had assumed a martyred air when he talked to me about it after it was all over. There was no use trying to do anything to help the town, he said. The old-time spirit of loyalty and solidarity seemed to have gone out of it; all that people were thinking about was making money. Nobody wanted to make the town a good place to live in; the big idea now was to make it attractive to outsiders, so that they would stop there and spend their money. And if he tried to do anything to bring the townspeople back to their senses they'd get angry and tell him he was a mossback or a monkey wrench in the wheels of progress.

He left my office in a very depressed state of mind. "I'm afraid," he said, "the old town is going to the demnition bowwows." He had not been gone five minutes before he was back with more bad news—and in a much more animated state. More and more, it seemed to me, Andy enjoyed being the bringer of bad news. The rumor he was bearing on this occasion was not of a grievous or a melancholy nature, though I was sorry to hear it—the story was going around town that Joe Spears was selling out to a chain. Joe had spent his life in that general store of his, and he had kept it general against the competition of a number of specialists. He sold as many dry goods as the dry goods store almost next door, and he sold as many groceries as the grocers. First and last he disposed of a lot of hardware, probably as much as either of the regular hardware stores, though he had nowhere near so large a stock. There were certain hardware lines that he refused to handle, and once after I had heard him refuse a very urgent offer of the exclusive representation of one of these I asked him if there was something the matter with the line.

"Oh, no," he said with a laugh, "nothing at all. It's really better than what I am carrying."

"Then why not put it in?"

"I wouldn't want this to go any farther, but if I'm going to keep my competitors in business I've got to let them have something to sell."

This puzzled me. "But why keep your competitors in business," I asked.

He pushed his spectacles up on his forehead and turned his faded blue eyes on me with a little extra twinkle in them. "As you know, my competitors are not what you'd call keen business men. As long as they stay here I'll get my full share of the trade, but if I should drive them out some smart young feller might come in here and take it all away from me."

Andy's report proved to be more than a rumor. Old Joe came in that same afternoon to have me go over a long printed form of contract that the agent for the chain had left with him. It was a "shotgun" agreement with clauses to cover almost any contingency. Many of these were struck out, but the deal went through. Joe was not particularly anxious to sell, he said, but he preferred to have the Blue Front a successor rather than a competitor.

Old Spears was the first of the merchants in town to sell out to a chain, but others were not long in following. The new road made it easy for the supply trucks to get in, and we were a halfway spot between Geneva and Newark. Soon the electric light company that we had fought so hard to get was in the hands of a utility company covering several counties, and in time even the produce man who bought the farmers' crops was working for an out-of-town commission merchant. These things did not happen all at once, but they began with the coming of the new highway and they seemed to be part of a great standardizing force that was flowing along in the wake of the swift and easy travel made possible by the development of the motor car.

Up to this time very few women had learned to handle a motor car. Burgess Harper had taught his sister Zelda to drive his car and she drove it well. The papers had given prominence to the motoring prowess of Alice Roosevelt; and Maude Adams and some of the other stage favorites had obtained wide publicity by having their pictures taken at the wheel or tiller of a motor car. However, the honor of being the first American woman to receive a driver's license went to Miss Julie E. Bracken of Chicago, in 1900.

Women drivers began to be seen on the roads with some frequency in 1907 or 1908, though they were rarely seen alone, tire trouble being such as it was, and the necessity for hand cranking of motors being an ever-present possibility and requiring a stronger right arm than the average woman was supposed to possess. Zelda was really a fine driver, but unless she was accompanied by a male escort she was not allowed to go beyond the village limits. She was constantly begging Tom to get on with his starting device, for by this time everybody in town knew he had one under construction.

"Somebody else will beat you if you don't hurry up," she used to tell him. "Women all over the country are screaming for a starter, and if you don't make it for them somebody else will."

I used to encourage her to keep after him, for I, too, was apprehensive that if somebody did not arouse him to action another inventor would beat him to the punch. Tom claimed to be working on it every waking hour not given up to making a living. This was probably true, as he was a prodigious worker. But somehow the construction of the experimental machine dragged on interminably. I heaved a sigh of relief when one day he told me it was practically finished—but only an hour later he came panting into the office with another idea. He was going to add an hydraulic jack that would raise the car by compressed air so that in case of a puncture the driver would no longer have to jack up the car by hand.

This hydraulic jack was really a clever idea. The lifting unit was to be built into each axle, integral with the axle itself. At the pull of a lever a sturdy iron jack dropped to the ground, and when the air was applied the entire axle slowly rose to the required height, lifting both front or both rear wheels, as the case might be.

It completely won me over, and in spite of the added delay I felt that he must go ahead with the improvement.

Tom was pleased all through. He was pleased with himself for thinking of the idea and he was pleased with me for liking it.

"Zelda's going to like this, too," he said. "It will bring her one step nearer to complete motor car independence."

"Poor old Zelda," I murmured.

"What's the matter with her?" he asked quickly.

I shook my head. "Nothing very serious. She's just feeling down in the mouth."

"Anything gone wrong with their car?"

"No, it's a little more serious than that."

Tom gave me a very puzzled look. "What's any more serious than having your car go wrong?"

With a smile I answered, "Heart trouble."

"Has she got *that?*"

"Perhaps I'd better call it suspicion of heart trouble."

He still looked concerned. "Well, even that sounds bad."

I thought I had carried the joke far enough. "The real trouble is that she thinks Asa is getting ready to propose to Lucy," I said, watching him closely to see how he would take it.

He had his emotions under control, for all I could see was a definite interest, and some bewilderment. "What makes her think that?"

"Oh, he's been moody and absent-minded. She says she has seen it coming on for a long time."

"Moody—and absent-minded? Those signs could mean a lot of different things."

"I suppose she is taking them into consideration with other indications she has uncovered—or imagined."

He nodded his head slowly. "Must be."

"Zelda is around with Lucy a great deal, and she sees a side of all this that we don't get."

"You mean Lucy's viewpoint?"

"That isn't exactly what I was referring to, but she sees Asa and Lucy together."

"Do you imagine you can always tell by that?"

"Well, no; I can't. I'm often puzzled to know what people really do think of each other. Now I know that Zelda's in love with Asa for the very simple reason that she has told me so. I think I would have known that anyway; but I haven't the slightest idea how Asa feels about Zelda—way down deep in the bottom of his heart."

"If he has any bottom in his heart," said Tom.

Coming from Tom this surprised me. I think it surprised him, too, as he so seldom spoke out about people in this way. "Why do you say that?" I asked.

"Because I think Asa has a very calculating nature."

"Don't you know he's the most popular fellow in town?"

"That doesn't change my opinion."

"You don't think he would drag politics into his love life?"

"I certainly do."

"But if Zelda is right about it—and he does pop the question—do you believe Lucy would have him?"

"How could she?"

"But why not?" I asked.

"Because Lucy's a real person."

"Oh—I didn't know you thought much of her."

"Can't you know whether people are real or not without thinking a lot of them?"

And that's as far as I got with that.

29

Comfort at Last

THE COMFORT OF THE DRIVER WAS ONE OF the last things the motor car builders took into consideration. Soft upholstery, to be sure, went into the rear seats at a very early date. High, wide, and handsome doors. Armrests and footrests galore. Robe rails, pockets, compartments in the doors for ladies' gloves, goggles, and knickknacks. But doors on the driver's compartment did not appear until 1910. The motor car had come a long way by that time. My "Silent Six" of that year had a sixty-horsepower motor. Speedometer top said seventy miles an hour. The lubrication was by force feed, and the ignition by magneto. There was a folding glass windshield in front and a trunk rack on the back. But, beyond all else, it was the first car I had ever seen that was equipped with front doors—and these came only halfway up. I think it must have been these doors that sold the car to me—those and a persuasive gentleman called "Zimmy," who has long since gone to his reward.

That year the total production of cars in the country topped 180,000, and still the drivers of practically all of them sat with their legs and feet exposed to the weather. Doubtless, to begin with, the motor car followed the general design of the coach—which never did get around to enclosing the feet of the driver. Nor did the coach show much interest in putting a covering over the driver's head. The theory was that the driver of horses needed a lot of elbowroom in which to wield his whip and, being a hardy fellow, was able to put up with almost any kind of weather. The driver of a motor car was also supposed to need plenty of room, and the reason given by salesmen for leaving his feet uncovered was to provide him with an easy means of exit in case of emergency.

I mention this merely to show how the creature conveniences lagged behind the mechanical improvements in the development of the motor car. Efficiency came first: the car must run. Then economy began to get in its work: the car must not cost too much to run and to maintain. But motoring was well along in its thirties before we began to hear about ten-inch upholstery and the individual springing of wheels. However, the end of the first decade of the century saw the motor car swift, efficient, and powerful, though it still had to be cranked by hand and was surrounded by a host of minor inconveniences.

When I started on my drive across the continent in 1912 the tank was filled by pouring in the gas with a gallon measure, and it was a big tank holding twenty-five gallons. The ubiquitous curb and filling station pump of today may have been down on paper at that time, but nobody had ever seen one. Except at the country stores you had to drive inside to get your gasoline. We saw only one outdoor filling station between New York and San Francisco. It was in a suburb of Chicago, and was so great a novelty and curiosity that, although our tanks were well supplied, we drove in to be "serviced"—a new and rather comical word regarded by the professors as about as barbarous as being "burglarized." Indeed the two terms had quite a little in common.

In those days the gasoline was drawn from a tank or barrel into a strange-looking bucket with a large spout. You had to take the attendant's word for the amount this container held. The fuel was poured into the car through a large strainer, and the careful motorist usually carried a chamois with him by which he attempted to strain the water out of the gasoline. This took time and was always an annoyance to the garage hand or the store clerk who happened to be waiting on you. So it was supposed to call for a liberal tip, the amount of which was determined by the size of your purchase. The truth of the matter is that the motorist was a long time in putting his confidence in a pump which emptied directly into his tank without giving him a chance to count the number of gallons.

Cylinder oil was also a very considerable problem in the early days of motoring. Lubricants were not so carefully graded, brands were not known, and often the dealers could not tell whether the oil was light or heavy, and sometimes they were not sure that the lubricant was not intended for steam cylinders rather than a gasoline motor. On a long trip I always carried a five-gallon can of my own brand on the running board. It was the only way to be sure of what you were getting. Some peculiar fluids were put into motors by careless or stupid attendants, the most peculiar that I ever heard of being a gallon of maple syrup poured into the crankcase of a motorist touring in Vermont. The luckless motorist, who had ordered a change of oil, assured me that he had "sugared down" before he had gone a hundred yards on his way.

Perhaps the greatest inconvenience with which the early motorist had to contend was the absence of road signs. With the aids to highway navigation furnished by the states and the municipalities today there is little excuse for a driver to lose his way so long as he is able to read. Nowadays the motorist can drive from California to New York in less than a week without once asking or losing his way. But on a two weeks' tour through New England in 1910 I must have been off my road more than fifty times, and I probably stopped to inquire my way twenty or thirty times a day. The big difficulty then was the absence of road signs. Garages were among the first to take advantage of this situation by posting signs at intersections, telling the distance to their various places of business. That same year one of the big tire companies spent thousands of dollars in advertising their tires on gaudy signboards, with a little postscript at the bottom of each, telling the mileage to this place or that, presumably where the tires were for sale. They were a great convenience and much appreciated by the public, though it was the *Automobile Bluebook* which really saved the life of the touring motorist.

This *Bluebook,* the official product of one of the big automobile associations, was the tourist's Baedeker. It was a leather-bound volume of slightly under octavo size, covering routes, roads, landmarks, history, points of interest, and accommodations, giving their general character and prices. It listed garages and repair shops, places of worship, amusement parks, and even telephone numbers. Distances were given from various starting points in the principal cities. In New York it was Columbus Circle, in Boston it was the Hotel Touraine, in Indianapolis the Soldiers' and Sailors' Monument, and so on.

Go north with car tracks to R.R. bridge (1.3). Pass under bridge and immediately turn right, past abandoned carriage factory on left (1.7), and baseball park on right (2.8). At watering trough in fork (3.4), go left, following riverbank, etc., etc.

Little detail maps were threaded along the margin of the page beside the running directions, and folded into each volume were comprehensive road maps of the entire district covered by that particular volume; for so detailed and explicit were the directions that the volumes had to be somewhat limited in their scope. Thus the whole of New England would be included in one volume, but only the states of New York and New Jersey in another. The various oil companies were not at that time clamoring to get you to accept their maps. They had no maps, indeed some of the most aggressive of today's oil companies were not even on a map in these gay old *Bluebook* days.

The arrival of the state highways with their permanent signs, further clarified by the naming and numbering of the through routes, relieved the motorist of the annual necessity of finding $2.50 for each of the *Bluebooks* he was going to need, for the new roads were being put in so fast and the landmarks changed so continually that the latest edition was somewhat out of date by the time of publication.

Another service of the *Bluebook* greatly appreciated by the motorist was the tip-off service it conducted on speed traps. If your name was on the mailing list you would receive these every little while, perhaps weekly. They told where the traps were being operated, how to avoid them, and what to look out for. On some of the main arteries sentries to warn members would be posted a mile or so before reaching the trap. Another service they performed was to provide local guides to conduct the motorist around some of the unmarked detours. But that was in the days when only half-a-dozen motorists would pass in the course of an hour.

On the Post Road a few miles south of Albany was a notorious speed trap run by a rapacious justice of the peace with the aid of a couple of constables. Motorists tried every way they could think of to get rid of this mendacious old brigand. But the signs erected to warn motorists of the trap were promptly torn down in the name of the law, and if the publicity in the press became too glaring the conspirators would move the trap to a new location and go right on with their robbery. At last one of the big automobile associations took a hand in the game and secretly sent out an engineer to check the measured course then in use. By great good luck they found it short, and persuaded one of their members who had been fined there to bring suit for restitution. Having won his case the member promptly filed another suit for damages, alleging false arrest, and recovered a fairly sizable verdict. Thereupon the association rounded up hundreds of the victims and filed so many suits that the perpetrators of the speed trap were forced to take refuge in the bankruptcy court.

It was such things as this—added to tire trouble, motor trouble, bad roads and an insufficiency of good hotel accommodations—that used to take some of the pleasure out of touring; and yet every summer you tried your best to get off in the car for two or three weeks. Somehow my compass turned east, taking me at one time or another over every main road in New England. Twice I tried Canada but was driven out by the execrable roads. In New England one could be sure of the roads, one could be absolutely sure of the scenery, and one could be fairly sure of the hotels—if one could get into them.

Year by year there was a steady infiltration of motor

cars across the state from the populous centers of the Middle West. Through June and July, and perhaps the early part of August, the drift was eastward. Then like the tide it would turn and go the other way. Year by year, as the roads improved, the tide became heavier and heavier. For quite a few years this was almost entirely pleasure traffic —people out for a good time and all ready to spend some money to get it. There was a gaiety to motoring in those days, a vacation spirit, a *camaraderie* of the highway that is almost unbelievable today. Nobody could have believed that so simple a pleasure would, in a single generation, grow into a monster called Traffic.

If you stopped with a flat tire you would have a dozen offers of assistance, and people that you had seen repeatedly on the road during the day's run would come up to you in the hotel in the evening and make themselves known. The next morning the breakfast tables of the hotel dining room would be filled with people bending over *Bluebooks* and mapping out the day's run—the women in dusters and with veils wrapped around their hats, the men bolting their food and hoping, with a little anxiety, that the car would start all right when cranked in the garage before a lot of strangers. Some of these same people you'd see at lunch, and a few of them at dinner. Occasionally you would be "rained in" at some hotel with them for a day or two, when there would be a chance to become better acquainted. You might get caught in a storm and have to come in through the rain, but no reasonably prudent driver would ever be rash enough to set out on mountain roads while they were wet and muddy. The smooth treads and unprotected turns formed an almost unbeatable combination; and the changing of a flat tire on a muddy road was an experience not soon to be forgotten.

Most of these tourists fell into the middle age bracket, somewhere perhaps between thirty and fifty. Some of the groups were families, a father and mother with one or two teen-age children, or an in-law party including a married son or daughter with spouse. There were few if any cars made up exclusively of young people—now and then a bride and groom who had borrowed the family car for the honeymoon, but no flaming youth, and absolutely not a jalopy on the road. In those thrifty, post-Victorian days motoring was thought to be too costly for the young —and it smacked a little too much of danger. And as for taking a helpless infant about the country by so hazardous a means—it simply was not done.

Andy Brackett was right. This traffic went roaring over the roads at high speed—twice the speed of the best of road horses. There was hardly a car that did not go twenty-five miles an hour over the open road. Of course they slowed down going through the town, notices of the speed limit being frequent and peremptory; but the leisurely atmosphere of gentility had been completely destroyed.

Andy would walk along the street shaking his head over it, muttering more and more often, "Like living in the middle of the county fairgrounds."

This speech always seemed to imply that the person he was addressing was somehow to blame, and he would frequently supplement his muttering with the further remark that he supposed the listener had heard that the railroad company had dropped another train from the schedule. He told about these trains so repeatedly that I never knew whether it was the same train or another one. It might easily have been another one, for with the great upswing in the registration of motor cars that followed the introduction of the mass-production methods of manufacture, the railroad was shuffling off trains like cards from the bottom of the deck. Then one day I heard more about the trains from an entirely different source. It was the Green Pack Peddler.

He came into my office and set his pack on the floor with more than the usual caution. "It's full," he said. "I haf to be careful how I hendle it."

"Then you're just starting out?" I asked.

He laughed ruefully, shaking his head. "The contrary iss true. I am on my way home."

"But how does it happen to be so full?"

He shrugged. "Just another casualty of the machine, you could say it. I am victim of the horseless age. I should take my seat beside Andy Brackett, my friend Gid, and railroad company. Tommy iss smart one. When comes machine, he jumps on; he will take a ride."

"Are you telling me that people won't buy your stuff any more?"

"Egzactly. I can't sell it."

"But why not? Don't the people need it as much as they ever did?"

"They don't need it and they don't want it, because it iss no longer novelty to them. If it heppen they haf not a car to visit five-and-ten every week or so, then it iss traveling five-and-ten brings it to the door. The peddler who travels on his feet must now starve or find another job."

"How long have you known this, Sol?" I asked.

"Oh, I haf long time suspect it. I haf not been here in two year."

I shook my head. "Doesn't seem like that long."

"But iss true. Two year. I make no mistake, for I will not soon forget that trip. You could call it, I suppose, a minor disaster; for first time since I put pack on my shoulder I do not make expense. My brother who keeps store, he pulls long face when he open my pack. 'Sol,' he say to me, 'take off your coat and get behind counter. You are peddler no more. Now you are nothing but salesman. These goods, I will put it back in stock.'

"For two years my coat hang on the nail. We are doing good bus'ness, but I am restless. I miss wandering around, I want to see my frien's, I like to know what iss going on. It iss not easy for me in cage like bird. So once more I fill pack and put on my shoulder." He shrugged and slowly shook his head. "It iss no go. The world iss completely change. Nobody need the Green Pack Peddler any more. If I go to farmhouse, do they buy my goods? No, they try to sell me the farm. When I want to get to next town, can I take train as always before? No, service is reduced. I must wait all day."

We sat and talked for half an hour, and when he rose to go, saying that he must stop in to see Tom, I walked along with him, having a little business with Tom myself. As we were passing the livery stable we saw Gid sitting in the doorway and stopped for a brief exchange of greetings. I had not been there for a long time and was surprised at the deserted air that hung over the place. Half the stables were empty, and the long row of vehicles standing with the shafts and poles propped up to get them out of the way looked as if they had not been used in months.

I waited around while the two old friends whacked each other on the back and exchanged friendly insults, each accusing the other of getting old and going to the dogs, each bragging about the big business he was doing and offering to take the other in as soon as he was down and out.

"I'm gonna need a good stable hand," said Gid, "and I think you'll do—if you'll just get over this notion of carryin' that damn pack around on your shoulder all the time. The hosses won't like it."

Sol smiled, his round moon-face beaming as of old. "What hosses?" he asked, pointing a fat finger at the empty stalls.

"Yeah, most the nags are out today," Gid lied cheerfully. "All these are on reserve. Prob'ly be gone in another hour."

"I'm glad you keeping so busy." Sol ran his eyes around the big barn cluttered with the unused gear of what had once been a busy stable. "But I see no space here for the storage of the motor-ve'cle. You have plenty room and could make nice return without investment."

Gid shook his head with great positiveness. "Guess you don't remember how Andy feels about them hossless buggies. He couldn't stand the stink of the damn things. I couldn't myself."

Sol winked at me. "How about the horses?" he asked as we rose to go. "Do they object also?" Gid did not deign to answer.

As we came up to Tom's garage after the little interlude at the stable we found Ike Meeker sitting on the bench looking, as Sol said to me in an aside, a little whiter, a little more wrinkled, but with the same unmatchable laziness.

"And how iss the family?" asked Sol after the usual exchange of amenities.

Realizing that Sol was fully aware of the probable result of this inquiry I passed on inside, but as I went through the door I could hear Meeker saying, "I don't

know as I ever told you, but the fact is that I married inter a kinda problem on my second venture. I got me a young wife, but I hadn't figgered on gettin' me a cold one . . ."

When I told Tom what was going on outside the door

he smiled dubiously. "I'm afraid old Ike has been guilty of a little misbehavior lately."

"Ike? What kind of misbehavior?"

"Well—what you'd expect of him. I left him here to keep an eye on the shop while I went to Geneva one day, and when I got back I found that same peculiar perfume that I've found here before when I've left him in charge."

"It wouldn't by any chance be the perfume of Nellie McKim?" I guessed.

He nodded. "Exactly. That's just what it is."

"But I should think his wife would smell it on him when he gets home."

"She does."

"And how does he get out of that?"

"He tells her that it's the smell of the grease soap I use here in the garage."

30

Demonstration

I HAD NEVER LIKED ASA PARKER. I HAD NEVER gone around with him much, for the truth is that Asa and I did not click. Our ambitions, our interests, our ideals were totally unlike. The old saying that opposites attract certainly did not work in our case. The only reason that I had taken him to the party over beyond Alloway was because we were the only two people in town who were going, and the hostess had called me up and asked me if I would bring Asa with me. I said I would be glad to oblige, which was stretching the truth a bit, though I really did appreciate having him along when I was faced with the necessity of tightening the clutch.

When Asa came walking into my office the morning after the little misadventure on the Alloway hill I can't say that I was surprised, though he had rarely come in there before unless he had some favor to ask or wanted some free legal advice on a political question. Father had started the precedent of dispensing free legal advice to all the local political parties, and in his absence they all expected me to carry on the old family tradition.

Asa was tricky, but he was far from being shrewd, and he had not been in my office five minutes before I knew that he was really upset over what had happened the night before and was much concerned by the knowledge that I "had something on" him. Quite naturally he did not tell me this; politicians try to keep such things covered up and to achieve their results by subtleties. Asa's subtlety consisted of trying to convince me that, entirely for my own good, I ought not to let the slightest inkling of that story leak out. His position was that he had dodged out of sight so quickly that he had not been recognized. And he reminded me of my remark that with all the grease on his face his own mother would not have recognized him. He also admitted that he knew the Judge only very slightly, having met him at quite a large gathering, and he wasn't entirely sure that the Judge would have known him even if he had taken a good look. This was a surprise to me, since he had previously given me to understand that he and the Judge were quite "close"—to use another of his political expressions.

I gave Asa no reassurance on this point, laughing the affair off as just one more of the comic incidents into which the use of a motor car had plunged me. The effect of this treatment was to make Asa more convinced than ever that not only did I have something on him, but that I meant to keep it for possible use at some subsequent time.

Another thing that began to trickle out while we were talking was Asa's growing interest in the motor car. This surprised me, for Andy's complete dominance in the past had precluded anything of that kind.

"Quite a job we did there last night," he said.

I was a little amused at the "we" but I let it go. "Yes, quite a job."

"It's all in knowing what to do, isn't it?"

"Not quite all. There's a certain knack you have to develop."

"Oh, yes, you've got to have the knack of it, but almost everybody knows how to use wrenches and things. Take yourself, for instance—did you ever have any interest in machinery before you got an automobile?"

"I was always pretty fair with tools," I said. "I could usually make things go."

"But you never worked much on machinery, did you?"

"Well, no; to tell the truth, I didn't."

"Just carpentry and stuff like that?"

"That's right. Mostly woodworking. I could pound my thumb with the best of them."

"That's my point exactly," said Asa. "Anybody with average intelligence can learn how to drive and take care of an automobile—isn't that right?"

He did not get to any definite point that day, but I could see that the yeast was at work in him. He came in to see me again only a few days later, and this time he began to talk quite learnedly of the various makes of car. He thought the Pierce too heavy and the Ford altogether too light. Packard and Peerless were all right, but they cost too much money. The Maxwell at $1750 looked very good to him, and he wanted my opinion of the Oldsmobile "Limited," a giant of a car with a 5x6 motor and 42-inch wheels. I shook my head over those big wheels and said that a new tire for one of them would upset my budget for the whole summer.

That threw him into a discussion of tires, during which my cue was to sit and listen. Somewhere, somehow, he had learned a great deal about tires, most of which was untrue. But eventually I discovered what he had come for: he wanted to find out how hard it was to learn to drive. In a weak moment I said I would take him out in my car and let him see for himself what it was like—and

· 348 ·

after that he hounded me until I did take him out, not once but several times. And, strange as it may seem, he caught on very quickly. He had no idea what was going on under the hood or under the floor boards. All he knew was that in one position the gear lever was in low and in another it was in second or high; if he pushed down on the throttle with his foot the car would go faster, whereas if he let up on it the car would slow down. But he was enough of an egotist to take naturally to a big, powerful machine which would go surging resistlessly forward at his bidding. I could see that he would be an aggressive driver, but I had a feeling that, so far as his own progress was concerned, he would be a good one.

I was curious to know whether he was really going to fly in the face of his patron and buy a car or was just flirting with the idea. He was serious enough about it, but he had something on his mind that he wanted to attend to first. So he stepped over to Brackett's one evening and made a proposal of marriage to Lucy.

Asa was not the most reticent person in the world, but he did manage to keep this particular incident to himself, and I heard nothing about it until late in the afternoon of the following day, when Zelda came to my office with a troubled look on her face. Zelda's family and especially her brother Burgess had scant affection for Asa. Burgess's opinion, as expressed to me, was that Asa was a big stiff. Doubtless her parents would have put it in slightly different words, which would have sounded a little more dignified but would have meant much the same thing. Under the circumstances, when Zelda reached the point where she felt she needed advice, she had to go away from home for it.

"Well, he's done it," she said as the door of my private

office closed behind her. Small, dark, shapely, her large brown eyes glistening with the tears she was struggling to hold back, she was a picture of despair as she stood there.

I suspected at once what she meant, but I pretended not to. "Who's done what?" I asked.

"Asa—" She swallowed, unable to go on.

"Then he's proposed?" I said.

She slowly nodded her head.

"And Lucy accepted him," I guessed. "By George, you're done for," I added, trying rather heavy-handedly to lighten the gloom.

But she shook her head. "No, she did not accept him. She very gently but quite definitely refused. Lucy came over and told me about it this morning. She did her best to let him down as softly as possible, but all she succeeded in doing was to make him very, very angry."

"What reason did she give for refusing him?"

"The best reason in the world—she said she was not in love with him." Zelda came over and sat across the table from me.

"And he would not take that for a sufficient reason?"

"He wouldn't believe it was the reason. He blamed it all on her Uncle Andy."

"But why should he blame it on Andy?" I asked.

"That's what we can't make out. Asa went stamping out, muttering something about being wounded in the house of his friends. That's what frightens me."

"I don't see what there is to be frightened about," I said. "Looks to me as if you had all the elements there for a happy ending. He proposed—she rejected him—he'll get over it—and there you are."

"But he won't get over it. He's in a terrible rage. He's got the idea that Andy Brackett wants to throw him overboard politically—and he's not going to have it. He's going to do something, and it will be something desperate. I suppose it's no secret that they haven't been getting along lately. Asa thinks that Andy's a back number, that he's hurting the party, and that somebody ought to take his place."

"What do you think Asa will do?"

Very slowly Zelda shook her head. "That's what I don't know. That's what I'm worrying about."

"You think he might pick a fight with Andy?"

"Oh, I wouldn't worry about a fist fight," she answered quickly. "That might do them both good. But if Asa is unwise enough to start a political brawl and drag Lucy's name into it—well, Andy will kill him. You know how he is about Lucy."

As I thought about it, that didn't seem unlikely. Asa was uncouth enough to drag Lucy or anybody else into a political brawl if he thought that by so doing he could help himself to win. And I knew, or thought I did, how Andy would act if anyone should make such an absurd and unwarranted use of her name. I was a little scared myself though I did not let Zelda know it. As it turned out, however, Asa went about the starting of his political brawl in quite a different way. He used a species of horse sense of which I had never suspected him to precipitate what turned out to be a bloodless revolution.

It was the day after my talk with Zelda that Asa had the Maxwell agent up from Geneva with a demonstrator. There was nothing unusual about having a demonstrator in town, but the way Asa handled this one was very unusual. He did not have the car demonstrated to himself so much as to his friends. He insisted that, since his friends were going to do most of the riding in the car, he intended to get one that they would like. He had the car brought right into the center of the town and then went from one store to another calling his friends to come and try it. He must have had thirty or forty people out in the car that day, and after the demonstration was over he stood right there on the street and signed an order for a 4-cylinder Maxwell touring car, priced at $1750.

The gesture was so typical of Asa and was carried off with such noisy publicity that everybody in town knew what was going on. And for those who did not know, the story was in the paper the next day.

When Andy discovered what was happening he kept out of sight, and it is probably just as well that he did, with Asa running in and out of this store or that office to get somebody to come out and try the car, and conspicuously avoiding Andy's place, though he noisily entered those on either side.

Gid left word at my office the next morning that Andy would like to see me, and after I had looked at my mail I went over there full of curiosity; I couldn't imagine what he wanted. His office was empty when I went in, and I stepped out on the little back porch hoping that I might see Andy somewhere about. His chair was there, and Gid's, and on the railing I saw a stumpy briar pipe that I recognized as belonging to Gid. On the floor were the scattered sheets of the *Post-Express*. So this was where the two had been spending their evenings.

The grass in the horse pasture was now rough and uneven. There was no longer enough stock, I thought, to keep it nibbled down like a lawn. A broken limb hung dangling, like a fractured arm, from one of the towering elms, doubtless a casualty of a storm that had occurred more than a month ago. Two blowzy mares stood head to tail, switching each other, in the shade of a tree on the farther side of the lot. An air of dilapidation and decay hung over the place. The idyllic picture of horses grazing on a rolling turf, that Andy had so loved, was forever gone. I quickly withdrew and walked around to the barn. Hearing voices as I came up, I found Gid and Andy sitting in the office among the dust-covered circus posters and lithographs of trotting horses with high-wheeled sulkies. Andy was in the barrel chair and Gid in the easy chair by the table.

Gid rose as I came in and offered me his seat, saying that he had some work to do and was just keeping Andy company until I came. He went limping out and down between the rows of empty stalls. The room was the same as when I had seen it before, and in spite of the desolation of the almost empty barn it looked lived-in and cozy. So this was where the two old cronies spent their time, dreaming of the past and living in a day that was no more.

"Well, young fellow." Andy never could quite understand that I was growing up. "That father of yours has a way of being off somewhere whenever I need him most. Where is he now, by the way?"

"The last letter I had was from Paris."

"Ah, what a place! Most wonderful horse racing in the world—and not all the fun on the track, by any means. Such atmosphere you never saw, felt, tasted, however you want to put it. But I didn't get you over here to talk horse racing. I've got something else on my mind. . . . I'm getting to be an old fogy—out of step with the times. This isn't the town it was when I took it over. That town is gone. What we need is a young fellow they can all unite on, somebody who hasn't got any old grudges piled up against him. What do you think?"

"Do you know of any such person?"

"I certainly do." He pointed his finger at me. "What about you?"

I burst out laughing. "You ought to know better than that, Andy."

"Well, I know your father would like it if you'd show a little interest in politics."

"I'd do a lot to please him, but not that."

"Do you know who'll get it if you don't take it?"

"I don't care who'll get it, so long as I don't have to."

Andy laughed softly. "I was afraid you'd take it that way. But, after all, that wasn't why I sent for you. I want you to write me the kind of a letter of resignation that your father would fix up for me. Something elegant, something with a ring to it. Can you do it?"

I shook my head. "Not as well as he would—but I'll do the best I can."

"All right, now I'll tell you the points that I want you to cover."

After we had finished with our business Gid came stumping in, wiping his brow. "I got more work to do around here than I had when we was stablin' fifty nags." He sat down in the straight-backed chair with the wired-on legs and tipped it expertly back against the wall without demolishing it. "How's that stink-wagon of yours?"

"About the same."

"Been up over the Manchester road lately—that new stretch put in a couple of years ago?"

"No, not lately," I said. "Why?"

"All goin' to pieces," said Gid. "Coupla years more and there won't be no road left. And lemme tell you some'pm, when these here new roads go to pieces, they're worse'n any *old* road you ever see. All full of pitch-holes—bad for a hoss's feet."

"It's easy enough to repair those roads with a little oil and gravel, but what makes you think there'll be any horses left to step on them?" I asked, rising to go.

"Don't you worry about that, boy!" shouted Gid with spirit. "There'll always be hosses, whether we've got any roads or not!"

"I think he's right," said Andy. "Can you have that letter ready for me this afternoon?"

I nodded and started back to my office, thinking as I went along of the two tough-bitted diehards sitting around that old livery stable waiting for the new roads to break up. It was thus that the old sailing men had stood out against the coming of steam. They had died still hopeful, but the great white wings had never come back. Little white wings, yes, but only as toys, adjuncts of sport. And I could not help wondering if old Dobbin would ever come to that. It seemed to me at the moment that he was much more likely to follow the trail taken by his friend the buffalo.

31

Self-Starter

BURGESS HARPER CAME INTO MY OFFICE and dropped a letter on my desk for me to read. It was from the state board of Bar Examiners and notified Burgess that he had passed his examination and was eligible for admission. Burgess sat down in a chair and put his feet on the desk. He said he wanted to see how it would feel to be a lawyer.

"But are you going to practice law with your feet?" I asked.

Burgess grinned. "Yes, I probably will for the first two or three years."

"Where—here in town?"

He shook his head. "Not a chance."

"Why do you say that? Don't you like your home town?"

"Love it. There's no place like it in the world; but it simply isn't the kind of place where I want to practice law."

"Why not?"

"Not enough wealth here—not enough people—not enough scope. I want to go to some place where the sky's the limit. I'd never be satisfied just to be a useful citizen like—like—"

"Like me, for instance?"

"No, not like you. I don't think you are a useful citizen.

Besides, we're not discussing you, we're discussing me. I'm going to start in with Rochester. There's a live town. Lots of wealth, fine people, good old families, and all that. But if I find out it isn't big enough to suit me after I've been there four or five years—I'll go to New York. Rochester will be nice, though. It's so near I can run back and forth in the car as often as I want to."

"Why don't you try the county seat for a starter? That's only fifteen miles away and you could live at home."

He pulled his feet down from the table and slammed them on the floor. "Not big enough. I've got it all thought out." He stood up, a fine, clean-cut, ambitious young American, looking for some good, tough worlds to conquer. Plenty of bumps ahead of him, but he'd get along all right, he'd come through. "Want to ask a little favor," he said. "Will you be one of my sponsors when I'm sworn in?"

I said I would and offered him my warmest congratulations and best wishes, and he went out beaming at being over the first hurdle. He did not realize that there would always be another one just ahead waiting to test his skill and endurance. Burgess had not been gone five minutes when Tom Hunter came striding in. He was clutching a newspaper in his hand and gesturing with it as he spoke.

"Here's the greatest thing that's ever happened to the motor car since they put the first gas engine into it. It's what I should have been working on all the time. This really does the trick. It draws all the various elements into a single unit, and the best part is that it doesn't add twenty pounds of unnecessary weight. See what I mean?"

"No. What is it?"

"It's an electric starter with lights and ignition all in a single unit! Neatest thing you ever saw. We *have* to have electricity for our ignition; can't get along without it. All right, why not make the supply just a little larger and have enough to take care of lights and starter? What beats me is why I never thought of it myself. Come to think of it, I did, and I'll tell you what threw me off the track— the battery people told me that a storage battery couldn't be built with enough power to start a motor, and I believed them. This fellow in Dayton wouldn't take No for an answer. He told them to go ahead and build him one anyway—and they did, and it *worked!* I never thought about hitching the lights into the same system, but probably it would have come to me."

"But, Tom," I asked with some trepidation, "what about your—your compressed air starter?"

"Oh, that!" He waved it into oblivion with a broad sweep of his newspaper. "That's out of the window. Let's forget it."

"But, Tom, you've spent years on it, and you must have spent hundreds of dollars."

"Aw, forget it—forget it. That was one of the ideas that didn't come through. I got a thousand ideas—they keep coming all the time, and one of these days an idea of mine will click and I'll put over something like *this!*" He slapped the paper with enthusiasm and admiration.

The door opened a crack and a feminine voice was heard outside. "May I come in?" It was Lucy Brackett.

When we both called to her most cordially to come in, she pushed open the door and paused in the doorway. "I'm sorry to interrupt, but I have a wonderful piece of news. . . . Asa's new car came this morning, and he and Zelda have eloped in it!"

I leaped to my feet. "When?"

"Not an hour ago!"

"But Burgess was just in here and he never mentioned it."

"Burgess doesn't know it. I'm the only one who knows it—and I wouldn't have known if Zelda hadn't run in to borrow a clean pair of white gloves to be married in. Oh, isn't it romantic and thrilling!"

"It might be—if it was anybody else but Asa," said Tom.

"But Zelda adores him—she's always adored him—she'll be unutterably happy."

Tom smiled dubiously. "What makes you think so?"

"Because she loves him so much."

"He'll treat her like a dog."

"What difference will that make so long as she loves him? Is there anything else that really matters?"

For some moments they stood there looking at each other—saying nothing. What a pair they were, so perfectly matched, so vital. When they left the office a little later I watched them from the window. This time they were not quarreling. As they walked along they kept gazing at each other as if neither had ever seen the other before—and I don't believe they really had.